Anatomy
of the
Ship

The Submarine
ALLIANCE

Anatomy of the Ship

The Submarine ALLIANCE

John Lambert
and David Hill

CONWAY MARITIME PRESS

Frontispiece
1. *Alliance* leaving Portsmouth, 17 April 1952, to lay wreaths over the site of the *Affray* loss. The *Alliance* was originally completed with a hinged snort and twin Oerlikons; the Oerlikon mounting was removed shortly after completion. In this photograph the bow cap of one of her twin forward external torpedo tubes can clearly be seen. These, together with the externals, were removed in 1953.
CPL

First published in 1986 by
Conway Maritime Press Ltd,
24 Bride Lane, Fleet Street,
London EC4Y 8DR

ISBN 0 85177 380 X

Designed by Jonathan Doney
Typesetting by C R Barber (Highlands) Ltd
Printed and bound in Great Britain by
R J Acford, Chichester

Contents

AUTHORS' FOREWORD AND ACKNOWLEDGEMENTS

When, in 1981, work was completed on the preparation of HMS *Alliance* as a museum ship and as a memorial to the 4334 British submariners who gave their lives in both world wars and to the 739 officers and men lost in peacetime submarine disasters, she became the first British submarine to be permanently opened to the public. And it is primarily for this reason that *Alliance* was chosen for inclusion in the 'Anatomy of the Ship' series.

Warships, and submarines in particular, have always been the subject of considerable interest to both the general public and the warship enthusiast, and every year books appear covering the many aspects of their development and operation both during and between the wars. However, the purpose of this book, and indeed of the whole series, as the title suggests, is to look at the subject in greater depth, to trace the development of the design, and to detail the armament and machinery they contained.

The 'A' class were the only ocean-going class of British submarine designed during the last war and although completed too late to actually see any action, they embodied all of the developments made in British submarine design during the final years of conflict. There is little doubt that had the war continued longer they would have given excellent service in the waters for which they were designed. In fact, in the years following the war many of the class operated comfortably in both tropical and arctic waters, establishing new records for both surface and submerged endurance. To illustrate this, in 1953 HMS *Andrew* carried out the first ever submerged crossing of the Atlantic; and earlier, in 1947, *Alliance* spent a record 30 days submerged off the coast of Africa.

'A' class submarines remained in service until well into the 1970s and it was an 'A' class boat, HMS *Andrew*, that carried out the Royal Navy's last submarine gun action in December 1974. The sense of occasion was not lost on her commanding officer who reported in his signal to the Flag Officer Submarines – also relayed to the Australian, Canadian and American navies – 'The reek of cordite has passed from the Royal Navy's Submarine Service. Last gun action surface conducted at 03 1330 Zulu. Time to first round, 36 seconds. May the art of submarine gunnery rest in peace but never be forgotten.'

HMS *Alliance* remained in service until March 1973 when she paid off for the final time and went to HMS *Dolphin*, the submarine base at Gosport to replace HMS *Tabard* as a static display ship and floating classroom. There she remained until August 1979, when following the decision to preserve her as a submarine memorial she was towed from Gosport to Vosper Ship Repairers Ltd at Southampton to have her keel reinforced prior to her being lifted out of the water and placed on permanent display.

For anyone contemplating a visit to Portsmouth a visit to the Submarine Museum at Gosport and a walk through *Alliance* is certainly worthwhile. The submarine has been restored to her active service condition and looks exactly as she did when last at sea. The tour of the submarine usually lasts about 45 minutes and is conducted by trained guides – usually ex-submariners. The experience is quite unique and together with the exhibits and photographs in the museum itself gives an excellent impression of what conditions were like in a wartime submarine. A more recent addition to the exhibits at the Submarine Museum is the Royal Navy's first submarine the *Holland 1* which was salvaged virtually intact in 1982 after nearly 69 years on the seabed. Dwarfed by HMS *Alliance*, *Holland 1* is now being restored to her original condition and visitors to the museum are encouraged to look inside this tiny vessel and make their own comparisons with her much larger descendant.

In the preparation of this book many months were spent researching at the Royal Navy Submarine Museum at Gosport and the authors are endebted to the staff for their help and co-operation and in particular to: the curator, Commander Richard Compton-Hall, MBE, RN (Retd); Captain Alec Wale of the *Alliance* projects office and of course to Gus Britton, the museum's assistant curator who served as a signalman on *Alliance* in 1949–50. And finally thanks to our wives, Kim and Sheila for their patience, help and support. But mostly for their patience . . .

David Hill
John Lambert

Introduction

'A' class submarines were designed primarily for operation in the Far East, to replace the very successful T-boats that had first been introduced in 1937. Although the first of the class, *Amphion*, was not completed until March 1945 it was as early as 1941 that plans for the construction of this new type of submarine were first approved. Wartime pressures had enabled great strides to be made in the use of welding in British shipbuilding yards and the development of the 'A' class illustrates very clearly how the introduction of these new methods radically influenced the techniques employed in submarine construction during the latter stages of the war.

From the submarine designer's point of view the advantages of welding were obvious, offering not only the prospect of improved hull strength and the tactical advantages of greater diving depths but a greater degree of flexability during construction than had previously been possible with riveted hulls. At first these new construction methods were introduced to vessels of existing designs already in production (primarily the later vessels of the 'S' and 'T' classes), but it was quickly realised that the development of a new design, taking full advantage of welding would enable the production of submarine hulls to be greatly speeded up.

Another consideration arguing in favour of a new type of submarine was that the war in the Far East called for submarines with a higher surface speed and greater endurance than those currently in production. The patrol areas in this new theatre of war were considerably larger than those that British submarines had previously been operating, namely the Mediterranean and the North Sea, and the distances between bases was far greater. This required the boats to remain at sea for longer periods, so improved habitability was another major consideration for the new design. These, then, were some of the factors that led to the introduction of the 'A' class. Nevertheless although the design was developed with the greatest possible speed, such was the overriding need to maintain their current output that none of the class was included in any new construction programme until the building yards felt able to accept them into their schedules with the minimum of disruption to their existing submarine construction rates. This was not until 1943 when a total of 46 vessels was ordered, the lion's share of the work going to Vickers-Armstrongs and the remainder being distributed amongst Cammell Laird, Scotts and the Royal Dockyards at Portsmouth, Devonport and Chatham. Simultaneously the emphasis shifted away from any new production of the 'S', 'T', 'U' and 'V' classes and this resulted in many orders for these vessels being cancelled.

The change from partial to complete welding of submarine hulls was taken up by the building yards with great enthusiasm and new building techniques were introduced to take full advantage of these new methods. The 'A' class, for example, were fabricated in sections, the sections being brought together on the slipway by overhead travelling gantries. The introduction of radiographic examination of the welds also contributed to a greater sense of confidence in the new techniques that were being employed.

It is interesting to note that in the years prior to commencing work on the 'A' class a great deal was heard about the superiority of German submarine design and methods of construction. However, in 1941 the *U 570*, a Type VIIC U-boat, was captured virtually intact by British forces, and some of the discoveries made after her capture proved to be quite revealing. Samples of steel from the pressure hull plating were tested and analysed and found to be quite inferior in quality to the British equivalent. Needless to say, for some time afterwards uninformed talk of German submarine superiority simply died away.

The first of the class, HMS *Amphion*, was laid down in November 1943 and the mass production of the 'A' class was embarked upon very shortly afterwards. However, Britain at the time was fully committed to a vast wartime programme of merchant shipbuilding, warship production, refitting and repair and, apart from one brief period when the 'A' class were in production, submarines were never given the highest priority. Consequently, only *Amphion* – which was running her first-of-class trials in Scottish waters on VE Day, and *Astute* – were completed before the war ended. A further fourteen vessels were eventually completed but the sudden ending of hostilities in the Far East saw a greater number, thirty in all, being cancelled.

In the construction of the 'A' class certain variations in building techniques occurred from yard to yard. At Cammell Laird's, for instance, large sections of the hull were fabricated under cover and then transported in a semi-finished state to the slipways where they were welded together. Light steel portable covers were lifted by crane over the sections being welded to prevent any disruption of the work due to bad weather. At Chatham, the pressure hull was built up in sections varying in length from 10ft to 28ft, the governing factor being the capacities of the lifting appliances at the slip.

One particular problem that had to be faced by the builders by the time the work had reached an advanced stage was maintaining the integrity of the pressure hull during launching, when a large area of the hull was left open for the shipping of the main engines and motors. This was overcome by securing a portable plate, made water-tight by a rubber joint, which was secured by hook bolts and heavy longitudinal girders welded to pads on the hull at the forward and after ends of the opening. After launching the girders were then cut away to allow the main engines to be lifted in. The area was later sealed with a closing plate.

Production times compared to the similar sized 'T' class were short indeed, with an average of 8 months from keel-laying to launching. The average time for this stage to be reached by 'T' class submarines was nearer 15 months.

TABLE 1: **PARTICULARS OF THE 'A' CLASS**

Building programme:	1943 Emergency War Programme
Building yards:	Vickers Armstrongs 10, Cammell Laird 3, Scotts 2, Chatham Dockyard 1
Length overall:	281ft 4¾in
Length pp:	249ft 3in
Maximum breadth:	22ft 3in
Draught:	17ft
Displacement:	1120 tons standard, 1385 tons normal, surfaced; 1620 tons submerged
Operating depth:	500ft
Water-tight compartments:	7 including conning tower
Pressure hull plating:	⅞in plate reducing to ¾in
Armament:	Ten 21in torpedo tubes, 20 torpedoes carried One 4in QF gun Three .303 Vickers GO machine guns One 20mm Oerlikon anti-aircraft mounting 26 mines
Machinery:	Two shafts, 8-cylinder Admiralty or Vickers diesel engines, 4300bhp; English Electric motors, 1250shp
Performance:	18½kts surfaced, 8kts submerged
Oil fuel:	159 tons
Endurance:	10,500 miles at 11kts surfaced; 16 miles at 8kts submerged; 90 miles at 3kts submerged
Complement:	61

It is interesting to speculate how the 'A' class would have fared under operating conditions had the war continued longer. Up to the end of hostilities in 1945 both 'S' and 'T' class submarines had been operating for several years with great success in the Far East. However it is fair to stress that neither of these classes was designed for operations in tropical waters, and their successes speak volumes for the endurance of their crews, who were forced to cope with inadequate ventilation systems and limited supplies of fresh water. There is little doubt that the 'A' class, with their improved habitability and greater endurance would have done very well in these waters, and certainly their formidable torpedo armament would have enabled them to take full advantage of the longer patrols they were capable of. Fortunately, they were never given the opportunity to prove it!

'A' class submarines were in production for a little over four and a half years, and although they began to leave the slipways too late to see any action during the war they subsequently proved themselves capable of adapting well to the developments made in submarine design and equipment during the postwar years, giving good service until well into the 1970s.

CONSTRUCTION

The pressure hull was constructed of ⅞in plate, reducing to ¾in, welded over internal frames spaced 21in apart. It was circular in cross-section throughout and had an internal diameter of 16ft. At either end of the parallel body, which was 129ft in length, the hull tapered to 13ft and then to 9½ft in diameter, the domed ends being of 1⅛in plate. The internal division was good, the pressure hull being subdivided into six water-tight compartments.

The forward section, 15ft in length housed the four forward internal torpedo tubes and their firing gear. The firing bottles were located beneath the tubes, forward of the Asdic dome, access to which was gained through a water-tight manhole let into the floor plates immediately below the inner tube doors. The compartment also housed the forward hydroplane tilting cylinder and turning-in gear.

The next compartment aft was the torpedo stowage compartment, 24ft 3in in length, providing space for the six 21in reload torpedoes. Access to the compartment from the fore deck was through the forward torpedo loading hatch and immediately forward of this was an escape hatch. The lower deck spaces were taken up by the forward trimming tank, a torpedo operating tank, an air bottle stowage and a small store. The upper section of the third compartment going aft, which was 45ft 6in in length, provided space for four mess decks. From forward they comprised: the Seamen's mess, the Stokers' mess, the Petty Officers' mess and the Engine Room Artificers' mess. A companionway led aft along the starboard side and it was here that more berths, the forward battery fuse-breaker, a cold cupboard and, in some boats, a small toilet were located. Most of the below-deck space was taken up by the forward battery and oil fuel tanks.

The next compartment aft was also the largest, 54ft in length, containing the officers' wardroom at its forward end, the control room amidships and in the after section the radar and radio offices, the galley and the toilets and wash places for the crew. Below deck was the magazine, the after battery and an auxiliary machinery space.

The engine room was 49ft 3in in length and housed the two 1250hp diesels and electric motors. Fuel and lubricating oil tanks took up much of the space in the lower section of the hull.

The final compartment aft, 35ft in length, was the after torpedo stowage compartment containing two 21in diameter torpedo tubes. Four reload torpedoes, two on either side, were stored here and an access and escape hatch were situated in the deckhead above.

The keel was generally rectangular in section and consisted of the Asdic dome and its casting at the forward end, forward and after ballast boxes, a quick-diving tank and a number of cast iron keel blocks weighing between 5 and 9 tons each. Both periscopes and one radar mast extended through the pressure hull to the bottom of the keel, where the sole plates were 2in thick.

External tanks. The main ballast tanks on the 'A' class were of a double hull construction. Welded to each side of the keel and extending up around either side of the pressure hull, the outer hull, which varied in thickness between ¼in and ½in contained the external ballast and oil fuel tanks. The heavier plate on the tank tops was originally fitted to give protection to the external fuel tanks which occupied the top section of each main tank. The plating was supported by angle bar frames and strengthened by sealed tubular struts welded to the pressure hull. Compensating tanks were fitted amidships on either side of the pressure hull and where these tanks were faired to the main tanks the construction was of a lighter 8lb plate.

Main tanks. The No 1 main tank was immediately forward of the domed end of the pressure hull and tapered towards the bow. Four oval-shaped free-flooding holes were let into the bottom plating and a telemotor-operated vent valve was situated inside the casing and connected to the tank's highest point by a large bore pipe. The four internal torpedo tubes passed through the tank and a free-flooding cable locker servicing the anchor was fitted into its after end. Nos 2, 3 and 4 main tanks were situated on either side of the parallel section of the pressure hull and were flooded through holes let into the sides of the keel section. Oil fuel tanks were built into the lower, forward, sections of No 2 main tank port and starboard. No 4 main tank could, if required, be used for additional oil fuel storage and it was for this reason that there were no free-flooding holes at the bottom of this tank. Instead, hydraulically operated kingston valves were fitted in the underside of the adjoining keel. Compensating tanks, cylindrical in shape and each with a capacity of 2388 gallons, were housed in the upper sections of the No 3 main tank. No 5 main tank was sited immediately aft of the domed pressure hull and tapered towards the stern. The tank was flooded through four free-flooding holes let into the underside at the forward end and was vented at its after end by a telemotor-operated valve. The two internal stern torpedo tubes passed through the tank, together with the operating shafting of the hydroplanes and rudder.

All of the main tanks were tested to 20lb per square inch.

Bow buoyancy tank. The original design called for a low bow and *Amphion* and *Astute* were completed in this form. However, after initial sea trials in rough weather it was found necessary to fit a buoyancy tank above the forward external torpedo tubes to improve stability. The tank raised the bow by about 4ft and gave the class its distinctive bow profile. The tank was open at the bottom and vented by two oleo-operated valves, one on the port side forward and the other on the starboard side aft.

External oil fuel tanks. Four oil fuel tanks port and starboard were housed within the double hull on either side of the pressure hull. No 1 external oil fuel tank was immediately forward of the No 2 main ballast tank, No 2 external oil fuel tank was fitted into the lower part of the No 2 main ballast tank, and No 3 oil fuel tank was sited immediately aft of the No 4 main ballast tank. The No 4 external oil fuel tanks were similar to the forward pair, long and shallow and situated high up in the after section of the outer hull. All of the external oil fuel tanks were tested to 20lb per square inch, with the exception of the No 4 tanks, port and starboard, which were tested to 15lb.

The conning tower. The 'A' class were unusual in that the Captain's cabin was situated in the bridge superstructure. Only the giant submarine cruiser *X 1* built in 1923, and some of the large ocean-going boats constructed in the 1930s, shared this feature. The cabin took the shape of a small water-tight cylinder mounted on the after end of the conning tower itself and was totally enclosed by the bridge plating. It housed a bunk, a small wardrobe, a folding toilet and a writing desk.

Habitability. Particular attention was paid to providing the highest standard of accommodation for the crew when the 'A' class was being designed. All of the accommodation spaces therefore, with the exception of the CO's cabin, were situated as far away from the engine room as posible, forward of the control room on the port side of the ship. A companionway, giving access to the various messes and also allowing passage between the fore ends and the control room, ran down the starbord side. Every effort was made to keep all noisy machinery away from the mess decks, and this included the exhaust fans for the No 1 main battery, over which the accommodation spaces were sited. In the final design they were squeezed into a store room beneath the ERAs' mess. The wardroom was situated in the adjoining compartment, adjacent to the control room where a small pantry was provided in the passageway opposite – although in some vessels this space was taken up by additional bunks. During a gun action the wardroom furniture would be pushed back to provide access to the gun tower, the lower lid of which opened above the wardroom table.

Because they were designed for service in the Far East, two air conditioning plants were provided to cope with the extremes of temperature and humidity that would be encountered in the tropics. They could be used either singly or together and each was capable of absorbing 55,000 BTUs per hour from 36,000 cubic feet of air per hour. A refrigerating system to cool the air was also provided. A fan drew air through the air cooler and passed it to the ship's ventilation system. Moisture from the air precipitated and was drained off into the radar mast well bilges. The ventilation trunking supplying the forward section of the submarine was 10in × 6in in section. Flap valves were fitted where the trunking passed through a water-tight bulkhead and smaller branch sections provided ventilation to the below-deck spaces and the magazine. A 10in × 3in trunking provided the ventilation aft. Two CO_2 absorption units were incorporated in the system. One was situated in the Seamen's mess forward, and the other below the floor plating in the motor room.

Fresh and distilled water systems. An electrically operated distilling plant was installed in the auxiliary machinery compartment below the wardroom. It was capable of distilling 15 gallons of water per hour. From the distiller the water was pumped by hand to a storage tank on the port side below the Petty Officers' mess. Distilled water from the tank could be transferred by means of a second handpump to portable hoses when required for topping up the main battery. The fresh water tanks, eight in total, were positioned in two groups on either side of the main batteries. The upper deck filling connection was situated over the forward torpedo stowage compartment and there was a cross connection to the distiller. A domestic hot water heater was squeezed into the galley, where opposite were the bathrooms and heads for the crew.

Refrigerating system. The refrigerating system fitted in 'A' class submarines maintained a cold room, a cool room and a ready-use cupboard. The plant, cold room and cool room were situated in the auxiliary machinery space and the ready-use cupboard in the accommodation passageway above. The main components of the plant, which had a capacity of 6000 BTUs per hour, were: a motor-driven compressor, a condenser, the evaporating grids in the cooled compartments and two thermostatic valves, one controlling the supply of gas to the cold and cool room grids and the other, the supply to the ready-use cupboard.

ARMAMENT

'T' class submarines, which the 'A' class were designed to replace, carried the heaviest torpedo armament of any class of British submarine put into production. The number of torpedoes carried had increased from sixteen in the first group to seventeen in the later boats. Not surprisingly therefore,

TABLE 2: **STATEMENT OF WEIGHTS, 1943**

Item	Weight (tons)	Item	Weight (tons)
Hull	571.03	Fresh and distilled water	27.78
Main machinery	140.00	Trimming water	10.00
Torpedo armament	70.00	Compensating water	23.95
Gun armament	13.26	Crew and effects	5.55
Electronic gear	11.10	Provisions and stores	12.00
Oil fuel	165.03	Hull spare gear	1.00
Lubricating oil	18.66	Ballast keel (including all keel structure and 'Q' tank)	117.68
Battery	118.85		
Main motors	37.00		
HP air compressors	3.14		
Air reservoirs	7.50		
Cooling plant	4.00	**Total**	1357.45

TABLE 3: REPORT ON SEA TRIALS, HMS AMPHION

The sea trials of HMS *Amphion* were carried out between 9 February and 12 April 1945. The programme was as follows:

9.2.45:	One-hour full power trial. Manoeuvring and astern steering. Interference on main circulating system of blowing main tanks. Hand steering. After hydroplane trials
11/12.2.45:	Diesel electric trial. 30 hours consumption trial. Measured mile runs at 1/5, 2/5, 3/5, 4/5 power
13.2.45:	Anchor trials. Diving trials
14.2.45:	Eight-hour full power trial. Measured mile runs at full speed
27.3.45:	Full power acceptance trial (2 hours)
28.3.45:	Full power surface speed trials with 5ft 7in pitch propellers. Submerged full power speed trials with same propellers
2.4.45:	Full power surface speed trials with 5ft 4in pitch propellers. Submerged full power speed trials with same propellers
3.4.45:	Dive to 300ft
12.4.45:	Deep diving trials to 400ft, 500ft, and 600ft

Speed trials. The propellers for 'A' class submarines were designed to absorb full power 3 months out of dock and the dimensions were: pitch 5ft 4in, diameter 5ft 9in, area 13.5ft². It was also decided to fit 'clean bottom' propellers to the first vessel for comparative trials. These propellers were of 5ft 7in pitch, 5ft 9in diameter and 13.5ft² area. The maximum speed achieved during the trials was 18.672kts at 473.6rpm, developing 4420bhp. This was at full power, with no load, with a sea state of 3–1 and a wind of 8–10kts. It was decided to adopt the 5ft 4in pitch propellers as the propellers for the class. It should be noted that the speed obtained during the preliminary sea trials was slightly less than had been anticipated; the vessel was examined in dock and it was found possible to blank approximately 100 free-flooding holes.
Steering trials. The most important point is that it was found possible to control the rudder on one cylinder only up to an angle of 30° to 33° at full speed. It was found that 33° of rudder was reached in 27 seconds but it should be noted that 30° was reached in only 15 seconds.
Hydroplane trials. The gears worked satisfactorily in power. In 'hand' the efforts on the after planes were on the high side but it was found possible for one man to operate the gear between 20° dive and 20° rise at 4.7kts in 30 seconds and between 'hard rise' and 'hard dive' at 4kts in 44 seconds. The latter met the requirements but the former should have been 6kts.

Deep diving trials. The deep diving trials of HMS *Amphion* were carried out east of Barm in the Sea of the Hebrides on 12 April 1945. The dives were carried out as follows:
1. To 400ft, returning to periscope depth.
2. To 500ft, during which strain measurements were taken both diving and surfacing, returning to periscope depth.
3. To 600ft, during which strain measurements were taken, returning to the surface.

The dives were entirely satisfactory. This was reported to the Admiralty, Admiral Submarines and Captain Submarines by signal immediately on surfacing.

Results
1. Strain measurements were taken at previously selected positions using the new type of clock gauge. These gauges were moderately successful.
2. It was necessary to pump out 450 gallons on going from periscope depth to 600ft, to maintain the trim.
3. Both ballast pump and trim pump operated satisfactorily at 600ft, although a relief valve lifted on the trim pump.
4. Hydroplane gears, water-tight doors, steering gear, were all operated satisfactorily at 600ft. The signal ejectors were tested dry at 550ft.
5. The pressure in the external oil fuel tanks was controlled throughout all the dives by the internal equalising valves – the external equalising tanks being shut off.
6. The maximum depth reached was 609ft, depth of water being 100–130 fathoms on the chart.
7. Periscopes were adjusted 1½in clear of their buffers in the lowered position at periscope depth. At 400ft the 7½in periscope had lowered 1⅜in and the 9½in periscope lowered 1¾in. At periscope depth there was 7/16in and 9/16in permanent stretch in the wires. This was taken up before diving to 500ft. At 500ft the wires had stretched approximately 2in in both periscopes. At 600ft the wires had stretched 2¼in and 2⅜in respectively.
8. Battens were rigged as follows:
   Between upper bow torpedo tubes – no deflection.
   Between after end of starboard upper bow tube and 26 bulkhead – maximum deflection, 0.45in, no permanent set.
   Between underside of gun access trunk hatch coaming and pressure hull – maximum deflection, 0.01in, no permanent set.

given the larger patrol areas in which they would be expected to operate, it was regarded as essential that the 'A' class should also be heavily armed, and that they should carry the maximum number of reload torpedoes.

However, great emphasis had also been placed on improving the diving depth of these new boats and the only way to achieve this was to make the pressure hull completely circular throughout. This of course, had the desired effect, increasing the diving depth from 350ft to 500ft. However, the shape of the pressure hull meant that only four internal torpedo tubes could be fitted forward. Two extra tubes were mounted externally in the bow and this brought the number up to six. Similarly, the shape of the pressure hull aft now allowed room for two internal torpedo tubes to be fitted. An additional pair of external tubes were mounted above these and this brought the total torpedo armament to ten 21in tubes with space for ten reload torpedoes inside the hull. Although the number of torpedo tubes fitted in the 'A' class was less than in the 'T' class, the fact that the after, internal tubes could be reloaded actually increased the number of torpedoes carried from seventeen to twenty.

The internal torpedo tubes fitted in the 'A' class were classified as Dry Semi-Slack Fit Type and each tube was made in two sections known as the inboard and outboard lengths. The inboard length was approximately 110in long and made of 0.375in steel plate rolled and welded to give an internal diameter of 21.75in. The outboard length was made up in two sections, a long section of ½in thick steel plate and a shorter section with an enlarged internal diameter which was known as the head space. The bow cap was hydraulically operated from the ship's telemotor system, the operation automatically opening a hinge bow shutter.

The external tubes were classified as the Dry Close Fit Type, each tube consisting of three gunmetal sections which were bolted together with spigot joints. In the early vessels the tube's outer door was opened by rod gearing from inside the submarine. This system was later improved by the fitting of a high-powered ram on the front of each tube.

Reloading the internal tubes was assisted by a power press fitted in the after end of each torpedo stowage compartment. However there were no suitable reloading facilities for the external tubes whilst at sea. The 'A' class were also equipped to lay mines through the internal torpedo tubes. They were usually Mk V mines and were stowed in the forward and after torpedo stowage compartments.

Gun armament. With the exceptions of *Andrew*, which was completed without anti-aircraft armament, *Artful*, which was completed without any gun armament and *Acheron*, whose guns were removed within months of

TABLE 4: **PARTICULARS OF DECK GUNS**

4in QF Mk XXIII				
Length	137.56in			
Weight with BM, but unloaded	14cwt 0qtr 1lb			
Weight without BM and unloaded	13cwt 0qtr 2lb			
Bore diameter	4in			
Length of bore	132.16in (33.04cal)			
Length of rifling	116.58in			
Rifling (1 turn in 25 calibres)	32 grooves			
Muzzle velocity	1750ft per sec			
The S2 gun mounting				
Weight	Ton	Cwt	Qtr	Lbs
Gun		14	0	1
Gun cradle and fittings		13	1	8
Gun carriage and fittings	1	1	0	20
Base		12	2	26
Gun shield and platform (see below)	1	11	1	19
Sighting gear		3	1	3
Total	4	15	3	21
Includes voice pipes, ammunition trough, range and deflection receiver brackets and supports				
Limits of elevation	+30° to −10°			
Training gear ratio	1 turn of handles to 2.95° of training			
Elevating gear ratio	1 turn of handles to 3° of elevation			
Initial compression on run out springs	1585lb			
Final load on run out springs	3170lb			
Recoil working	24in			
Metal to metal	26in			
Capacity of recoil buffer and make up tank	14.5 pints			
Liquid in system	Oil DTD 44D (OM1)			
Forces on recoil	14.2 tons			
Upward lift on mounting	10 tons			
Downward blow	12.25 tons			
Ammunition				
Weight of projectile	35lb 13oz			
Weight of charge	3lb 12oz			
Base of mounting	60in diameter			
Holding down bolts	1in diam, 24 bolts on 57.5in PC			

completion, 'A' class submarines entered service with a 4in Mk XXIII gun forward of the conning tower and a 20mm Oerlikon on a 'bandstand' aft. In view of the fact that A-boats were the last class of British submarine designed to carry deck weapons it might be useful at this stage to look briefly at the history of gun armament as it applies to the development of British submarines.

Small calibre guns were first introduced to British submarines during the 1914–18 war. From 1915 a 12pdr or other smaller weapon was fitted on the casing forward of the conning tower, although it was only later that construction allowed for gun hatches to be part of the design at the drawing-board stage. Once the idea was found to be practical, the ammunition used being cheaper to produce than the torpedo, it was introduced in all new submarine designs; 4in guns were mounted as standard on the larger units of the 'J', 'K' and 'L' classes. There were some notable exceptions of course, such as the 12in Mk IX gun fitted to the 'M' class laid down in 1916 and the 5.2in twin mountings fitted to the *X 1*, which was launched in 1923, whilst a 3in weapon was fitted in the 'G' class, *Nautilus* and *Swordfish*.

From 1925 a standard submarine gun and mounting was designed, to carry the 4in QF Mk XII gun on the S1 (Submarine) mounting. This was to become the standard weapon fitted to the large Royal Navy patrol submarines from the period between the wars through to 1945, and it was fitted with variously shaped gun shields and breastworks. Naturally, the design underwent a number of improvements and modifications during this period. In December 1942 the DNO (Director of Naval Ordinance) informed the Board that the development of a new 4in weapon was being put in hand. It was to fire fixed ammunition and would be less clumsy to handle than the existing round for the QF 4in Mk XII gun. It was also required to provide a shell of improved lethality with a range requirement of 8000yds (slightly over 4.5 miles) at 20° elevation. To achieve this an increase in calibre was considered and handling trials were carried out with 4.5in dummy ammunition. As a result, it was found that a new 4.5in round was too heavy for use on operations in submarines, and that the development of a new 4in gun on a totally redesigned submarine mounting, the S2, would therefore proceed.

In March 1943 the CEAD forwarded a design of 4in gun which included a simplified breech mechanism to replace the QF Mk XII and XII* guns, as carried on the existing S1 mounting. Fine details were discussed at the meeting in May and the Mark number XXII was allocated. The twist of rifling was increased from 1:30 to 1:25, to make the weapon more suitable for a 40lb shell, which was then under consideration, in order to provide a heavier explosive weight on the target. Thus the two aims came together for the design of the new equipment and the updating of the 'in use' submarine gun. With the development of the new 40lb shell, the range requirement could be met with a muzzle velocity as low as 1650fs. This permitted the use in the new equipment of a cartridge case shorter by about 6in than the existing QF Mk XII and XXII gun cases.

Later it was decided that the new shell, weighing only 37½lb instead of the original 40lb, would not be used in the Mk XII and XXII guns, but would be developed for use only in the new equipment with its shorter cartridge cases. Shell designs were approved for trial and test firings were arranged. A uniform twist of rifling of 1:25 was adopted. In February 1944, the CEAD reported discussions with Vickers-Armstrongs, and forwarded proposals for a 4in gun to fire a 40lb shell with a muzzle velocity of 1650fs. A muzzle brake was considered but the DNO decided that it be rejected on account of blast. The board entirely concurred with the decision, not only for the above reason, but also because the gun would be totally out of action if the muzzle brake was damaged. Nickel plating of the gun and mechanism was discussed and the above gun was called the Mk XXIII.

In October 1945, it was decided that the development of the Mk XXIII gun on the S2 mounting should proceed for new submarines, which included the 'A' class and 'T' class and for retrospective fitting. Pending the introduction of the 'Universal' shell, the existing 35lb shell would be used.

The main visual aid to identification between the two mountings, the S1, which during its long life carried Mk XII, XII* or XXII guns, and the S2, which mounted the much improved Mk XXIII gun, was that the earlier mounting was of the pedestal type, whilst the S2 was of a box type construction. In the S1, the recuperator and recoil cylinders were carried under the gun barrel, whilst the later S2 had the gun cradle, recoil and run out gear above the barrel, and thus plainly visible.

A little known fact concerning the deck armament designed for the 'A' class is that in April 1945 drawings were prepared proposing the

TABLE 5: **PARTICULARS OF ANTI-AIRCRAFT GUNS**

20mm Oerlikon		
Weight (with splined barrel)		141lb
Weight (without splined barrel)		150lb
Weight of shoulder piece with 300kt sight		32lb
Overall length		8ft
Calibre		20mm (0.8in approx)
Rifling		9 right-hand grooves
Muzzle velocity		2725ft per sec
Rate of fire (in automatic fire)		465–480rpm
Maximum range at 45° elevation		6250yds
Effective range		1000–1200yds
Magazine		
Capacity		60 rounds
Weight (full)		61lb
Weight (empty)		30lb
Weight of one round (nominal)		8oz 2 drams
Deck blows	**Mk VIIA S/M Mtg**	**Twin Mk 12A Mtg**
Upward lift	1.54 tons	0.52 tons
Downward blow	2.45 tons	1.65 tons
Recoil force	8 tons	1000lb (one gun)
Mk 12A mounting		
Maximum elevation		80°
Maximum depression		12½°
Muzzle sweep		4ft 2in radius
Height of trunnions above deck		4ft 7½in
Horizontal distance between gun centres		7½in
Weight of complete mounting less ammunition		20 cwt 3qtr 10lb
Outside diameter of base		2ft 6in
Holding down arrangements		10 ⅞in BSW bolts on 27¼in PCD

installation of a 6pdr gun on the after casing between the Oerlikon platform and the engine room hatch. The gun was to have been supported on a single, portable mounting and five ready-use ammunition lockers capable of holding a total of 125 rounds were included in the design. Given the type of area in which the 'A' class would have been operating during the war, the desirability of such a weapon is clearly understandable. However, with the sudden ending of hostilities and the subsequent cancellation of many of the boats the gun was never fitted.

Anti-aircraft armament. From 1941 the 20mm Oerlikon gun became available for close defence against enemy aircraft, and was fitted as a single mounting carried on a small bandstand aft of the conning tower, where it had a good field of fire – at least from astern. With the exception of the 'U' and 'V' classes, it was added to vessels then building and to older vessels during their refits, particularly boats of the 'S' and 'T' classes.

Briefly, the 20mm Oerlikon was an automatic gun designed for high-angle close-range anti-aircraft fire, with an effective range of 1000-1200yds. The barrel and breech did not recoil, and the gun mechanism was operated by the pressure generated by the explosion of the cartridge or round in the chamber. The empty case was blown back against the breech, forcing it to the rear against the tension of the barrel springs. This backward movement ejected the empty case, and as the momentum was all but expended the barrel springs reasserted themselves to carry the breech mechanism forward, loading a new round from the magazine into the chamber for firing. The breech was not locked at the time of firing, which took place just prior to the round being fully home in the chamber. The neck of the shell case expanded with the explosion to form a gas-tight seal. The gun could be left cocked ready for instant action for long periods in surface ships, but would not be left in that condition in submarines.

The single Mark I, II, II USN and IV USN guns (all were interchangeable) were produced in the United Kingdom and the USA and supplied under lease-lend. The Mk VIIA mounting was modified for use in submarines and was then known as the Mk VIIA Submarine Mounting, the main differences being that a splinter shield was not fitted and drainage holes were cut in the lower part of the pedestal and the access hole cover plate was omitted. Other items were made of stainless steel or rust-proof material.

The Mk VII mounting is still in use today, and proved very useful in the Falklands War, in the role for which it was designed all those years ago. It may be recognised by the gun and its cradle being unevenly balanced (muzzle-heavy) in the trunnions in order to provide a short working radius in elevation, to the rear end of the gun. To counteract this uneven balance, to each side of the rear end of the cradle is attached a large cam with a chain secured to, and passing round, the outer periphery of each. Limits of elevation were from 15° depression to 85° elevation, which was later reduced to 75° as a result of war experience. To obviate rust formation, the upper bearing and counter-balance guide rollers were constructed of stainless steel.

A twin 20mm hand-worked Mk 12A mounting was fitted experimentally to HMS *Aeneas* for trials, and was also fitted to several other vessels, including *Alliance*, for short periods, but was not available for general issue as a wider bandstand was required to work the larger, heavier twin mounting.

MAIN ENGINES AND AUXILIARY EQUIPMENT

The main engines used in 'A' class submarines were either of the Vickers design or Admiralty pattern. They were arranged on two shafts and each was capable of producing 2150bhp at 460rpm, giving a maximum surface speed of 18½kts. Although basically similar in general construction there were minor design differences between the two types.

The Vickers main engine. These were eight-cylinder, single-acting, four-stroke supercharged engines. The cylinder bore was 17.4in and the stroke 18.5in.

Supercharger: A positive displacement, three-lobe Rootes blower was driven off the after end of the crankshaft through a train of single helical wheels and a friction clutch. A cushion drive was incorporated in the train.

Fuel injection: Fuel was supplied to a common rail by two blocks of three pumps driven off the forward end of the crankshaft through a cushion driving wheel in a train of five wheels incorporating drives to a fuel booster pump and an 'Amal' drain pump. The fuel spray valves were mechanically operated and their timing was independent of the pumps.

Turning gear: The engine could be turned by an electric motor or by a ratchet hand lever, the drive being transmitted to a wheel on the engine clutch.

Air starting: The engine was started by high pressure air which was supplied to each cylinder by a cam-operated distributor in the centre of the engine and then through a combined air start and relief valve on the back of each cylinder.

Engine clutch: The main drive was transmitted through a telemotor-operated dog clutch secured to the after end of the crankshaft.

TABLE 6: THE VICKERS MAIN ENGINE

Cycle	4-stroke
No of cylinders	8
Firing order	Port 16748325 Stb 15238476
Bore	17.4in
Stroke	18.5in
Compression ratio	12.65
Crankshaft journal diameter	11.40in
Camshaft journal diameter	3.8in
Weight of engine dry, complete with supercharger, damper, turning gear and motor and holding down bolts	35½ tons
Weight of engine wet	36½ tons
Weight of engine clutch	1½ tons
Maximum power	1613bhp; supercharged 2150bhp
Maximum rpm when propelling on both engines	460rpm; supercharged 460rpm
Maximum pressures when developing max bhp	690lb per sq in; supercharged 860lb per sq in
Exhaust temperatures when developing max bhp	760°F; supercharged 850°F
Supercharger	
Induction air pressure to full power	4.72lb per sq in
Induction air temperature at full power	150°F
Supercharger rpm at full power	1865
Power to drive the supercharger at full power	200hp (approx)
Air start system	
Normal starting air pressure	350lb per sq in
Air start bottle pressure	900lb per sq in

TABLE 7: THE ADMIRALTY MAIN ENGINE

Cycle	4-stroke
No of cylinders	8
Firing order	Port 13258674 Stb 14768523
Bore	17.5in
Stroke	18in
Compression ratio	12.56
Crankshaft journal diameter	11.5in (11.75in in No 11 main bearing)
Camshaft journal diameter	4.5in
Weight of engine dry	38⅙ tons
Weight of engine wet	39 tons
Weight of clutch	3⅚ tons
Maximum power	1510bhp; supercharged 2150bhp
Maximum rpm when propelling on both engines	390rpm; supercharged 460rpm
Maximum pressures when developing max bhp	780lb per sq in; supercharged 970lb per sq in
Exhaust temperatures when developing max bhp	870°F; supercharged 975°F
Supercharger	
Induction air pressure at 460rpm of engine	4.5lb per sq in
Induction air temperature at 460rpm of engine	Not to exceed 105°F
Supercharger rpm at 460rpm	1720rpm
Supercharger power to drive at 460 engine rpm	210hp
Air start system	
Normal starting pressure	1000lb per sq in
Starting bottle pressure	2000lb per sq in

Exhaust system: Twin exhaust valves were fitted to each cylinder head and discharged through an exhaust manifold, a group exhaust valve and then to an exhaust tank located in the superstructure.
Cooling arrangements: The cylinder liners, heads, exhaust valves, exhaust manifold, group exhaust valves, supercharger air coolers, main motor coolers and lubricating oil coolers were all sea-water cooled. Three motor-driven main circulating water pumps supplied the cooling water and two emergency pumps, driven from the propeller shafts were also fitted.
Engine controls: The starting, running, engine clutch and supercharger clutch controls were all grouped together at the forward end of each engine above the fuel pumps. The principal gauges were contained on a panel above the controls.
The Admiralty main engine. This was an eight-cylinder, single-acting, four-stroke supercharged engine. The cylinder bore was 17.5in and the stroke 18in.
Supercharger: A positive displacement Rootes type blower, the camshaft and the engine-driven lubricating oil pump were driven off the after end of the camshaft through a train of eleven single-helical gearwheels. The blower was permanently incorporated in the gear train, except in the case of *Acheron* where an oil-operated clutch was fitted at the upper end of the gear train.
Fuel injection: An overspeed fuel cut-off trip gear operating at 530rpm and a fuel feed pump were driven from the forward end of the crankshaft. Fuel was supplied by eight independent CAV pumps, each sited alongside its own unit and driven by the camshaft. Bryce type fuel injectors were fitted but no fuel timing control was fitted as the pumps automatically advanced the point of injection as the fuel supply was increased.
Turning gear: The engines could be turned by a single electric motor placed between the engines. Both or either engine could be turned and a hand turning gear could be fitted to the top of the turning gear motor.
Air starting: This was similar to the system used on the Vickers engine.
Engine clutch: The main drive was transmitted through a Bibby spring coupling and a telemotor-operated Admiralty type radial-plunger clutch. The clutch could also be operated by a local handpump system. The cooling arrangements and engine controls were similar to those fitted to the Vickers engine.
Vessels fitted with the Vickers main engine. *Alcide*, *Alderney*, *Alliance*, *Ambush*, *Amphion*, *Anchorite*, *Andrew*, *Astute*, *Auriga* and *Aurochs*.
Vessels fitted with Admiralty pattern main engines. *Acheron*, *Aeneas*, *Alaric*, *Artemis*, *Artful* and *Affray*.
Ace and *Achates* were engined by J Brown.
Main engine shafting. The main shafting, between the engine clutch and the propeller, was in four lengths supported at the main motor bearings, the thrust block, the inner and outer stern tube bushes and the 'A' bracket bush. The end section between the propeller and the first coupling – which was immediately forward of the stern tube bush, was known as the tail shaft and could be withdrawn from outboard. The shafting up to the main motor shaft had a diameter of 7in, except in way of the 'A' bracket and the inner and outer stern bushes where it was increased to 7½in and in way of the thrust block and tail clutch where it was increased to 7¼in.
Propellers: The propellers were made of manganese bronze and were

three-bladed, the port one being left-handed and the starboard one right-handed. They were supported by an 'A' bracket which consisted of a forged steel shell secured to the plating of No 5 main tank by two forged steel arms.

The stern tube: The ¾in thick stern tubes had an internal diameter of 14½in and were welded into position after the pressure hull was completed. Liners were contained in either end of the tube to take the inner and outer bushes. The entire assembly was tested to 300lb per square inch.

Shaft brake: The shaft brake consisted of two Ferrodo lined steel straps hinged to a bottom casting. To stop the shaft rotating the two straps were drawn together by an operating screw and handwheel which caused them to bind on the shaft coupling. The purpose of the brake was to stop the shaft rotating and thus enable the tail clutch to be engaged.

Tail clutch: The purpose of the tail clutch was to disconnect the tail shaft so that the main motor, when it was clutched to the main engine, could be used to recharge the main batteries. Generally it was of the hand-operated dog type, although in *Aurochs* and *Alaric* telemotor-operated friction clutches were fitted.

Thrust block: The purpose of the thrust block was to transmit the thrust of the propellers to the hull and support the weight of the shaft. Six Michell thrust pads were mounted on either side of a thrust collar, the entire assembly being contained within a cast steel and aluminium housing.

Main motors. The main motors were compound wound, the field magnet being under the influence of two windings, a shunt coil and a series coil. Each pair of armatures were mounted on a single shaft and the entire assembly was enclosed within a water-tight casing. Two 500-watt heating elements were fitted to prevent the motors from becoming too cold. They were attached to the inside of the casing and supplied from the CP ring main.

Coolers were provided to prevent the motors from overheating. Each motor was fitted with a variable speed fan which was secured to the outer casing. The fan drew air from the motor room and discharged it into the motor casing through an air duct. After cooling the motor the heated air finally passed through either the forward or after coolers and back into the motor room. The coolers were supplied with sea water from the after circulating water system.

Main battery. The main battery used in 'A' class submarines was made by the Exide, D P Kathanode and Tudor Battery companies. The battery was in two equal sections and consisted of 224 lead acid cells with a designed capacity of 6630 ampere-hours at an average pressure of approximately 2 volts. The two sections gave a nominal pressure of 220 volts, the sections being connected in parallel.

No 1 battery section was stowed in No 1 battery tank beneath the central part of the accommodation space, a clearance of about 10in being left between the top of the cells and the deck of the accommodation space. Access to the tank was gained through rubber seated screw-down battery boards, through which all the cells could be reached. The tank was lined with Rosbonite to prevent corrosion of the ship's structure by acid. The cells stood on waxed teak gratings to which were secured rubber pads to prevent contact between the cells and the ship's structure. The tank floor sloped aft to a sump which could be sighted through a port in the Engineer's store.

No 2 battery section was stowed in No 2 battery compartment under the aft end of the control room. The cells were arranged in tiers, a cell top to deckhead clearance of about 3ft being left in the centre. One access hatch was provided and portable fore and aft gangways were sited each side of the battery centreline to provide access to all the cells. In the No 2 battery compartment the sump was at the forward end of the compartment. The battery tanks were ventilated through natural air intakes and two 10in × 3in exhaust fans were fitted in the exhaust trunking of each battery.

Oil fuel system. Diesel fuel was carried in thirteen storage tanks which were arranged in six separate groups, two inside the pressure hull and four outside. All the tanks which used sea water to displace the fuel supplied to the engines and to compensate for the weight of fuel consumed. An equalising and expansion system was fitted so that when the submarine was dived the pressure in the lightly built external tanks could be balanced with that of the sea outside. No 4 port and starboard main ballast tanks could be used as additional fuel tanks. The capacities and grouping of the tanks is shown below:

Fuel group	Tank	Capacity (gallons)
Forward internal	No 1	4465
	No 2	4465
	No 3	1795
	No 4	1950
Aft internal	—	3125
Port forward external	No 1	2505
	No 2	3420
Starboard forward external	No 1	2505
	No 2	3420
Port aft external	No 3	4040
	No 4	2790
Starboard aft external	No 3	4040
	No 4	2790
No 4 port main ballast tank	—	7205
No 4 starboard main ballast tank	—	7205

Total fuel capacity using No 4 main ballast tanks: 55,720 gallons.
Total fuel capacity without No 4 main ballast tanks: 41,310 gallons.
These figures have to be approximate because tanks are not always of exactly the same size in submarines.

Two De Laval Type 4014 centrifuges were fitted in the engine room. They were used for purifying oil fuel and lubricating oil. They were driven by 1¼hp continuously rated electric motors through a friction clutch and worm gearing and had a maximum capacity of 250 gallons an hour.

AUXILIARY MACHINERY

The trimming system. In 'T' class submarines the forward and after ballast pumps were used for trimming purposes, suctions being taken off the 'main line', which ran down the port side of the submarine. However in the 'A' class an entirely separate trimming system was fitted. The trim line, which also ran down the port side, connected the forward and after trim tanks to a reversible 'Mono' type trim pump which was situated in the control room. Additional tanks for adjusting transverse stability were located outside the pressure hull amidships inside No 3 main ballast tanks port and starboard. They were called 'O' tanks and each had a capacity of 2400 gallons.

Incorporated in the system was a control box. The control box had a wheel with two positions, so by using the pump in either forward or reverse four operations were possible: sea water could be admitted to the 'O' tanks port and starboard or transferred from one side to the other. However, water from the forward trim tank could only be pumped aft and vice versa. The pump was capable of discharging 12 tons per hour at a depth of 100ft and 7 tons per hour at 300ft. A flow meter was fitted to measure the volume of water pumped.

The ballast pump. A Drysdale four-stage electrically driven ballast pump was fitted on the starboard side of the engine room forward of the starting position. It was used primarily to adjust the trim and also as a bilge pump. The pump installation comprised a rotary air pump, an electric motor and a four-stage centrifugal water pump. The unit was silently mounted and was capable of discharging from 150 tons per hour at 80ft to 10 tons per hour at 628ft. The motor developed 29hp at 1880 revolutions.

The pump was connected to a 4½in diameter main line, which ran down the starboard side and by means of a six valve chest was able to take a suction from either forward or aft, discharging into or pumping from the sea. Valve chests were situated throughout the submarine enabling various internal tanks to be connected into the main line. Hose connections were also provided for bilge clearance and cable washing.

The low pressure blower. A Reavell low pressure rotary blower was fitted in the auxiliary machinery space below the wardroom. Its purpose was to bring the submarine to full buoyancy after surfacing thus preserving precious high pressure air. It could also be used for compartment testing and salvage blowing on the surface. The unit comprised of an electric motor driving a rotary blower and both motor and blower were bolted to a common, resiliently mounted bedplate. The blower took its suction from the atmosphere and discharged into the low pressure line through a screw-down non-return valve. Tankside connections were fitted to all five main ballast tanks.

High pressure air service. High pressure air was stored at 4000lb per square inch in fifteen bottles giving a total volume of 136.5cu ft. The bottles were arranged in four groups, any one of which could be used to supply air to the HP ring main or to the main blowing panel in the control room.

HP Air Groups

Group	*Position*	*No of bottles*	*Capacity*
No 1	Torpedo stowage compt (stb)	3	27.3
No 2	Torpedo stowage compt (port)	3	27.3
No 3	Engineer's store	5	45.5
No 4	Auxiliary machinery space	4	36.4
			136.5

The groups could either be recharged by two motor-driven air compressors or through a shore charging connection immediately forward of the gun.

Air compressors. Two Reavell four-stage air compressors were fitted, one in the auxiliary machinery space below the wardroom and the other in the engine room forward of the port starting platform. They were driven by 40hp electric motors and cooled by sea water.

Telemotor system. Hydraulic power for operating equipment such as the periscope and radar masts, the main vents, the hydroplanes, steering and torpedo tube caps was provided by the ship's telemotor system. In the 'A' class the system comprised two 'Imo' telemotor pumps supplying two 6000cu inch capacity air-loaded accumulators, a telemotor oil replenishment tank and an oil storage tank. The supply and return lines, which were of 1in and 1¼in bore respectively ran along the inside of the boat on the port side. Handpumps, in the event of a pump failure were situated in both the forward and after torpedo stowage compartments.

A working pressure of between 1200 and 1500lb per square inch was maintained by the two pumps, the forward of which, together with its air-loaded accumulator was situated in the auxiliary machinery space beneath the wardroom and the after pump in the control room just forward of the wireless office. The after air-loaded accumulator was situated in the motor room.

HYDROPLANES AND STEERING

Hydroplanes. In keeping with normal practice, two sets of hydroplanes were fitted in submarines of the 'A' class. The forward pair were mounted above the waterline, and could be turned in against the bow superstructure to safeguard against damage whilst entering harbour or in a heavy seaway. The after pair were 'fixed' in the 'drowned' position beneath the stern of the submarine and so placed as to take full advantage of the effects of the propeller wash. Both sets of hydroplanes were normally operated from the control room by means of hydraulic power from the ship's telemotor system. Alternative means of control were fitted in the tube space forward and the torpedo stowage compartment aft.

There were two types: (a) cast steel frame with a skin of 8lb plating; (b) fabricated steel frame with a skin of 17lb plating. Cast iron weights were included to balance the hydroplanes about their shafts when immersed in salt water. The inside surfaces were coated with a bituminous solution. The principal components operating the forward hydroplanes, which were situated in the superstructure above the tube space, were: the housing piston, which was used to supply power to fold the hydroplanes up against the sides of the casing when not in use; the tilting piston, used to control the angle of the hydroplanes when in operation; and the handgear, providing power to operate the hydroplanes manually should the telemotor pressure fail. Interlocks were fitted to prevent damage to the system whilst in use.

The after hydroplanes were mounted on a fin immediately forward of the rudder. The tilting piston was secured horizontally just inside the domed end of the pressure hull, the tilting action being transmitted to the hydroplane shaft by a bell-crank lever and connecting rods inside the No 5 main ballast tank. Handgear was also provided for emergency use. The hydroplanes were operated from the control room, the controls being situated on the port side, aft of the steering position. The control valves were originally operated by large wheels. These were later replaced by 'tapper bars', which incidentally had always been the German practice. The principal equipment consisted of: a deep diving gauge, two shallow diving gauges, two clinometers, Evershed transmitters to the local control positions, an after hydroplane locking control valve, and a fore planes housing indicator.

Steering gear. The rudder fitted in 'A' class submarines weighed 4.17 tons and had an effective area of approximately 60sq ft. It was made of fabricated steel and was free flooding. It was supported by the stern fin. A portable gudgeon, secured to the bottom of the fin carried a crown metal bush, into which the rudder pintle fitted, and a hardened steel pad upon which the pintle rested. This gudgeon supported the whole weight of the rudder and was secured to the pin by six 1¼in diameter fitted bolts. A crosshead was keyed to the top of the rudder stock which protruded into the free-flooding space above the No 5 main tank. Connecting rods pivoted at the end of each of the crosshead arms.

The maximum working angle of the rudder was 35° either side of amidships and stops were fitted to prevent more than 37° of movement either way. Lift stops were fitted to the rudder stock bearing casting to prevent the rudder lifting more than $^1/_{16}$in. Two operating cylinders were fitted as there was insufficient room for one large one owing to the space taken up by the two stern internal torpedo tubes. The principal components of the steering gear were: the power cylinders, one port and one starboard, mounted under the torpedo tubes inside the pressure hull (the working stroke of the cylinder was 17.2in and the bore 8.75in); the Hunting gear transmitter, connected by an actuating lever to the port cylinder; the VSG pump, which provided hydraulic power to either side of the steering rams; the Brown's receiver and the Brown's transmitter, transmitting hydraulically the movement of the steering wheel; and finally the Hunting gear receiver (the Hunting gear checked the movement of the rudder once it had reached the desired position; the system was similar to the Brown's system and was charged with a mixture of glycerine and water).

Local control was fitted for use in the event of an hydraulic failure and interlocks were provided to prevent damage to the system whilst in operation. The steering wheel in the control room was later replaced by a 'tapper bar' of the type used to control the hydroplanes. There was no bridge steering position.

THE SNORT MAST

Although Dutch submarine designers had first shown an interest in the principle of running the diesel engine whilst submerged by drawing air through an air mast, it was Germany that developed the idea and began to include first folding and then periscopic schnorchel masts in their submarines during the war. Britain, however, was slower to take up the idea and it was not until 1946 that a 'T' class submarine, HMS *Truant*, became the first British submarine to be equipped with such a mast (christened 'snort' in RN service). During the development stage of the 'A' class serious consideration was given to the possibility of including a snort mast in the design, and a review of the problem showed that no technical difficulties stood in the way of fitting this new equipment. However, it was felt at the time that there were no pressing operational requirements for such a device and the idea was not taken up. Consequently, it was not until as late as 1947 that the snort mast first began to appear on 'A' class submarines.

In all, four variations of snort mast were fitted to the 'A' class. The original design featured a combined snort induction and exhaust pipe. The two were attached to one another and were raised and lowered hydraulically. The mast housed into the casing on the port side at the after end of the conning tower and the snort induction head valve was float-controlled. This type of mast was originally fitted to *Aurochs*, *Alliance*, *Ambush*, *Anchorite*, *Andrew*, *Aeneas*, *Artful* and *Acheron*.

Very shortly after its introduction the system was modified by repositioning the snort exhaust pipe in a fixed position on the after end of the ANF radar mast, so only the snort induction mast was raised and lowered. The second modification to the system involved replacing the float-controlled induction head valve with an improved 'ring float' head valve. This type of head valve was first fitted to HMS *Andrew* in 1949 and with the exception of the *Affray*, which was lost before the modification could be made, was fitted to all of the class. It is this system which will now be described in greater detail.

TABLE 8: **SNORT MASTS**

Type: Combined snort induction and exhaust.
Fitted during building, 1947–49: *Aurochs, Alliance, Ambush, Anchorite, Andrew, Artful, Acheron.*
Fitted after completion: *Aeneas*

Type: Snort exhaust fixed to ANF radar mast.
This was a modification; no vessels were completed in this form; fitted 1948–57: *Amphion, Astute, Alderney, Affray, Auriga, Aeneas, Alcide, Alaric, Aurochs, Alliance, Ambush, Artemis, Anchorite, Andrew, Artful, Acheron.*

Type: 'Ring float' induction head valve; snort exhaust fixed to ANF radar mast. From 1949: All vessels except *Affray*

Type: Periscopic snort induction mast, housed in an extension to the after part of the fin.
Fitted 1965–74: *Auriga, Aeneas, Alliance, Ambush, Artemis, Anchorite, Andrew, Acheron.*

The 'ring float' controlled head valve. The float and valve assembly was fitted over a galvanised mild steel guide pipe which was bolted to the snort mast. The float, which was made in four parts, was constructed of aluminium alloy and alloy sheet. To prevent the valve from freezing under arctic conditions a heating element was fitted in the space between the valve and the hood, supply for the assembly running inside the guide pipe and induction tube through a gland at the foot of the snort mast.

A galvanised mild steel hood covered the entire assembly, the bottom half of which was pierced by ten flood and drain holes covered with galvanised wire mesh. The air intake was through two top sectors and four side ports cut in the after side of the hood and covered with galvanised wire mesh.

The induction tube. The mast consisted of a galvanised tube 28ft long and streamlined in section. An internal strengthening plate, perforated for lightness divided the mast along its entire length. The head valve and its guide pipe were secured to the top of the mast by a sixteen-bolt flange, whilst the base was machined and welded into a hollow steel forging about which the mast pivoted and was known as the mast trunnion bearing. When raised to its full elevation the mast was secured to the after end of the conning tower by a locking plate and bolt, which was secured from inside the submarine.

Water trap. A water trap, which was a light steel cylinder fitted with a transverse baffle plate was used for separating any water that happened to splash down the mast whilst 'snorting' (running submerged on diesels). The water was drained into 'R' port compensating tank through a hull valve and the drain was known as 'snort drain one'. It was kept open during snorting and was also used to drain down the system before snorting commenced.

Mast raising ram. The induction mast was raised and lowered hydraulically by the action of an operating cylinder applying leverage to a forked crank arm welded to the mast base. The hydraulic pressure was supplied by the ship's telemotor system. In order to prevent an oil leak from betraying the submarine's position, the telemotor cylinder and piping was totally enclosed by a pressure-tight steel cover.

Induction hull valve. The induction hull valve was enclosed by a cast steel pressure-tight dome secured by studs to a shaped pad on the engine room pressure hull. A telemotor-operated ram opened and shut the valve by means of a fulcrum lever and operating rod which were situated below the valve in the engine room.

Snort muffler valves. When running on the surface the main engines discharged their exhaust gases through a group exhaust hull valve to a muffler tank in the superstructure above, and then overboard. When snorting, the exhaust gases were diverted forward via the group exhaust hull valve to a snort muffler valve and thence to the standing snort exhaust pipe. The purpose of the snort muffler valve was to shut off the snort exhaust when running on the surface. The valve was operated manually from inside the submarine and was provided with a high pressure air blow to enable water to be expelled from snort exhaust pipe just prior to starting the engines.

The snort system was further modified during the mid 1960s by the introduction of a periscopic induction mast. This modification was carried out on *Auriga*, *Aeneas*, *Alliance*, *Ambush*, *Artemis*, *Anchorite*, *Andrew* and *Acheron* and involved the removal of the original folding induction pipe, trunnion bearings and lifting press, extending the after end of the fin by some 3ft, and installing the new periscopic unit immediately behind the ANF radar mast. Improvements were also made to the head valve, and the water trap was replaced by a helical dryer which removed any moisture from the incoming air by imparting a swirling effect, centrifugal force throwing out the heavier water which was then drained away.

THE TROPICAL 'SNORT' CRUISE OF HMS ALLIANCE

The tropical snort cruise of HMS *Alliance* lasted for 30 days, from 9 October to 8 November 1947. During this period she covered a distance of 3193 miles, the route taken being approximately from south-east of the Canary Islands to Cape Verde, then due south, due east along the Equator, altering north-east to Cape Palmas, and then northwards up the African coast to Freetown. The object of the cruise was to obtain information about the living conditions onboard a submarine on an extended snort patrol in tropical climates and was conducted entirely with the use of the snort, with the exception of three nights when the *Alliance* went deep to take bathythermograph recordings and to work the battery.

The *Alliance* left Portsmouth on 1 October 1947, and after calling at Gilbraltar for fuel and water, dived in a position south-west of the Canary Islands. From the very beginning it was recognised that boredom, especially among the ratings, would be a major problem. Fortunately it had been possible before leaving Portsmouth to obtain the loan of a cine-projector and about a dozen films, together with numerous records and a number of BBC record programmes. Film shows were held nightly in the forward torpedo stowage compartment during the dog watches and despite the full torpedo load carried it was possible to accommodate about a third of the ship's complement at each performance. This turned out to be a greater success than had been anticipated as it had the effect of reducing the number of people occupying the messes at the time. Unfortunately, however, during the last week of the cruise a fault developed in the sound circuit of the projector completely scrambling the sound track.

From the very start of the cruise *Alliance* developed problems with her electric distillers. A salt water leak had put one of them out of action at a very early stage and the output of the other was greatly reduced. The consumption of fresh water began at an unacceptably high rate and after several unsuccessful attempts had been made at rationing the consumption, orders had to be given forbidding the use of fresh water for washing. The only alternative was to use the air conditioning plant condensate, of which about a ton a day was being drained into the bilges. A semi-rotary pump was rigged, and a rubber hose led up the radar mast well into the control room. Anyone wanting a wash badly enough had to trust the panel watchkeeper to fill his bucket with uncontaminated water and disappear below to earn the privilege of such a luxury.

For one extremely unpleasant 24-hour period the air conditioning plants were shut down completely, and the snort flap valve changed over to the ships's ventilation trunking, so that warm, humid air was drawn down the snort mast and into the ventilation system. The effect was the immediate sweating of men and machinery. Men awoke in the morning soaking in sweat and feeling 'perfectly lousy'. It was a day that few aboard would have cared to repeat and had it continued longer would have resulted in an outbreak of prickly heat. As it was, only one mild case was reported during the entire cruise. However, the experiment did have the effect of impressing on those aboard who took such things for granted the value of air conditioning plants.

The general conditions prevailing in the boat were such that shirts and shorts could be worn without discomfort, barring any strenuous exertions, and although cramped, life was considered to be fairly tolerable. The most uncomfortable watchkeeping position in the ship was on the distillers in the auxiliary machinery compartment where there was very little air movement, very high humidity, and temperatures of up to 114°F.

The main engines behaved well during the cruise, although one major defect occurred to the port supercharger drive, which was found to have been aggravated by a manufacturing error in the cushion wheel drive. The snort exhaust valves, as had been expected, were a bone of contention. They proved to be unreliable from a water-tightness viewpoint due to distortion and required constant attention to prevent the operating and grinding gear from seizing up. On more than one occasion sea water found its way into the cylinders when stopping the engines. Because of this defect every effort was made to avoid shutting off both engines together in cases of emergency. The practice adopted if the snort head dipped for a considerable period was to shut down on one engine just before 6in of depression was reached and to take out the engine clutch to make the electric motor available to regain the trim. Meanwhile the exhaust valve was ground in. This ensured that one engine was dry, and available to start, in case the second engine became flooded in the event of that also having to be stopped. The fact that the exhaust from both engines 'married' before entering the snort mast ensured that no flooding back would occur so long as one engine was running at medium speed.

The maximum depression reached during the cruise was about 8in of mercury, but *Alliance* was fortunate in having fair weather all the way, so that there was very little 'pumping' of the atmosphere in the boat – if it goes on for long enough this can have a demoralizing effect on the crew. The condition is caused by several heavy swells passing over the snort head, or even more acutely by repeated loss of depth control due to bad weather. 'Pumping' did however occur for short periods and this had the effect of lowering the dew-point sufficiently to produce fogging in various parts of the boat, notably in the wardroom. The tinned foods carried onboard often reacted noisily to the various states of atmospheric depression as the ends of cans buckled under the fluctuating pressure. No insurmountable difficulties were experienced during night snorting. The chief problems were those of visibility, especially on moonless nights. A slightly shallower depth of 35ft was maintained at night for this reason.

Depth-keeping trials were carried out at intervals, using the after hydroplanes only. The success achieved in these early trials was such that for the last 7½ days only after hydroplane control was employed, and this included one dive to 340ft for bathythermograph records. The success of this method was largely attributed to the halving of the human error by only having one hydroplane operator. This, however, did not pass off without moments of interest, since when error crept in it did so with a vengeance: twice during the last week the 'bubble' was chased off the inclinometer, fortunately forward, until *Alliance* was ploughing herself steadily along with the fore-end depth gauge reading 5ft, and the after end one 50ft!

At 0900 on Saturday 8 November 1947 *Alliance* surfaced and both conning tower hatches were opened together for the first time in 30 days. The stench of marine life drawn down into the boat was at least a change – if not unpleasant. Later that day *Alliance* closed on a native fishing boat from French Guinea, the occupants of which offered to sell some snapper at 10 dollars a piece. Fortunately a more appropriate form of currency was found, which resulted in the most delicious dish of fish and chips imaginable. *Alliance* then headed for Freetown, arriving alongside King Tom Jetty at 0800 on Sunday 9 November 1947.

THE ARCTIC 'SNORT' CRUISE OF HMS AMBUSH

HMS *Ambush* left the Clyde on 12 February 1948 to carry out a prolonged snort cruise between Jan Mayen and Bear Island. She returned to the Firth of Forth on 18 March. This was the third in a series of long snort patrols, the first having been carried out by HMS *Taciturn* in temperate waters, and the second by *Alliance*, as described above, under tropical conditions. The objects of *Ambush*'s patrol were:

1. To gain further information on the physiological problems associated with snort propulsion, in particular under conditions of cold and rough weather.

2. To obtain further data on speeds, fuel consumptions, engine loading, etc, in order to deduce the most suitable and most economical methods of snorting for long periods.

The readings required to achieve the first object were taken by a medical officer, whose main consideration was the effect which vacuum fluctuations would have on the ears of the crew, and the readings required to achieve the second object were taken by the boat's own complement. During the patrol, both icing conditions and exceptionally rough weather were experienced. It was therefore possible to assess the limiting effect which these factors impose on a submarine fitted with a snort mast. On 15 February an attempt was made to start snorting in a position just inside the arctic circle and due north of the Faroe Islands. However, owing to a leak in the bridge induction master valve it was found to be impossible to drain the water out of the air intake trunk of the snort mast. The valve, which is usually left open when running on the surface is situated close to the waterline, and normally only accessible in flat calm weather. Therefore it was decided to return to the Faroe Islands to carry out an investigation.

The cause of the trouble was found to be a stray bolt which appeared to have been in the trunking since building. It had been carried down to the valve during the rough weather where it had become securely lodged under the valve. The bolt was removed, and after a test dive *Ambush* returned to her diving position in the arctic. Snorting was started on 19 February and a northerly course was maintained until Jan Mayen Island and the ice barrier were sighted. The course was then altered towards Bear Island, where pack and brash ice were met several times over the next few days. A rapid fall in sea temperature below 37°F invariably indicated approaching ice and on one occasion it dropped from 39°F to 31°F in less than one hour. These low temperatures did not adversely affect the running of the engines and the jacket cooling water and lubricating oil were always sufficiently warm.

Air temperatures inside the boat while dived were not as low as had been expected and the special warm clothing that was carried was regarded as a convenience rather than a necessity. External air temperatures, however, had a considerable effect while snorting, and freezing up took place inside the submarine while on the surface. When the wind was blowing from a northerly direction, ice was deposited on the head of the snort mast and on the periscopes and radar masts if these were raised. The ball float valve became completely frozen-up on several occasions. Final freezing was preceded by an erratic 'build up' of vacuum, which indicated that ice was being formed inside the valve box thus restricting the air flow. It was always possible to thaw out the valve by dipping it below the surface for several minutes, but on attempting to restart snorting it froze up again in a very short time. The submarine was then forced to dive deep until conditions improved.

Rough weather also had a limiting effect on the ability to snort for long periods. If the sea and swell were excessive it was impossible to control the submarine at periscope depth, particularly in a following sea. While running on the surface a considerable amount of ice formed on the superstructure. This inevitably affected the trim on diving but did not appear to cause any serious reduction of surface stability. More than ten degrees of frost was experienced in the control room and several salt water systems, including the trimming pump, depth gauges, and the sanitary water supply became completely frozen. These thawed out, however, after about half an hour dived.

Ambush's two electric distillers performed well during the cruise and were run continuously during the arctic patrol, the hours for one plant being 620 and the other 560. More than 4000 gallons of fresh water were produced with the result that it was never necessary to ration water for any purposes.

The arctic patrol of HMS *Ambush* was considered to be a great success and a considerable amount of useful information was obtained. *Ambush* was fortunate in that the results of the two previous patrols carried out by the *Taciturn* and *Alliance* were available and a repeat of some of the difficulties was obviated.

PERISCOPES

Two periscopes were fitted: one for general lookout purposes with binocular vision; the other, with monocular vision, was smaller and was used during attack. Both were bifocal.

	Forward	**After**
Type	CH66	CK14
Diameter	7½in	9½in
Vision	Monocular	Binocular
Magnification	HP 6×; LP 1½×	HP 6×; LP 1½×
Field of view	HP 10°; LP 40°	HP 6°; LP 24°
Sky search range	+30° to −15°	+54° to −15°
Height advantage between eye piece and top prism	40ft	40ft 3in

Both periscopes were equipped with sky search facilities, achieved by tilting the top prism. To keep the top windows as small as possible the prisms were made to move vertically down the tube when tilted upwards, and vice versa. Six times magnification was provided in high power but in low power a minifying telescope was swung into the field reducing the magnification to one and a half. An HT bronze tube provided the main strength of the periscope and was supported at the bottom by a crosshead. The tube passed through the hull via a blockhouse gland and bearing and was supported externally by two bearings in the periscope standard; the upper of which was a standard ball race.

Periscope hoisting arrangements. Both periscopes were raised and lowered on wires operating through hydraulic presses. In the 'A' class the presses were situated below the control room floor, mounted horizontally on the port side. The press for the forward or 'attack' periscope was sited above the main cold room and the press for the after periscope above 'R' compensating tank. The hoisting wires were clamped to the outer ring of the periscope crosshead and were supported by sheaves fixed to the inside of the pressure hull. The hoisting arrangement gave an inverse mechanical advantage of 1:8, a 2ft stroke at the ram produced a movement of 16ft at the periscope.

In the 1960s modifications were made to the after periscope. An electrically operated traverse was installed enabling the operator to sweep through 360° of vision whilst sitting on a revolving turntable. This modification was introduced to all of the surviving patrol type submarines of the time and is still the practice used today.

POSTWAR DEVELOPMENT

The 'A' class began to enter service with the Royal Navy against a background of rapid change in the role and operating requirements of British submarines. The sudden ending of hostilities had seen the cancellation of over fifty orders for submarines, of which thirty had been for vessels of the 'A' class. Many of the older boats still in service, namely the remaining 'H' and 'L' class, the 'O', 'P', 'R', 'River' and *Porpoise* classes and most of the early 'S' 'T' and 'U' class submarines were either sold for scrapping or expended as anti-submarine targets and the Navy began to look to the future to see what would be needed to meet the requirements of a peacetime construction programme.

Considerable progress had been made by the shipbuilding firms in warship construction during the latter part of the war. Submarine hulls, for example, were first riveted, then partially welded, then as techniques improved, completely welded. They could dive deeper, were faster, better armed and carried a sophisticated array of radar and communications equipment. As the war had progressed, so British designs had expanded to meet the operational demands made on them. Even so, it was the progress made by the German submarine designers, with their revolutionary Type XXI and Type XXIII 'Electric Boats' and experimental high speed 'Walther' designs, that seemed to indicate the direction in which the submarine was developing. British submarine design up to this time had developed very much along the lines of the 'tried and tested' principle. Changes occurred slowly and logically and with the exception of the steam-driven 'Swordfish' and 'K' class and the experimental 'M' class, were rarely innovative. The design for the 'A' class, for example, had provided a class of submarine that had met, and in some cases exceeded, all of the operational requirements laid down, but contained very little that was actually new. Although in fairness it must be said that in 1945 Britain and her allies were not facing a defensive war, so the problems facing British submarine designers at the time were not the same as those faced by Germany.

During the 4½ years that they were in production, 'A' class submarines were completed in no less than five different forms, reflecting the period of rapid change that occurred in submarine construction immediately after the war. The most obvious change was that British submarines began to lose their guns. First the Oerlikon mounting was removed and then later, the 4in gun. *Andrew* was the first of the class to be completed without an Oerlikon mounting. She was followed by *Artful* and *Acheron*, neither of which were given *any* gun armament. By the end of 1949 the Oerlikon had been removed from all of the class, although in some boats – namely *Amphion*, *Astute*, *Aurochs*, *Alliance*, *Ambush*, *Anchorite* and *Andrew* – the 4in gun was retained until they were streamlined.

Another change made during the early refits on both the 'T' and 'A' classes was the removal of the forward external torpedo tubes. In all cases this involved the removal of both tubes and their firing gear and the plating over of the openings, giving the bows a cleaner, finer line. Probably the most significant advance made in the years immediately following the war was the development of the snort mast. HMS *Truant* became one of the first British submarines to be fitted with a snort mast, during experiments carried out in early 1946 and by the end of 1947 nearly all of the remaining 'T' class submarines had been fitted with a schnorchel.

The modification of the 'A' class was no less rapid. In fact seven of the sixteen boats were actually completed with a snort, namely *Aurochs*, *Alliance*, *Ambush*, *Anchorite*, *Andrew*, *Artful* and *Acheron*, and the remaining boats had all been modified by 1949. In May 1953 *Andrew* carried out the first ever submerged crossing of the Atlantic, 'snorting' for over 2500 miles between Bermuda and the English Channel, whilst earlier, in 1947, *Alliance* established a record in remaining submerged for 30 days off the coast of Africa. The 'A' class were originally fitted with a folding snort mast which housed against the port side of the after casing and, like the early German designs, combined both induction and exhaust pipes. The mast was raised and lowered hydraulically and held in position against the after end of the conning tower by a locking pin operated from the control room. Shortly afterwards the design was modified by repositioning the snort exhaust in a permanent position against the after part of the ANF radar mast with only the induction tube being raised and lowered. In 1949 the system was further modified by replacing the float-controlled head valve, which was similar to the German type, with an improved 'ring float' head valve. Finally, in the mid 1960s eight of the class were fitted with a telescopic snort induction mast which was housed in an extension to the after part of the fin.

Wartime experience had shown the necessity for submarines to be developed with higher underwater speeds and greater endurance. However, practically all of the Royal Navy's submarines in service immediately after the war were still less than ten years' old and with little likelihood of any new designs becoming available for some years to come the Navy began to look at ways in which it could modernise its existing fleet. Streamlining seemed to offer the answer. In fact some of the Navy's first experiments in this field had already been carried out on the 'S' class submarine *Seraph*, which during the latter part of the war was modified experimentally to evaluate the feasibility of achieving higher underwater speeds. HMS *Tradewind* followed, appearing in August 1946 minus her guns and external torpedo tubes with a streamlined casing and conning tower, joining the 7th Submarine Squadron at Portland for experimental

TABLE 9: 'A' CLASS, CONSTRUCTION AND FATES

Name	Pen No	Builder	Laid down	Launched	Completed	Fate
Amphion	P 439	Vickers Armstrongs, Barrow	14.11.43	31.8.44	27.3.45	6.7.71 sold to T W Ward Ltd, Inverkeithing for breaking up
Astute	P 455	Vickers Armstrongs, Barrow	4.4.44	30.1.45	30.6.45	1.10.70 sold to Clayton & Davie Ltd, Dunston-on-Tyne for breaking up
Alderney	P 416	Vickers Armstrongs, Barrow	6.2.45	25.6.45	10.12.45	August 1972 arrived Cairnryan, Scotland for breaking by Shipbreaking (Queenborough) Ltd
Affray	P 421	Cammell Laird, Birkenhead	16.1.44	20.4.45	12.11.45	16.4.51, lost in the Hurd Deep, English Channel
Auriga	P 419	Vickers Armstrongs, Barrow	7.6.44	29.3.45	12.1.46	14.11.74 sold to J Cashmore Ltd, Newport for breaking up
Aeneas	P 427	Cammell Laird, Birkenhead	10.10.44	25.10.45	31.7.46	13.12.74 arrived at Clayton & Davie Ltd, Dunston-on-Tyne, for breaking up
Alcide	P 415	Vickers Armstrongs, Barrow	2.1.45	12.4.45	18.10.46	1974 sold to A Draper & Sons Ltd, Hull for breaking up
Alaric	P 441	Cammell Laird, Birkenhead	31.5.45	18.2.46	11.12.46	5.7.71 sold to T W Ward Ltd, Inverkeithing for breaking up
Aurochs	P 426	Vickers Armstrongs, Barrow	21.6.44	28.7.45	7.2.47	7.2.67 sold to the West of Scotland Shipbreaking Co for breaking up
Alliance	P 417	Vickers Armstrongs, Barrow	13.3.45	28.7.45	14.5.47	1981 preserved as a submarine memorial at HMS *Dolphin*, Gosport
Ambush	P 418	Vickers Armstrongs, Barrow	17.5.45	24.9.45	22.7.47	5.7.71 sold to T W Ward Ltd, Inverkeithing for breaking up
Artemis	P 449	Scotts, Greenock	28.2.44	26.8.46	15.8.47	1.7.71 sunk alongside the jetty at Gosport whilst refuelling; raised and sold to H J Pounds, Portsmouth for breaking up
Anchorite	P 422	Vickers Armstrongs, Barrow	19.7.45	22.1.46	18.11.47	24.8.70 sold to West of Scotland Shipbreaking, Troon for breaking up
Andrew	P 423	Vickers Armstrongs, Barrow	13.8.45	6.4.46	16.3.48	4.5.77 towed to Davies & Cann Ltd, Plymouth for breaking up
Artful	P 456	Scotts, Greenock	8.6.44	22.5.47	23.2.48	23.6.72 sold to Shipbreaking (Queenborough) Ltd, for breaking up
Acheron	P 411	HM Dockyard, Chatham	26.8.44	25.3.47	17.4.48	August 1972 broken up by J Cashmore Ltd, Newport
Incomplete boats						
Ace	P 414	HM Dockyard, Devonport	—	14.3.45	—	Sold to Smith & Houston Ltd, Port Glasgow for breaking up, June 1950 after the hull had been used for crush tests by the Royal Navy
Achates	P 433	HM Dockyard, Devonport	—	20.9.45	—	Expended as a target in 1947 after the hull had been used for crush tests by the Royal Navy

Cancelled boats: Vickers Armstrongs, Barrow – *Andromache* P 424, *Answer* P 425, *Antagonist* P 428, *Antaeus* P 429, *Anzac* P 431, *Aphrodite* P 432, *Approach* P 435, *Arcadian* P 436, *Ardent* P 437, *Argosy* P 438, *Atlantis* P 442. Vickers Armstrongs, Walker – *Admirable* P 434, *Asperity* P 444, *Austere* P 445, *Aztec* P 455, *Adversary* P 457, *Awake* P 459. Cammell Laird, Birkenhead – *Agile* P 443, *Aggressor* P 446, *Agate*, P 448, *Alcestis* P 453, *Alladin* P 454. Scotts, Greenock – *Astarte* P 461, *Assurance* P 462, *Asgard* P 458. HM Dockyard, Chatham – *Adept* P 412. HM Dockyard, Portsmouth – *Abelard* P 451, *Acasta* P 452.

anti-submarine duties.

However, the major programme of modernisation did not start until November 1948 when *Taciturn* was selected for conversion by Chatham Dockyard, reappearing eighteen months later with an additional 14ft of pressure hull inserted abaft the original engine room bulkhead to accommodate an extra battery section and an additional pair of electric motors. The gun, five external torpedo tubes and the bridge were removed and were replaced with a modified conning position and streamlined casing and fin enclosing her seven periscopic masts. The combination of additional motors, extra battery power and streamlining gave *Taciturn* over twice her original underwater speed. Between 1948 and 1957 eight of the welded 'T' class were modified in this way, whilst the remaining riveted boats were streamlined but not lengthened.

The modernisation of the 'A' class was less drastic, and between 1955 and 1960 fourteen of the original sixteen vessels were taken in hand. Only HMS *Affray*, which had been lost in 1951, and HMS *Aurochs*, which, although remaining in service until 1966, had previously been surveyed and considered to be in too poor a condition to be modernised, were omitted from the streamlining programme. HMS *Artful* was the first of the class to be modified. All of the external torpedo tubes were removed and a new, lightweight aluminium superstructure fitted. The conning tower was raised, enclosing the periscope standards and radar masts, to form a fin 26½ft high. The bow was also modified, giving it a flatter profile and the buoyancy tank dispensed with. At this stage the wireless transmitting aerial was supported by a frame abaft the conning tower. The aerial and frame were later removed and replaced by a folding 'whip' aerial which was sited on the starboard side of the fin and raised and lowered hydraulically.

The streamlining of the bridge and superstructure and the fining of the bow resulted in a marked improvement in the maximum underwater speed of this class, although, as one would expect, the results were not as dramatic as those achieved by the 'stretched' 'T' class with their additional electric motors and battery power.

During subsequent refits some internal modifications were also carried out. These mainly involved modernising the control room layout, the fitting of an automatic depth-keeping device, improved steering and attack instruments and the installation of a watchkeeping turntable for the after periscope. Some effort was also made to improve the habitability in the mess decks. The gun access tower was retained during the many periods of modification and even after streamlining some boats were fitted temporarily with a deck gun. In some cases this was of a light calibre: *Ambush* and *Alliance*, for example, shipped light calibre armament whilst serving in the Far East. Dependent upon operational requirements a 4in gun was also mounted from time to time (*Artemis*, *Anchorite*, *Andrew*, *Aeneas* and *Auriga* were so equipped).

In May 1961 a change took place in the numbering of the 'A' class, when, to enable all of the postwar-built conventional submarines to be numbered from S 01 onwards the pennant numbers were redesignated as follows: *Amphion* P 439 was renumbered S 43, *Astute* P 455 became S 47, *Alderney* P 416 became S 66, *Auriga* P 419 became S 69, *Aeneas* P 427 became S 72, *Alcide* P 415 became S 65, *Alaric* P 441 became S 41, *Aurochs* P 426 became S 62, *Alliance* P 417 became S 67, *Ambush* P 418 became S 68, *Artemis* P 449 became S 49, *Anchorite* P 422 became S 64, *Andrew* P 423 became S 63, *Artful* P 456 became S 96, *Acheron* P 411 became S 61.

In 1972 HMS *Aeneas* was loaned to the Vickers Shipbuilding group at Barrow and fitted experimentally with a unit for firing SLAM (a version of the Army's Blowpipe) anti-aircraft missiles from a retractable launcher installed in the forward part of the fin. Initially the idea showed great promise but the trials were not pursued because of the limited range of the missile and *Aeneas* was returned to Devonport in November 1972.

By 1969 all of the remaining fourteen boats had been in service for over twenty years and many were approaching the end of their safe hull-life. All of the 'S' class had been taken out of service and only one or two of the 'T' class boats still remained. The main strength of the Navy's conventional patrol submarine fleet lay in the eight *Porpoise* class and thirteen *Oberon* class in service at that time. These boats were faster, quieter and more technically advanced than the 'A' and 'T' classes. The 'A' class began to disappear rapidly from service and by the end of 1974 only HMS *Andrew* was still at sea. Attempts were made to preserve her after she 'paid off' for the last time but these failed and in 1977 she was towed out of Devonport to be broken up.

Fortunately, however, one vessel did escape the breakers' torch. In 1973 *Alliance* replaced *Tabard* at the submarine base in Gosport as a floating classroom and static display ship. There she remained until August 1979, when following the decision to preserve her as a submarine memorial she was towed from Gosport to Vosper Ship Repairers Ltd at Southampton to have her keel reinforced prior to being lifted out of the water and placed on permanent display where she can be seen to this day.

The Photographs

2. Right: The launch of *Auriga*, 29 March 1945. *Auriga* was one of ten 'A' class submarines built by Vickers-Armstrongs at Barrow and after her commissioning in December of that year sailed immediately to join the British Pacific Fleet in the Far East. *Auriga* enjoyed a long service with the Royal Navy, eventually being withdrawn from service in 1974.
IWM

3. Below: *Aeneas* photographed by her builders Cammell Laird & Co at the time of her completion in July 1946. Her gun armament consisted of a single 4in S2 mounting and twin Oerlikons Mk 12A. Both radar masts are raised in this typical 'completion' photograph.
MoD

4. Below: *Aeneas* at the time of her completion in 1946. The two after external torpedo tubes can clearly be seen, as can the D/F frame coil Type EM 11 and the Type 183 Asdic unit on the after casing. Also of interest is the twin Oerlikon mounting.
MoD

5. Below: *Affray* photographed by Cammell Laird at the time of her completion in 1946. The Oerlikon platform was later removed and a folding snort mast fitted. *Affray* was lost in the English Channel in 1951, the loss being attributed to a break at the base of the snort induction tube.
Author's Collection

6. Above: *Astute* photographed in 1946. She was originally completed with a low bow and shorter periscope standards, both of which were modified to improve her seakeeping qualities.
Author's Collection

7. Left: *Astute* surfacing during her acceptance trials in 1945. Note the original short periscope standards and the support bracket at the top of the ANF radar mast. Shortly after completion the periscope standards were raised by some 3ft and the upper bracket extended to include the radar mast. Also of interest is the guard rail for the 20mm Oerlikon at the forward end of the bandstand.
Author's Collection

8. Left: A rare photograph of *Amphion* taken during her first of class trials in 1945: note the original low bow and periscope standards. *Amphion* and *Astute* were the only two vessels of the class to appear in this form. The low bow was found to give poor seakeeping and was later raised to provide space for a buoyancy tank.
Author's Collection

9. Below: *Auriga* leaving Malta en route for the Far East to start her first commission with the British Pacific Fleet in early 1946. *Auriga* remained in the Far East until 1948, during which time she was equipped with a snort mast at the Naval Dockyard in Hong Kong. *Auriga* arrived back at Portsmouth on 19 October 1948.
Author's Collection

10. Right: One of two known 4in Mk XXIII guns on the S2 mounting on display. This one, from *Aeneas*, is on display at the RN Armament Museum, Priddy's Hard, Gosport; the other is displayed on the Pierhead of HMS *Dolphin* (I believe ex-*Andrew*).
MoD

11. Below: *Aeneas* after streamlining in 1962. Her gun armament has been removed and the bridge built up to form a fin enclosing the periscope and radar masts. The original deck superstructure has also been removed and replaced by a light aluminium casing. The streamlined dome on the bow is made of fibreglass and houses the forward Asdic mounting.
MoD

12. Left: An unusual view of *Aeneas* taken in 1966 showing the top of the 'fin'. The superstructure forward houses the gun access tower which was retained even after streamlining. One of the radar masts and a W/T aerial can be seen forward of the upper navigating position and a second radar mast between the two officers. The fin has been extensively modified and in its after section can be seen the head of the periscope snort mast. Note the gangplank in its recess on the after casing.
Author's Collection

13. Left: *Andrew* in 1962 after streamlining: at this time she was fitted with a 4in gun forward of the conning tower. *Andrew* was one of the last 'A' class submarines to be withdrawn from service and carried out the Navy's last submarine gun action in December 1974. Attempts were made to preserve her but these failed and she was sold for scrapping in 1977. Note the folding snort mast on the after casing.
Author's Collection

14. Right: *Andrew* in the Jahore Strait, Seletor Island. After streamlining at Devonport *Andrew* spent eleven years in foreign waters before returning to the UK in 1968. 'A' class submarines were well suited to working in tropical conditions, the theatre of war in which they were originally designed to operate.
Author's Collection

15. Right: *Ambush* at Bangkok in 1965. *Ambush* saw service during the Indonesian confrontation off Malaysia and is shown here fitted with a single 20mm Mk VIIA* gun forward of the conning tower.
MoD

16. Left: *Anchorite* probably in 1965. *Anchorite* was based at Singapore between 1961 and 1968 operating with the 7th Submarine Squadron. During her time in the Far East she visited Pakistan, India, Ceylon, Japan, Hong Kong and Australia and was fitted with a 4in gun during the Indonesian confrontation with Malaysia.
MoD

17. Below: *Auriga* 'paying off' for the final time at the end of her last commission in 1973, seen here arriving at Portsmouth. In November 1974 she was sold to J Cashmore Ltd for breaking up, leaving Rosyth in February 1975.
RN Submarine Museum

18. Above: *Artful* arriving at Portsmouth in 1972 at the end of her last commission. *Artful* was the second of only two 'A' class submarines built by Scotts of Greenock and was the first of the class to be streamlined in 1955. Note that she has retained the original folding snort mast until the end of her service.
MoD

19. Left: *Alliance* camouflaged during her part in the Indonesian campaign in the 1960s (the colours have not been identified). During this period several of the 'A' class were fitted with deck armament. Note the folding snort mast, later removed and replaced by a periscope mast in an extension to the after part of the 'fin', and the wooden planking on the fore and aft casing. This gave some protection to the cylinders for the Built In Breathing System (BIBS) mounted on the pressure hull above the escape compartments.
Author's Collection

20. Right: *Alliance* at Gosport in 1980 whilst being prepared for display to the public as a museum ship and memorial to the officers and men who lost their lives in submarines. This unusual view shows clearly the openings for the two after internal torpedo tubes, the rudder and hydroplane assembly and one of her two propellers. Note also the bilge keel on the underside of the hull on the port side.
MoD

21. Below: *Alliance*, showing a detail of the forward part of the fin showing the gun access tower. Other points of interest are: the outboard battery ventilation valve on the starboard side of the fin above which is a folding W/T antenna, the two radar masts and between them the after 'search' periscope.
MoD

22. Below right: *Alliance* at Gosport during the final stages of her conversion to a museum ship. The submarine has been raised out of the water and doors cut into the sides of the pressure hull on the starboard side giving access to the forward and after torpedo stowage compartments. Note the bow shutters and caps of two of the four forward torpedo tubes. *Alliance* was opened to the public in 1981.
MoD

The Drawings

SOURCES

The information for the Introduction and, particularly, for the drawings came from many sources. The general arrangement plans were based on originals in the National Maritime Museum at Greenwich and the Royal Navy Submarine Museum at Gosport. Details of the 4in guns and mountings were supplied by the RN Armament Museum, Priddy's Hard, while the 21in torpedoes depended on material lent by Vickers Engineering of Portland. However most of the information came from official handbooks (particularly the BR 1963 series on the 'A' class and BR 1803 series on submarine torpedo tubes) consulted at the Submarine Museum.

The scale plans are mostly reproduced at 1/192 ($^1/_{16}$in = 1ft) or variations thereof.

GLOSSARY AND ABBREVIATIONS

The following is a list of the principal technical terms, abbreviations and acronyms used in the Introduction and the drawing keys:

AC: alternating current
ADL plot: automatic detection and location plotting table, bringing together action data from all the boat's sensors
AIV tank: automatic inboard vent tank (for torpedo firing)
Amal: trade name
ANF: sea guard radar (probably NATO code)
APT: forward mast for Type 291W radar (probably NATO code)
Arens: trade name
ARL mountings: resilient and shock-proofed mounting of main and auxiliary machinery
AVG mast: probably code for snort induction mast
BIBS: Built In Breathing System, a bottle group to provide an unpolluted supply of air to escapers during the flooding-up period and immediately prior to ascent
BSW: British Standard Whitworth thread (for bolts)
CAV pumps: named after their designer C A Vandervelt
CEAD: Controller Engineering and Armament Department
CP: Constant pressure (electrical circuits)
DC: direct current
DP: dual purpose
DP and C: dual purpose and constant (pressure groups on electrical ring main)
DOT: dirty oil tank
EIV: emergency inboard vent (for use if AIV fails)
GA gear: gyro angling gear (torpedo tubes)
GAT: gun access tower
Gaco: trade name
HE cock: hand emergency cock (torpedo tubes)
HFV: hand firing valves
ICO: impulse cut-off
Imo pump: trade name for quiet running electrically driven telemotor pump
Iswas: early basic disc type torpedo attack calculator
JPC4, JPV3, C3D etc: junction, distribution and control boxes on various electrical circuits. Feeder boxes on the two ring mains were numbered from forward to aft, with 'V' or 'C' indicating either the variable or constant pressure main
LFV: large firing valve
Lolos: trade name for a self-cleaning strainer
Loran: longe range navigation system
LP: low power
MBT: main ballast tank
M/G: motor generator
MM: main motor
MT: main tank (4MT = No 4 main tank)
OF subs: oil fuel subsequent (filling line, only used for fuelling the boat, and drained at sea)
OMD: oil mineral detergent (lubricating oil, NATO code)
op: operating (switches etc)
PCD: pitch circle diameter
PO: power-operated
ROT: reserve (lubricating) oil tank
SEA: Stellite-faced valve seating rig
SFM: small firing motor
SFV: small firing valve
Stellite: trade name for very hard metallic ground-in working surface (to valves, etc)
Strum, or 'strum box': the well or collecting area for draining a tank or bilge (usually fitted with a strainer)
TO: telemotor-operated
TOT: torpedo operating tank
VP: variable pressure (electrical circuits)
VSG: variable speed gear
Weir: trade name
WRT: water round torpedo
W/T: wireless telegraphy (radio)

A Development of the class

'A' class submarines appeared in many forms during their 28 years of service. These profiles represent some of the major changes and modifications that were carried out during that period. All are reproduced to 1/384 scale ($^1/_{32}$in = 1ft).

A1 **AMPHION 1945**
Amphion was the first vessel of the class to be completed. She is shown here as she would have appeared during her 'first of class' trials with the original low bow and short periscope standards. At this stage the ANF radar mast was not joined to the top of the standards. *Astute* was also completed in this form.

A2 **ASTUTE 1946**
This shows how the *Astute* and *Amphion* appeared after the raising of the bow to improve stability. The periscope standards have been raised by some 3ft and the ANF radar mast fixed to the standards. *Alderney*, *Affray*, *Auriga*, *Aeneas*, *Alaric* and *Artemis* were all completed in this form.

A3 **AMBUSH 1947**
Ambush, *Alliance* and *Anchorite* were completed in this form. They were fitted with a folding snort mast, combining both the induction and exhaust, which housed on the port side of the casing abaft the conning tower. All three vessels were equipped with twin Mk 12A 20mm Oerlikons.

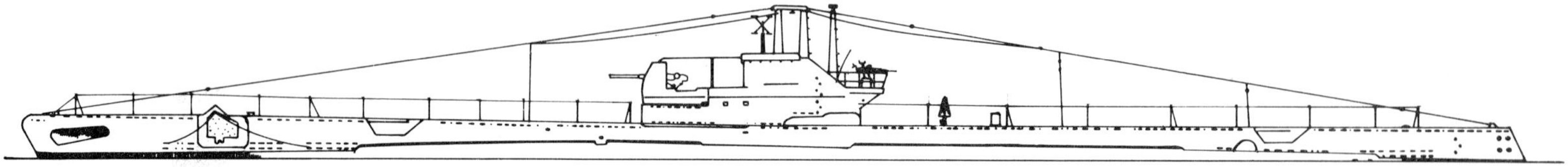

A1

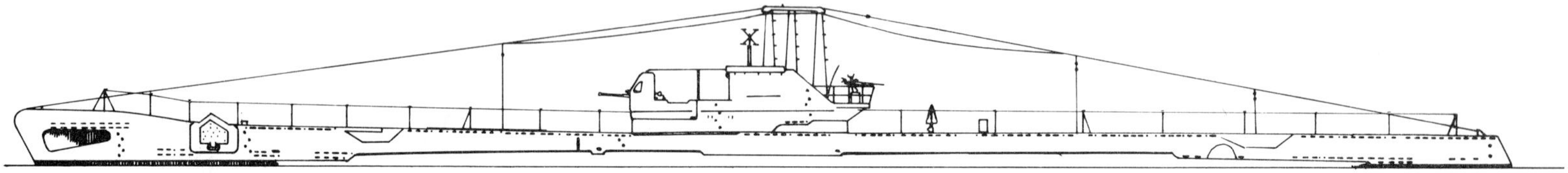

A2

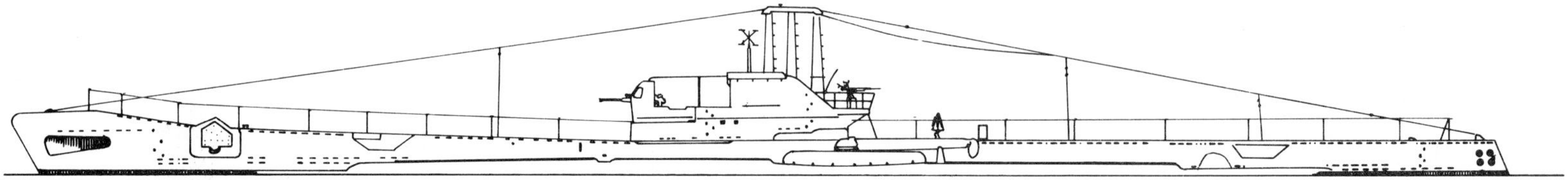

A3

A4 **ANDREW 1951**
Andrew was the only vessel to be completed in this form. She appeared with a combined snort induction and exhaust mast and a modified shield around the 4in gun. *Andrew* was never fitted with an Oerlikon mounting during her service.

A5 **AUROCHS 1954**
This shows *Aurochs* after the removal of her Oerlikon platform. The snort mast has also been modified, with the exhaust now attached to the ANF radar mast. *Amphion*, *Astute*, *Auriga*, *Alcide*, *Alliance*, *Ambush* and *Anchorite* all appeared in this form prior streamlining.

A6 **ALARIC 1954**
During the postwar years individual vessels were being modified continuously. *Alaric* is shown here after the removal of her guns and the addition of an experimental superstructure forward of the bridge. Also, the forward external torpedo tubes and the D/F frame coil on the after casing have been removed.

A4

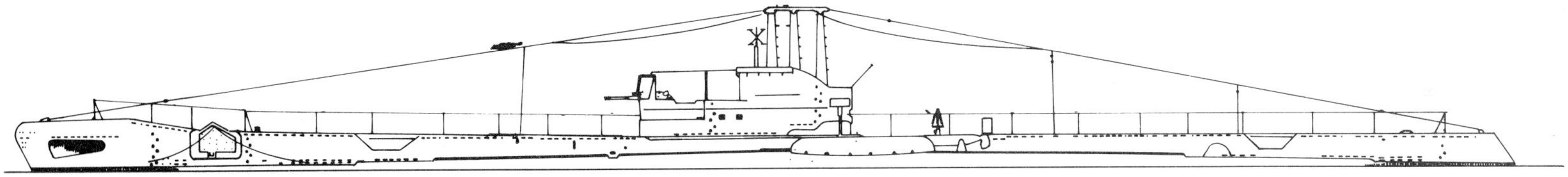

A5

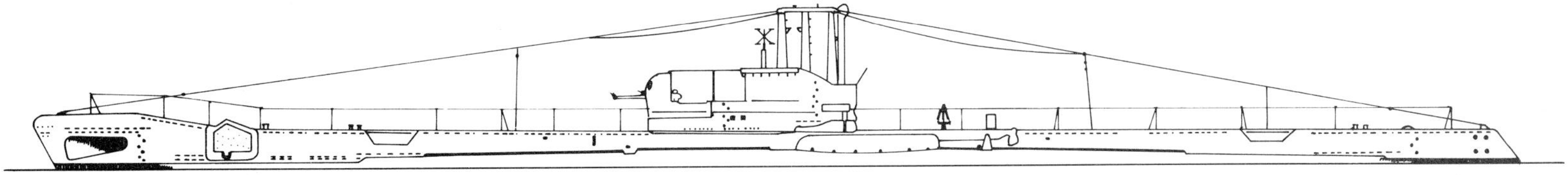

A6

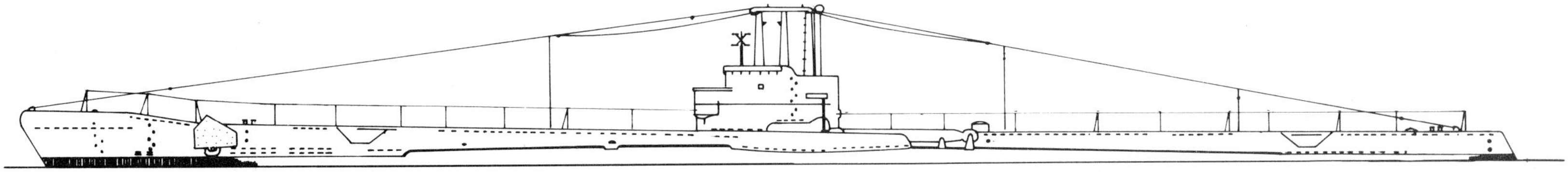

A Development of the class

A7 **ARTFUL 1956**
Only two vessels were completed entirely without gun armament; they were the *Artful* and the *Acheron*. Although similar in appearance the two vessels could be distinguished by the shorter platform forward of the conning tower in *Artful*. Also of interest, the fairing of the casing in way of the forward and after torpedo loading hatches housing the torpedo loading davit was not fitted to these boats.

A8 **ALDERNEY 1958**
During the mid-1950s fourteen of the original sixteen 'A' class were streamlined. The external torpedo tubes and 4in gun were removed and the bridge built up over the periscope and radar masts in the form of a fin. A light aluminium superstructure was fitted and domes added to the forward and after casing enclosing units for the Asdic and underwater telephone. When originally streamlined the wireless aerial was supported by a metal frame on the after casing.

A9 **ARTEMIS 1960**
Several vessels were fitted with a gun for short periods after streamlining. *Artemis* is shown here as she appeared in 1960. The wireless aerial was fixed to a single stub mast on the after casing and the Asdic unit on the bow given a distinctive 'float' shape.

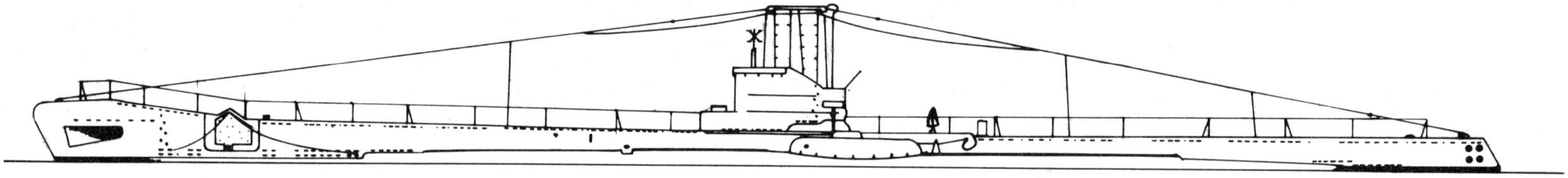

A7

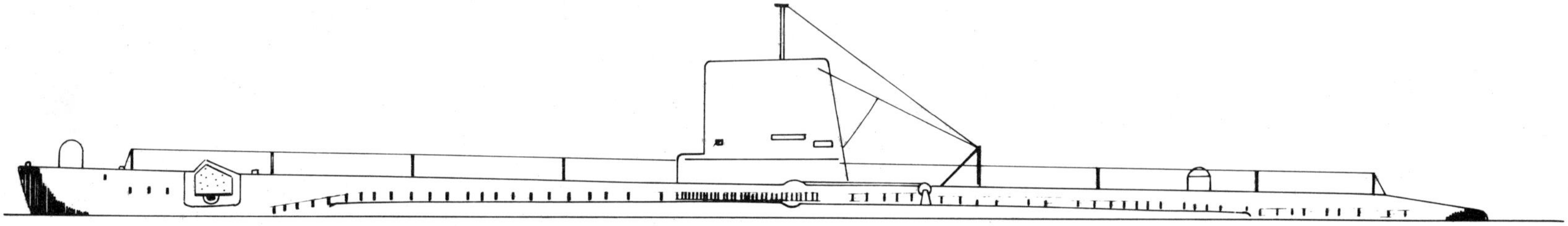

A8

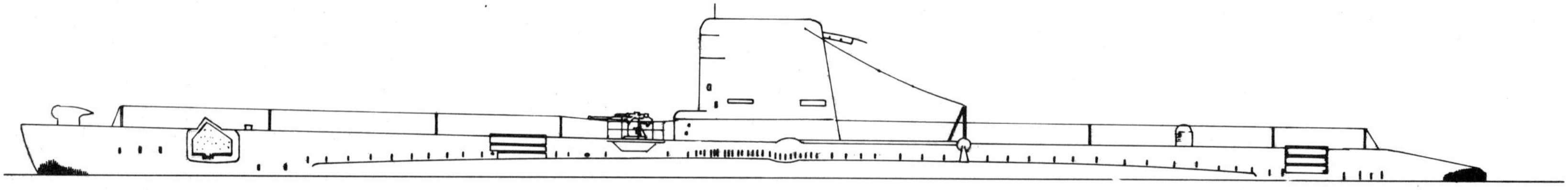

A9

A10 **AENEAS 1962**
Soon after streamlining the frame supporting the wireless aerial was removed and a folding 'whip' aerial fitted to the starboard side of the fin. Wooden protectors were added to the superstructure forward and aft in way of the BIBS cylinders and the Asdic unit on the bow improved and housed beneath a large free flooding glass fibre dome.

A11 **ALLIANCE 1966**
During the 1960s modifications were carried out to the snort mast of eight of the remaining boats in service. The fin was lengthened aft and an improved telescopic snort mast fitted: *Alliance, Auriga, Aeneas, Ambush, Artemis, Anchorite, Andrew* and *Acheron* were all modified in this way.

A12 **ANDREW 1970**
Andrew was the last 'A' class submarine to be taken out of service. She is shown here in her final form with a 4in gun forward of the conning tower.

A10

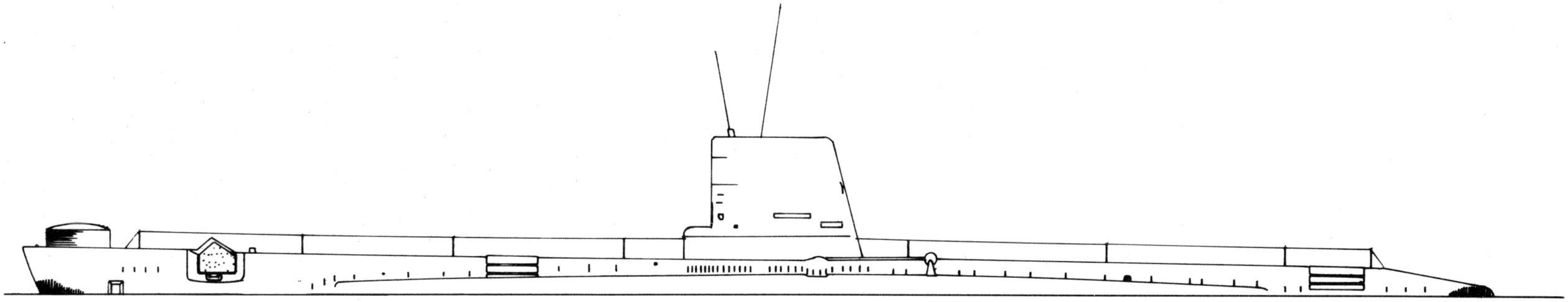

A11

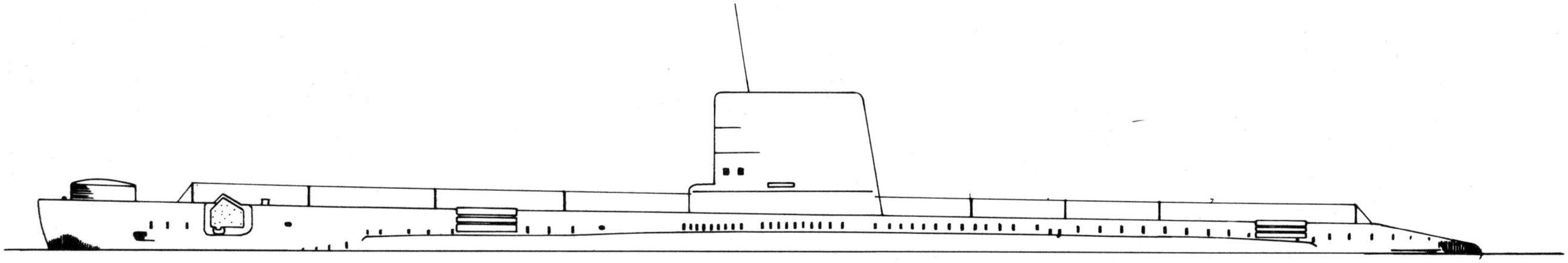

A12

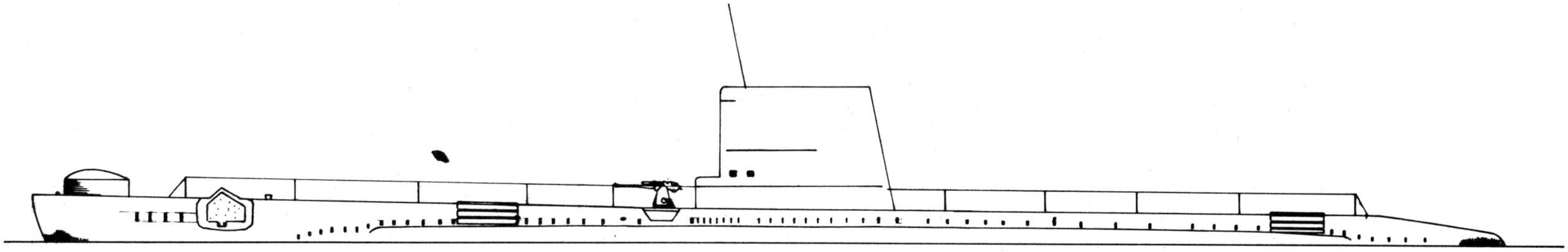

B General arrangements

B1 **'A' CLASS AS COMPLETED (Affray and Aeneas 1946; 1/192 scale)**

B1/1 **External profile**

B1/2 **Plan view of casing**

B1/1

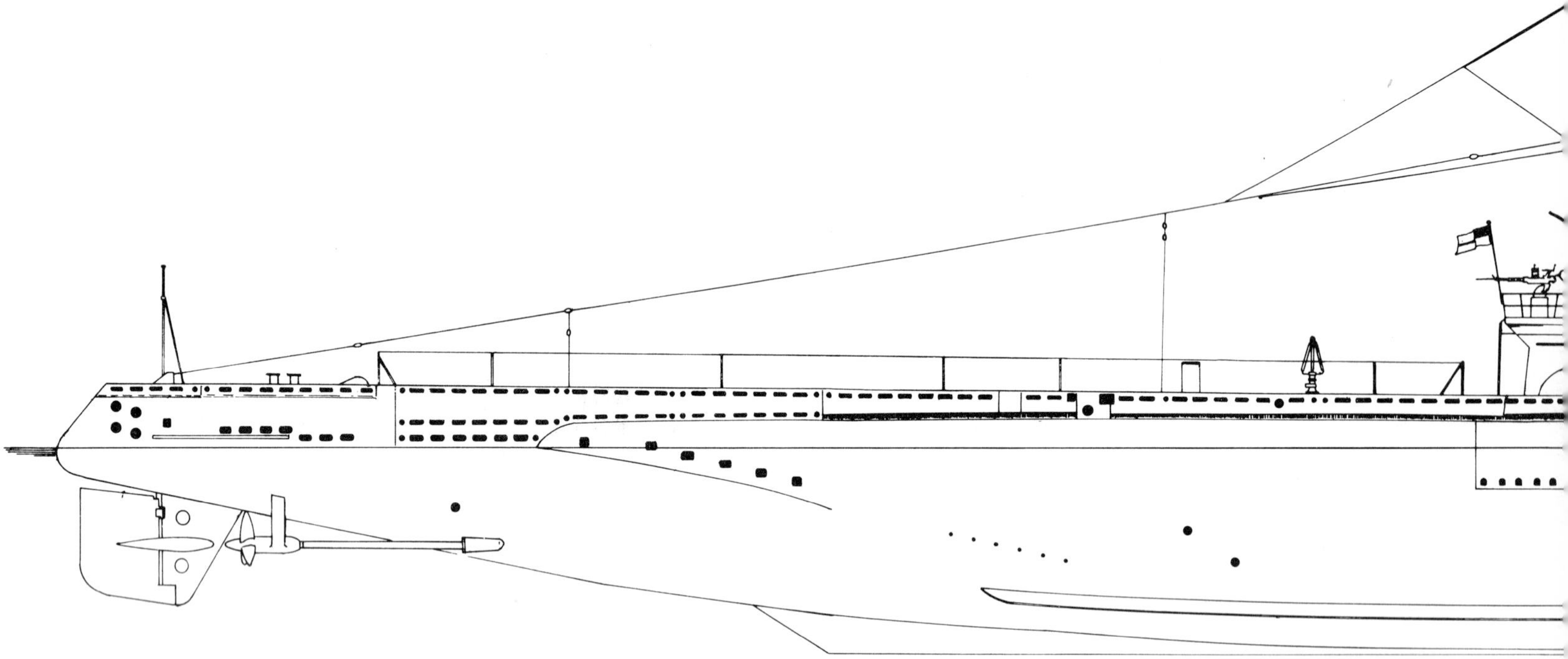

B1/2

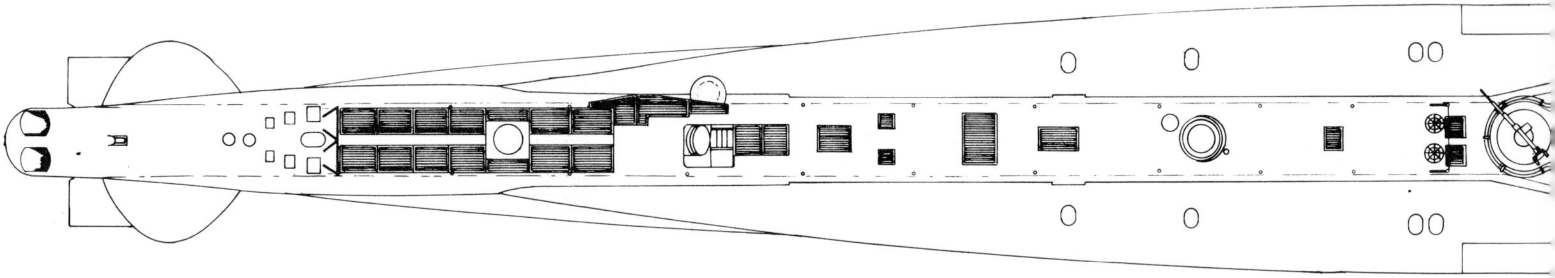

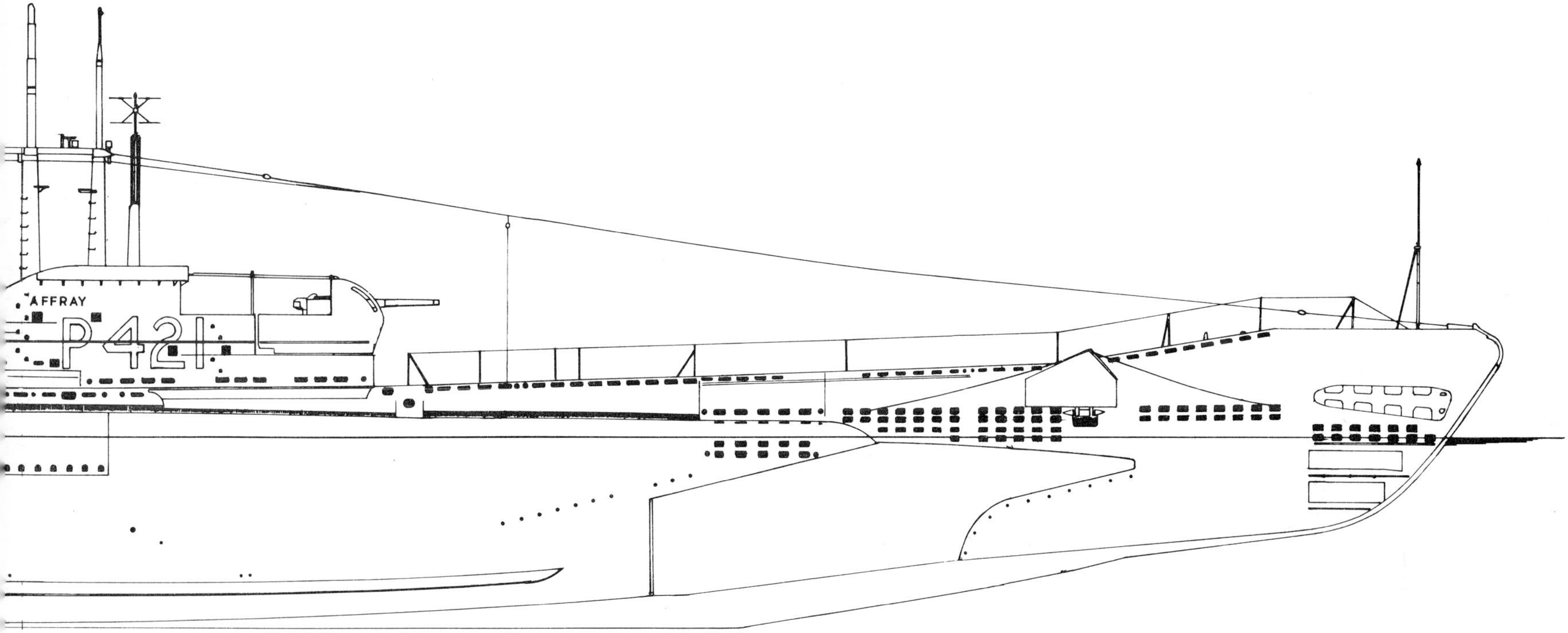
AFFRAY
P421

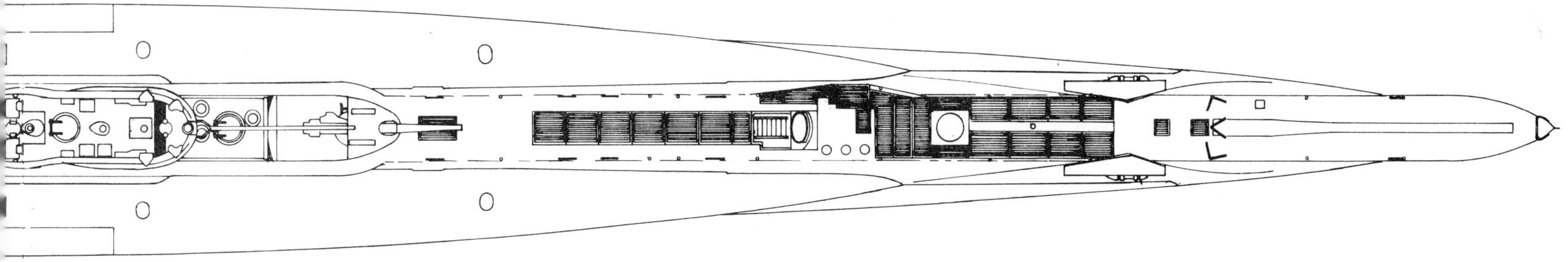

B General arrangements

B1/3 Internal profile

1 Open to sea
2 Torpedo operating tank
3 Torpedo firing and stowage compartment
4 Aft trim tank
5 Lubricating oil drain tank
6 Lubricating oil tank
7 Main engine and motor room
8 Galley
9 W/T (wireless telegraphy) machinery
10 W/T office
11 No 2 battery compartment
12 Air conditioning compartment
13 CO's cabin
14 Conning tower
15 Crew's washplace
16 POs' and ERAs' washplace
17 Officers' washplace
18 Crew's WC
19 Radar office
20 Anti-submarine office
21 Control room
22 Hydroplane in working position
23 Auxiliary machinery compartment
24 Wardroom
25 ERAs' mess
26 Gun access trunk
27 Petty officers' mess
28 Coxwain's store
29 Engineer's store
30 4in gun on S1 mounting
31 Gun support
32 Stokers' mess
33 No 1 battery compartment
34 Seamen's mess
35 Torpedo hatch
36 Torpedo tube compartment
37 Ballast box
38 Cable locker
39 Net cutter
40 No 3 oil fuel tank
41 No 1 external oil fuel tank
42 No 2 main tank
43 'O' compensating tank
44 No 4 main tank
45 No 3 external oil fuel tank
46 No 4 external oil fuel tank
47 Main tank no 3
48 No 2 oil fuel tank
49 Lockers
50 Distilled water tank
51 Passageway
52 Trim tank
53 Air space
54 W/T deck tube
55 'Q' tank
56 Bullring
57 Disappearing bollard
58 21in diam torpedo tube
59 Stern cap operating gear
60 Rudder operating shaft
61 Ensign staff
62 Hydroplane gear
63 AIV (automatic inboard vent) tank
64 Firing bottles
65 Portable gratings
66 Insulator
67 21in diam Mk XI torpedo
68 Portable centre girder
69 Wood lining
70 Recess
71 DSEA twill trunk
72 Overhead carriage
73 Escape hatch
74 Steering gear power unit

B1/3

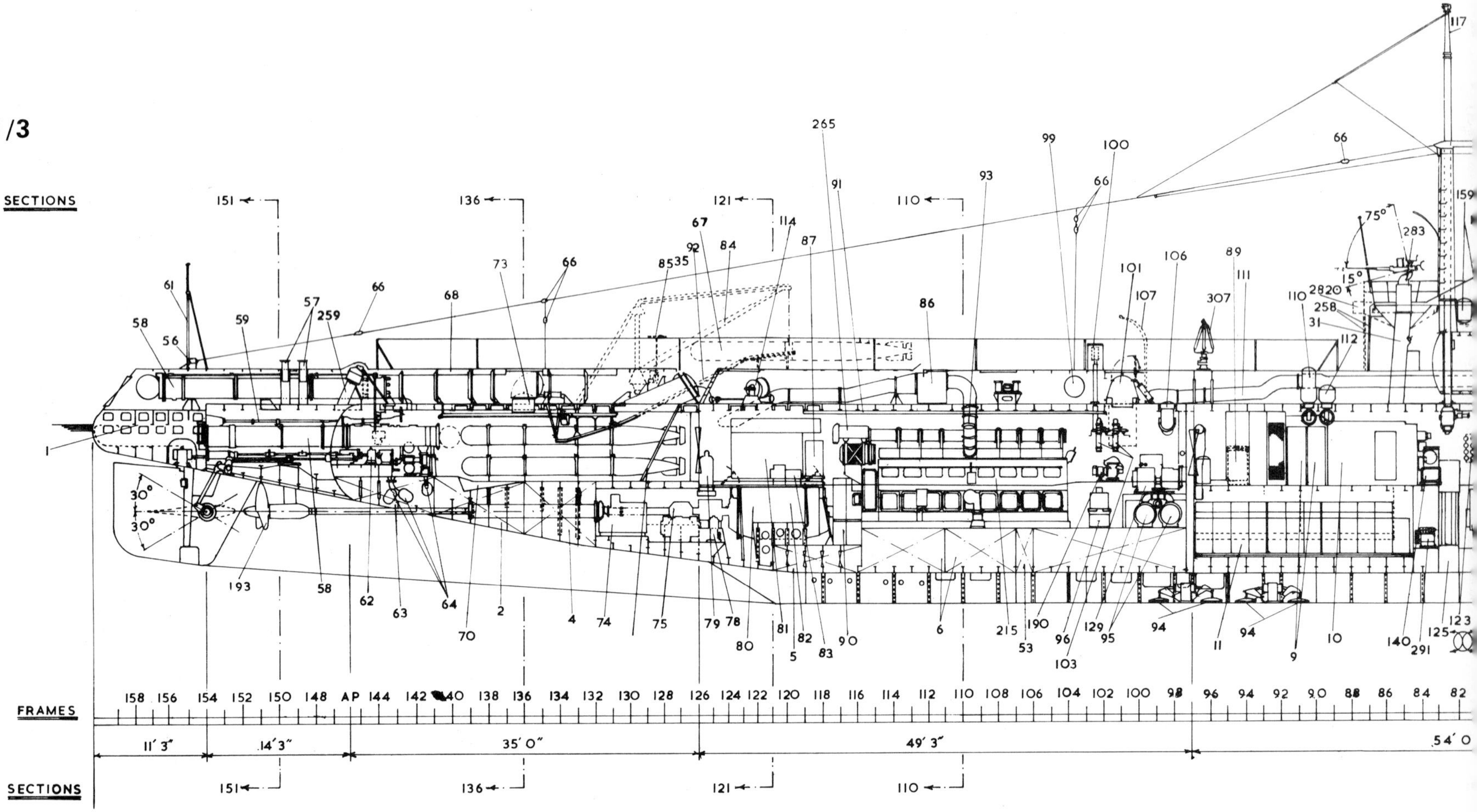

75 Thrust block
76 After clutch casing
77 Water-tight door
78 Oily bilge pump
79 Air-loaded accumulator
80 Main motor
81 Switchboard
82 Fan
83 Fan motor
84 Torpedo derrick
85 Torpedo derrick training handwheel
86 Exhaust tank
87 Regulator
88 Main engine supercharger
89 Galley range
90 Engine clutch
91 Lifting beam
92 Portable torpedo embarking rail
93 Inboard exhaust valve
94 24in diam hand-operated kingston valve
95 Oil cooler
96 Port circulating pump
97 Bollards
98 Mooring pipe
99 Oil fuel expansion tank
100 Type 138B Asdic
101 Engine room hatch
102 Ventilating valve
103 Signal ejectors
104 Air compressor
105 Oil fuel gravity tank
106 Engine induction valve
107 Engine room davit (portable)
108 Lubricating oil pump starter
109 Type FM 1 direction finder
110 No 4 main tank vent
111 Ventilation trunk engine induction
112 No 3 main tank vent
113 Battery vent
114 Torpedo derrick winch
115 Engine telegraph
116 Sanitary tank
117 ANF radar mast
118 9½in diam search periscope
119 7½in diam attack periscope
120 Type 253MW radar
121 Type 86M radar
122 Type 267MW radar array
123 Telemotor control panel
124 Trim pump motor
125 Radar mast well
126 Washing water tank
127 10-gallon water heater (Jackson)
128 Air bottles
129 HP (high pressure) air compressor
130 Gyro compass
131 Telemotor oil storage tank
132 Sewage tank
133 Radar mast hoist
134 'R' compensating tank
135 Main cold room
136 Ready-use cold room
137 Magazine
138 Distiller
139 Oleo press
140 Telemotor pump
141 LP (low pressure) rotary blower
142 Telemotor accumulator
143 4kW or 5kW machine
144 Desk
145 Wardroom wine cupboard
146 Rum cupboard
147 Three hinged beds
148 Steering wheel
149 Hydroplane indicator
150 Depth gauge
151 Bed (lockers under; hinged bed over)
152 Type 128A Asdic
153 Bridge seat

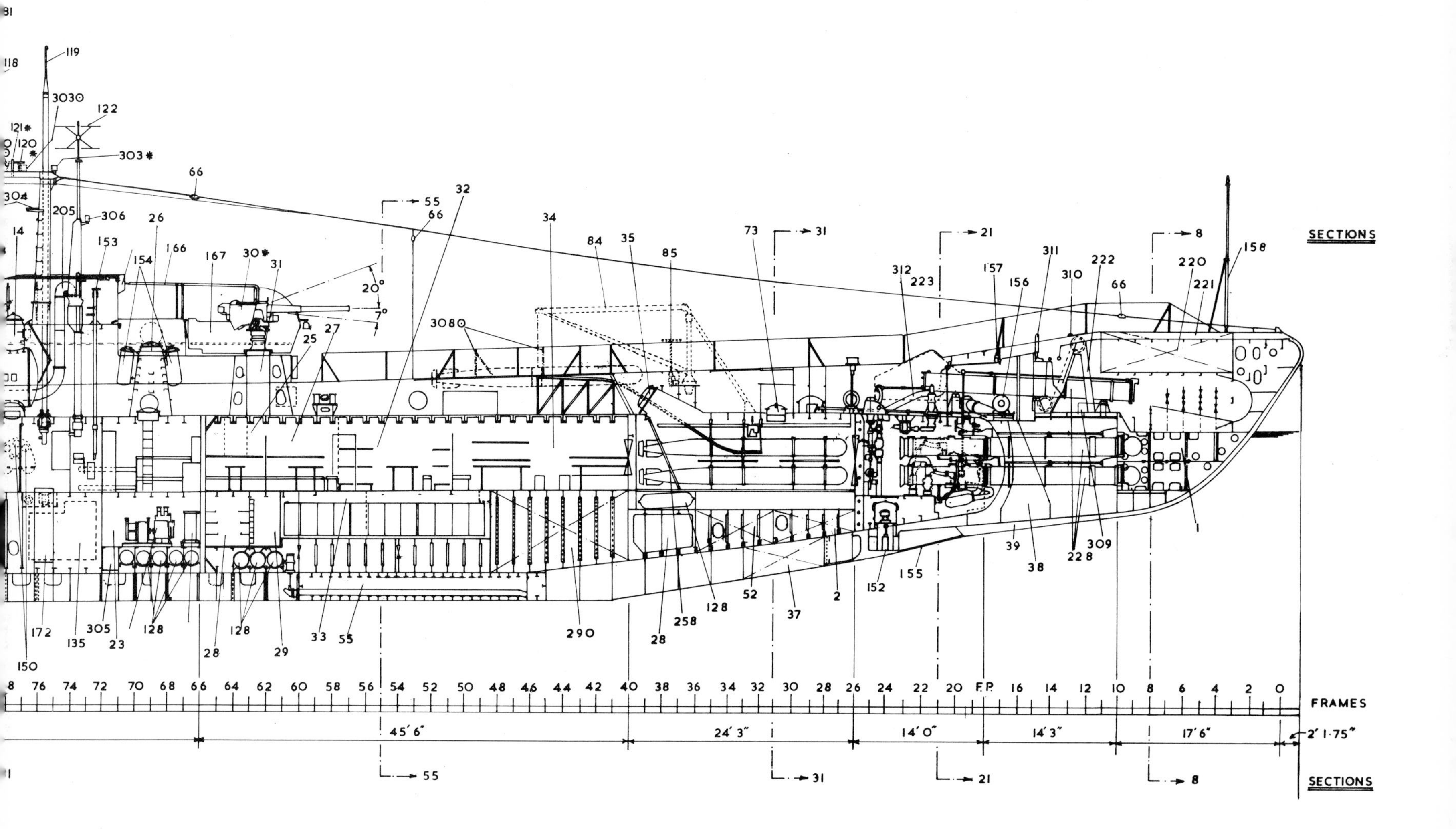

B General arrangements

B1/4 **Plan view of bridge**

B1/5 **Plan at superstructure**

B1/6 **Plan at greatest breadth**

154 4in ready-use ammunition locker
155 Stay
156 Capstan unit
157 Twin towing slip
158 Jackstaff
159 20mm Oerlikon ready-use ammunition lockers
160 Portable wood seat
161 Seat
162 Bow light
163 Socket for .303in gas-operated Vickers machine gun
164 Night sights
165 Azimuth repeater
166 Voice pipe
167 Revolving gun platform
168 H/F (high frequency) aerial
169 Wash basin
170 Walking flat
171 Guard wire
172 Periscope well
173 Firing gear
174 Firing panel
175 Hinged bed
176 Absorption unit CO_2 (*Affray* only)
177 Curtain
178 Table
179 Seat locker
180 No 1 battery fuse panel
181 Ice chest
182 Letter box
183 Urinal
184 Wardroom pantry
185 Gyro angle transmitter
186 Chart table
187 'Imo' pump
188 Circulating water pump starter
189 Lubricating oil heater
190 Lubricating oil separator
191 Lubricating oil pump starter
192 Ballast pump
193 5ft 9in diam propeller
194 Propeller shaft
195 Shaft bracket
196 No 5 main tank
197 Air cooler
198 Steering gear shafts
199 Torpedo bow cap shafts
200 Jumping wire stay
201 Periscope support bracket
202 Breakwater

B1/4

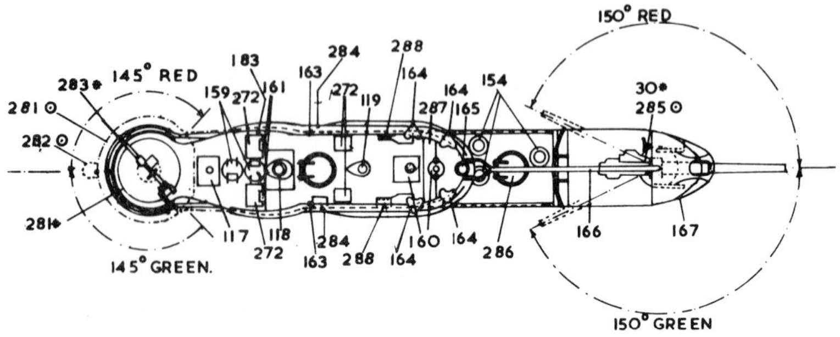

B1/5

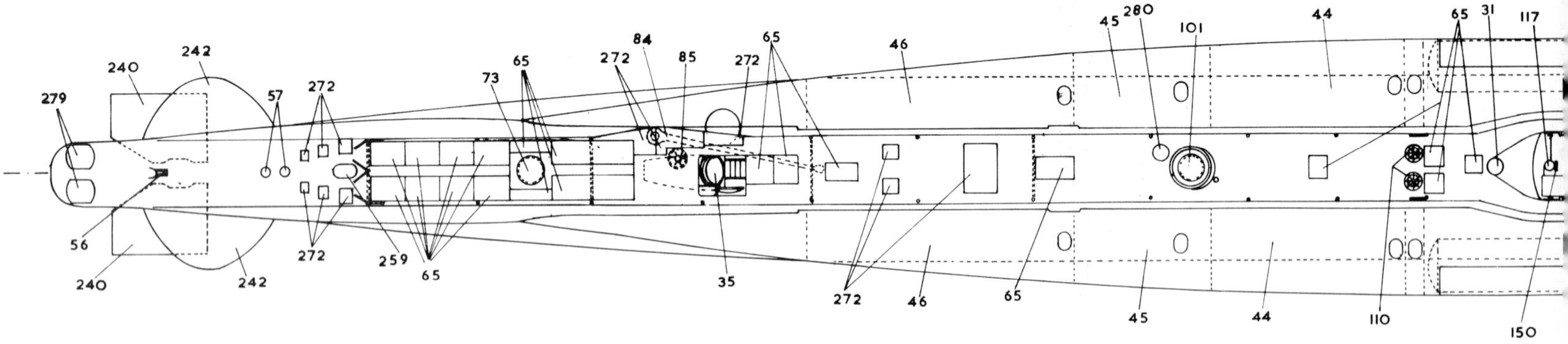

B1/6

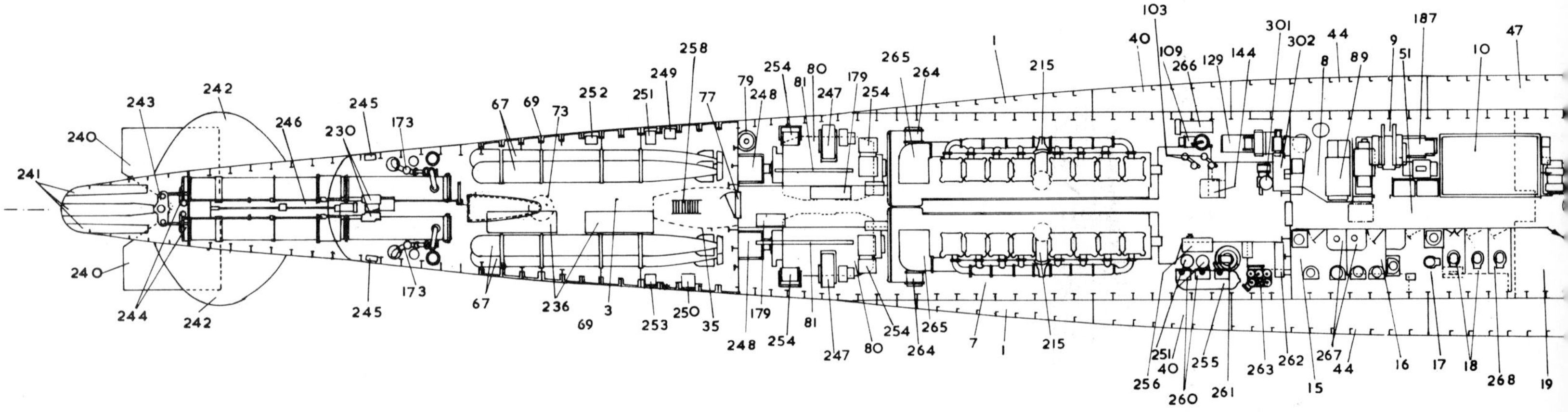

203 Bridge deck
204 No 3 main tank
205 Engine induction trunk
206 Gyro panel
207 Ballast keel
208 Bridge handrail
209 Torpedo embarking rails
210 Portable guardrails
211 Exhaust trunk
212 Handrail
213 Cast iron block
214 Main cables
215 Main engines (8-cylinder Admiralty diesels)
216 Engine turning gear
217 Ballast keel
218 Hinged bed
219 Seat locker
220 Bow buoyancy tank
221 Towing trough
222 Hawse pipe
223 Hydroplane guard plate
224 Bow shutter
225 Torpedo in loading position
226 Portable ramp
227 Trough
228 21in torpedo tube
229 Bow cap
230 Bow cap operating gear
231 No 1 main tank
232 External firing gear
233 Anti-submarine unit
234 Hot cupboards
235 Wood lining
236 Two hinged beds
237 First-aid cupboard
238 4-gallon urn
239 Spare 20mm Oerlikon gun barrels
240 Hydroplane
241 Torpedo guide
242 Hydroplane guard
243 Rudder crosshead
244 Stern cap
245 Heater unit
246 No 5 main tank
247 Main motor blower
248 After star clutch
249 Duplex pistol locker
250 Detonator locker
251 Signal cartridges
252 Grenades
253 Stowage rack
254 Cooler
255 Starting air bottle
256 Bench
257 Lubricating oil strainer
258 Ladder
259 Vent pipe
260 Circulating oil pump starter
261 Ballast pump
262 Lathe
263 Main line six-valve box
264 Silencer
265 Supercharger cooler
266 Lubricating oil heater
267 Shower
268 ERAs' and POs' WC
269 Rudder indicator
270 Hydroplane controls
271 Cable trough
272 Hinged cover
273 Portable accommodation ladder (alternative positions)
274 Cleaning gear locker
275 NUC (not under control) lights
276 Very light pistols
277 Identification flares
278 Lower conning tower hatch
279 External torpedo orifice
280 Anti-submarine dome (Type 138 Asdic)
281 Gun platform
282 Overtaking light (fitted in this position in *Aeneas* only)
283 20mm Oerlikon gun on Mk VIIA Submarine Mounting
284 Teak rail
285 4in gun on S2 mounting (*Aeneas* only)
286 GAT trunk
287 Sparred wooden platform
288 Engine induction
289 Fresh water tank
290 Oil fuel tank
291 Freon unit
292 Supply fan
293 Air heaters
294 Walking platform
295 Starter for blower
296 8kW motor alternator
297 Electrical store
298 Refrigerating machine
299 Sub-pressure pump

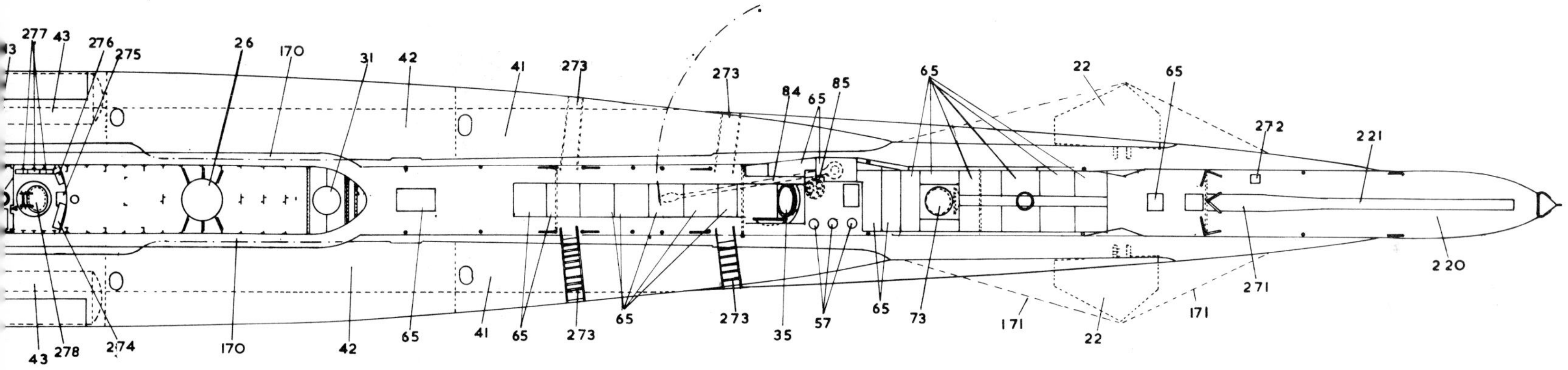

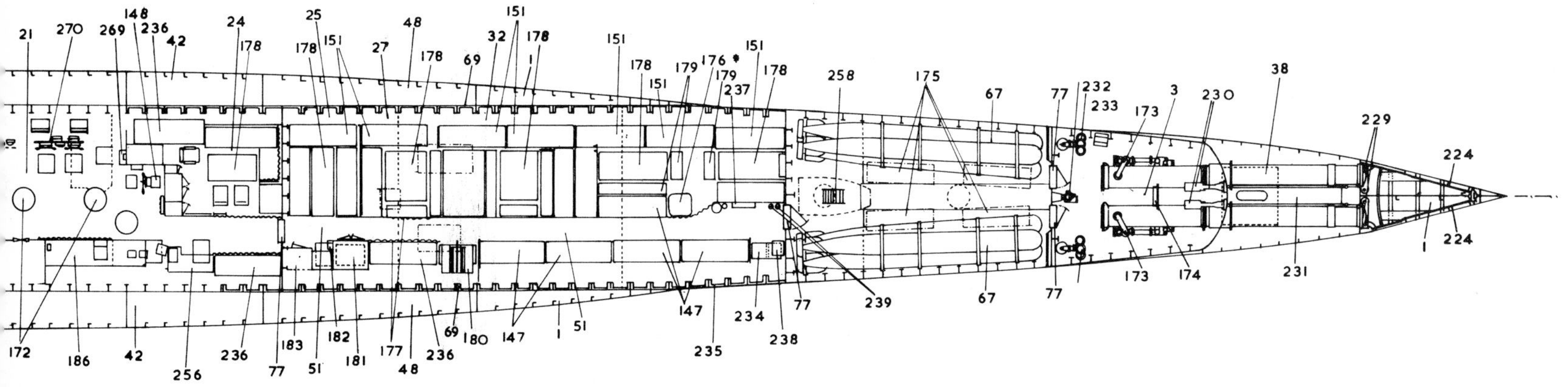

B General arrangements

300 Slop drain tank
301 Fuel oil separator
302 Fuel oil gravity tank
303 Steaming light (*Aeneas* only here)
304 Lookout platform
305 Brine tank
306 Emergency light
307 FM Type direction finder
308 Guardrail
309 Anchor recess (port side only)
310 Bolster
311 Bullring for breastrope
312 Firing pipe

B1/7 Plan below main flat (Frames 40–97)

B1/8 Section at Frame 150 (looking aft)

B1/9 Section at Frame 136 (looking aft)

B1/10 Section at Frame 121 (looking aft)

B1/11 Section at Frame 110 (looking aft)

B1/7

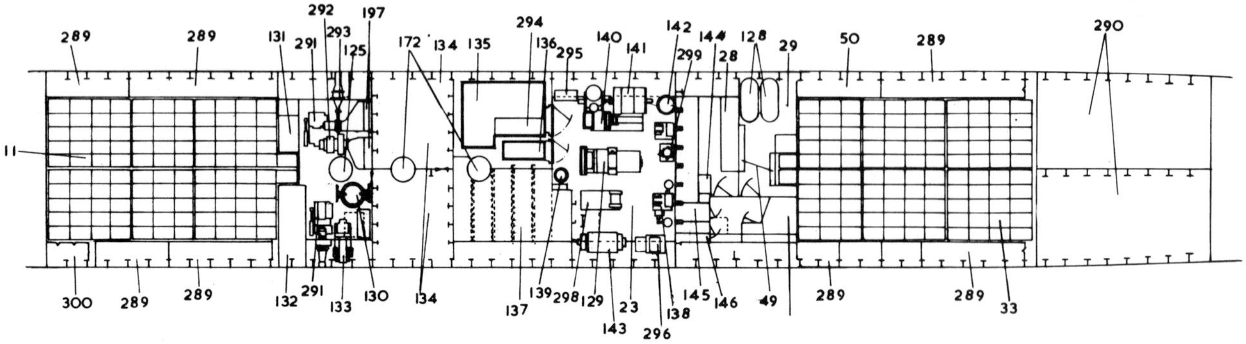

B1/8

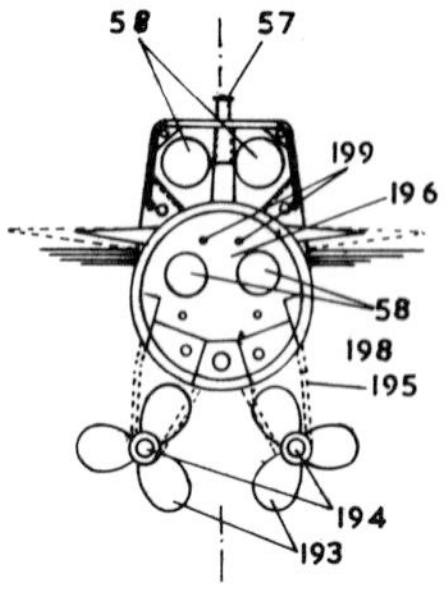

B1/9

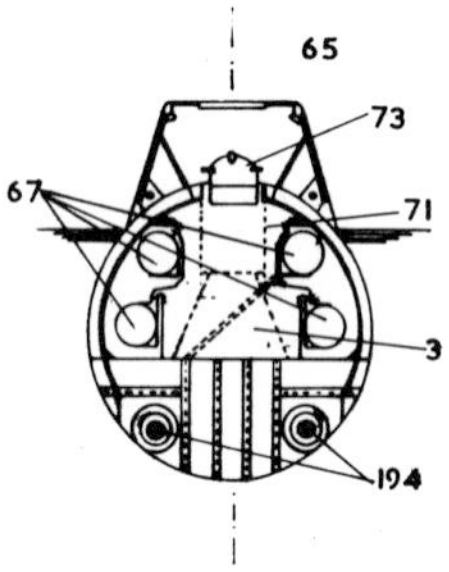

B1/10

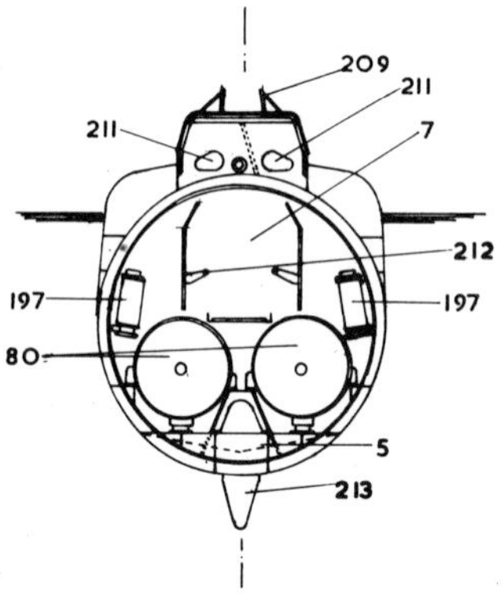

B1/11

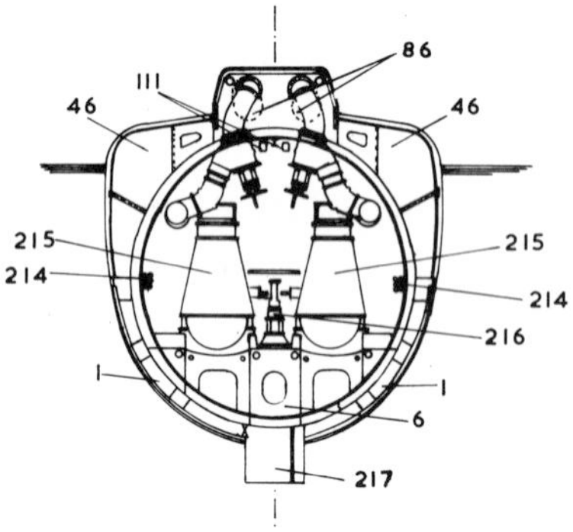

B1/12 Section at Frame 81 (looking forward)

B1/13 Section at Frame 55 (looking forward)

B1/14 Section at Frame 31 (looking forward)

B1/15 Section at Frame 21 (looking forward)

B1/16 Section at Frame 8 (looking forward)

B1/17 Twin Mk 12 Oerlikon mounting platform (Aeneas only; not to scale)

B1/12

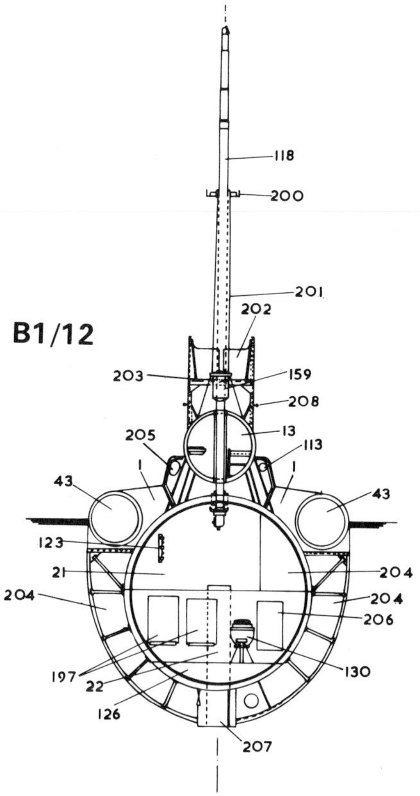

B1/13

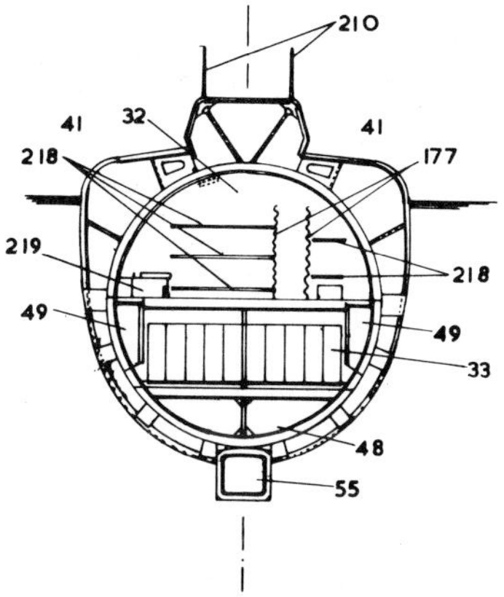

B1/14

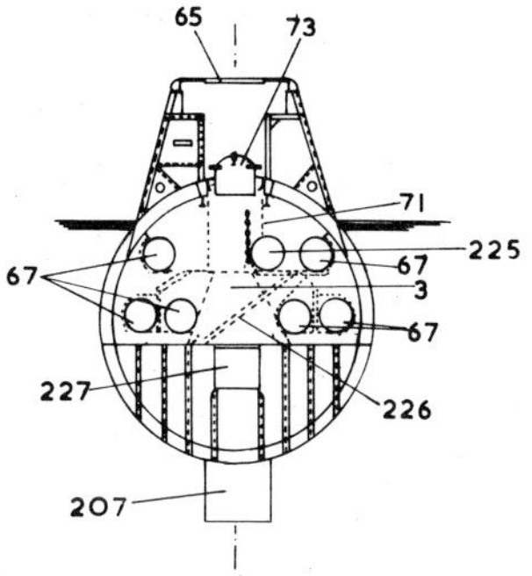

B1/15

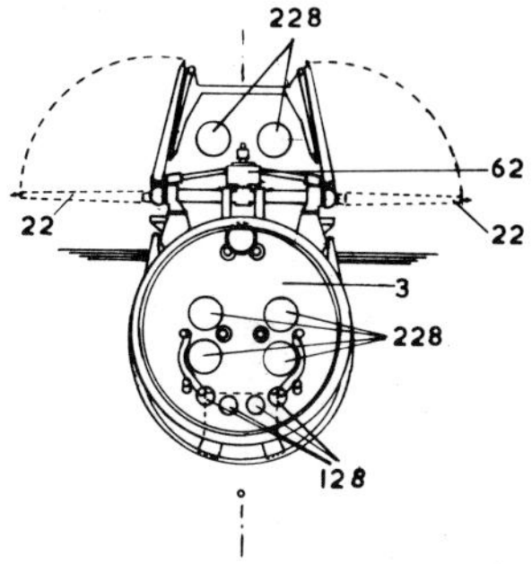

B1/16

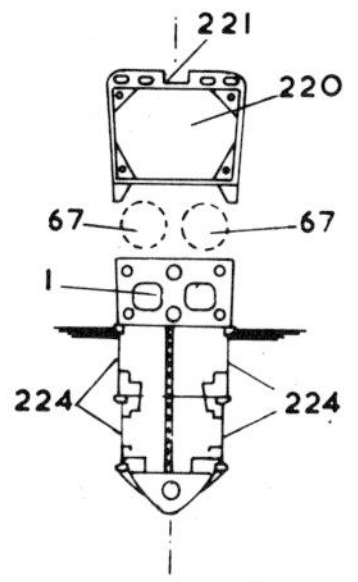

B1/17

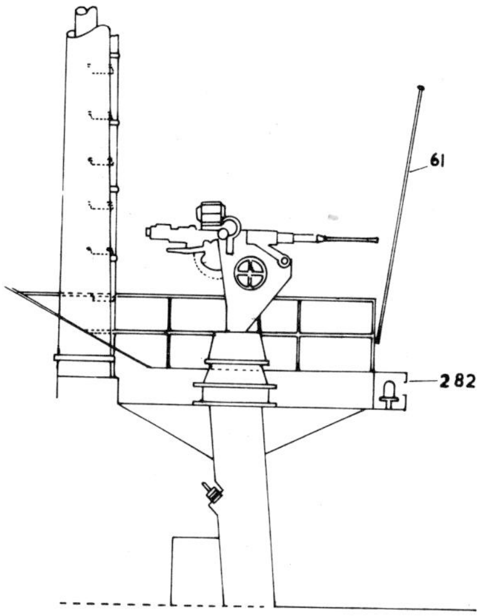

B General arrangements

B2 **PROJECTED ARRANGEMENT FOR ADDITIONAL GUN ARMAMENT FOR FAR EAST OPERATIONS (dated April 1945; 1/192 scale)**

B2/1 **External profile**

B2/2 **Plan**

B2/3 **Internal profile**

1 20mm ready-use ammunition locker
2 6pdr ready-use ammunition locker
3 Twin Mk IX Oerlikon mounting
4 QF 6pdr MK IIA gun on Mk VII mounting
5 CO's cabin
6 Engine room hatch
7 Enlarged Oerlikon bandstand
8 5ft 3in diam 6pdr platform
9 Oil fuel expansion tank
10 Type 138 Asdic dome

B3 **SECTIONS (1/96 scale)**

B3/1 **Ambush, Anchorite and Andrew (Frame 76 looking forward)**

B3/2 **Ambush, Anchorite and Andrew (Frame 81 looking aft)**

1 CO's cabin
2 'O' compensating tank
3 Air conditioning compartment
4 Control room
5 Fresh water tank
6 Main tank No 2
7 Main tank No 3

B2/1

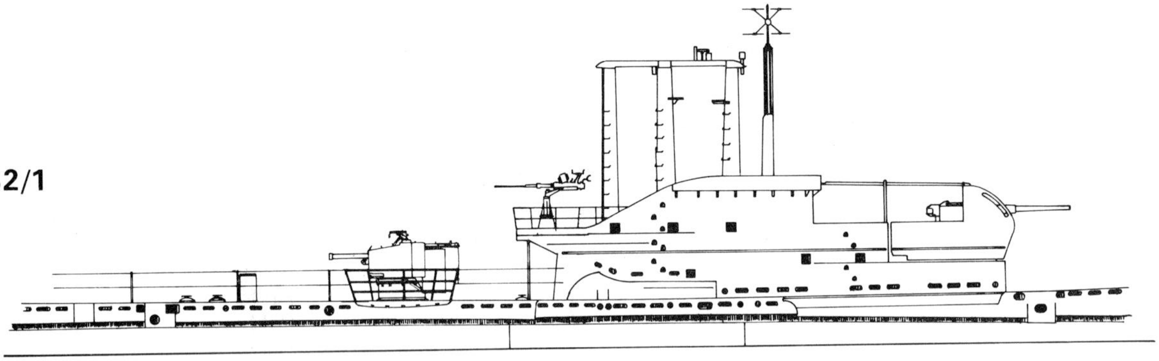

B2/2

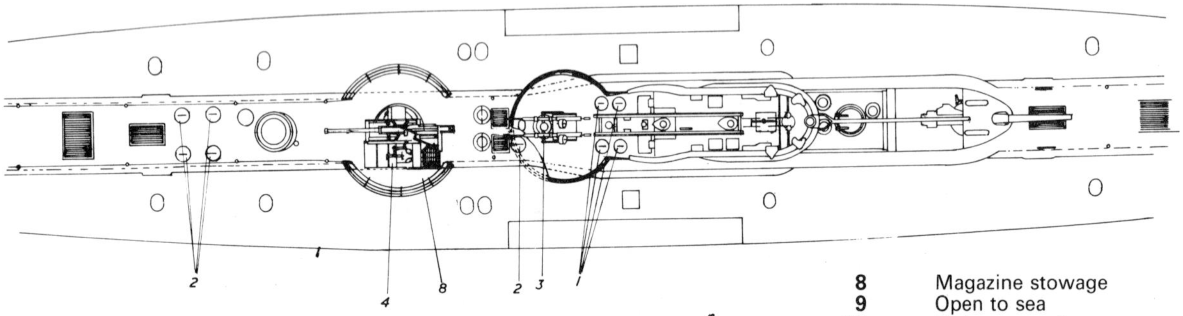

B2/3

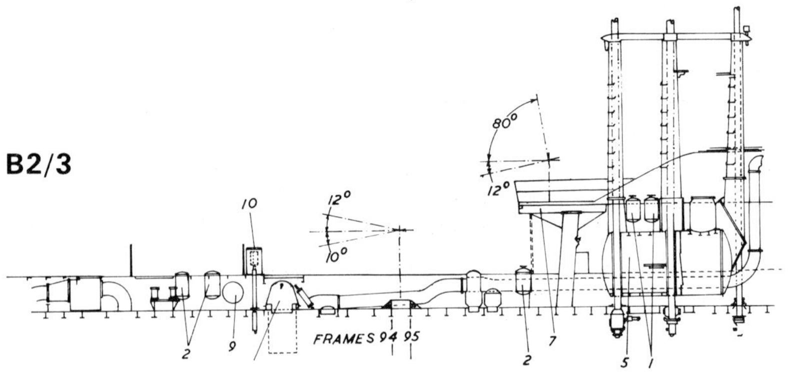

8 Magazine stowage
9 Open to sea
10 Periscope well
11 Ballast keel
12 Main cold room
13 Gun sponson
14 ANF array
15 ANF mast
16 Jumping wires
17 Main aerial support
18 ANF mast support
19 Oerlikon gun safety rail
20 Twin 20mm Oerlikon gun on 12A S/M mounting
21 Single 20mm Oerlikon gun on Mk VIIA* S/M mounting
22 Snort mast (1949 refit on *Andrew*)
23 Snort mast crutch
24 7½in diam periscope
25 Radar array
26 Main aerial
27 Periscope support bracket
28 Wind deflector
29 Standard compass
30 Socket for .303in gas-operated gun
31 Submarine night sight
32 Bridge handrail
33 Table
34 Bunk bed
35 Folding lavatory
36 Drawer
37 Railway type fan
38 8in battery ventilation
39 8in exhaust
40 14in engine induction
41 Vent trunk
42 Sluice valve
43 Battery fan control unit
44 Battery fan indicators
45 Main cables
46 Sliding door
47 Hatch coaming
48 LP fuse panel
49 Engine telegraphs
50 Forward telepump starter
51 Engine clutch indicator
52 ANF mast hoist
53 Freon unit starter
54 18in auxiliary cable run
55 9in auxiliary cable run
56 Telephone control box
57 Telemotor replenishing tank
58 Hydroplane control panel
59 Main motor speed indicator
60 Log master speed transmitter
61 Projector compass resistance
62 Torpedo orders forward tubes
63 Torpedo orders aft tubes
64 Gyro angling transmitter
65 Telemotor operated vent valve
66 Gyro steering repeater
67 Transmitter for torpedo angling circuit
68 LP junction box No 3
69 Junction box No 7
70 Range transmitter
71 Strobe generator
72 Steering wheel
73 Periscope press
74 Bridge front door
75 Trim pump starter
76 Fan 10in × 3in
77 Steel trunk
78 Grating
79 PPI radar set
80 Iswas
81 Chart table
82 ADL plot
83 Box fuses
84 Echo sounder recorder
85 Condenser
86 Freon unit
87 Trim pump
88 Gyro compass
89 Gun handrail
90 Transformer

B3/1

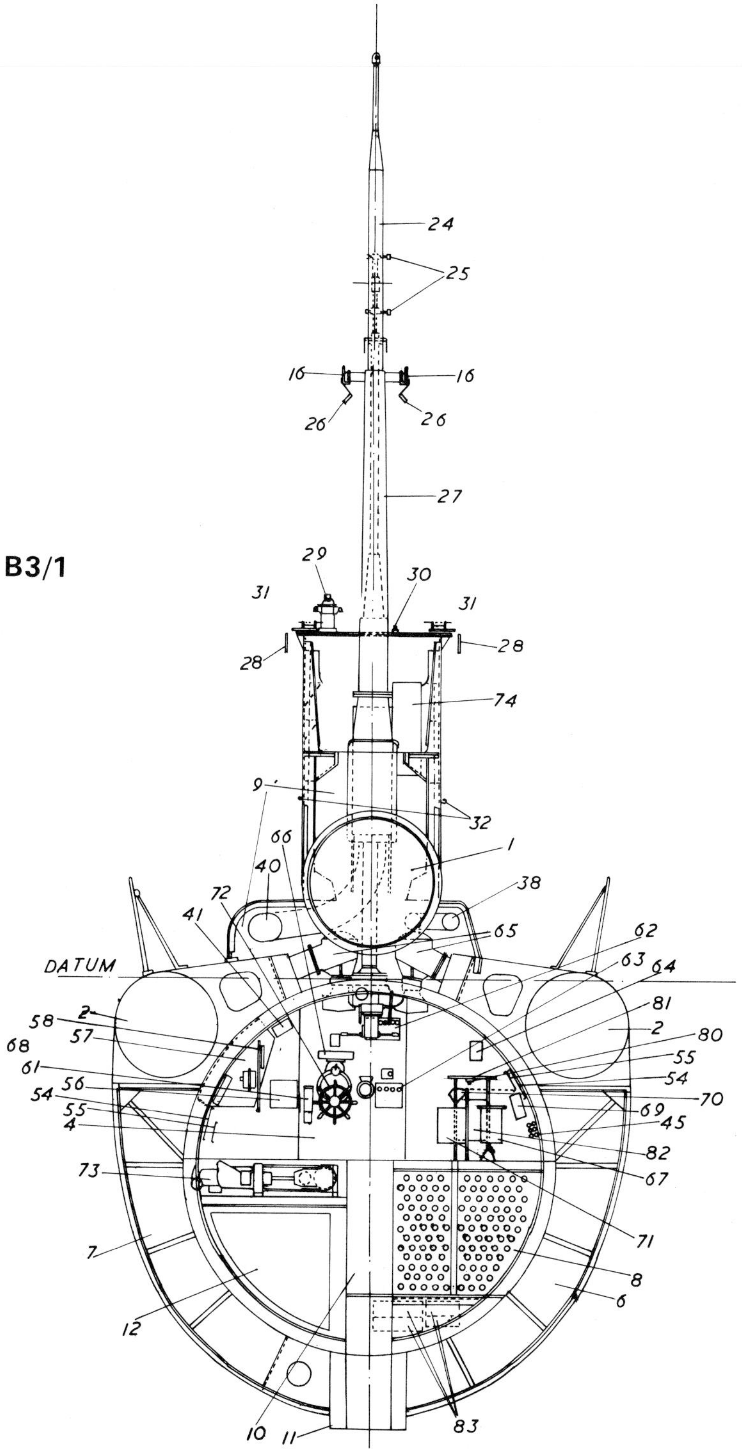

B3/2

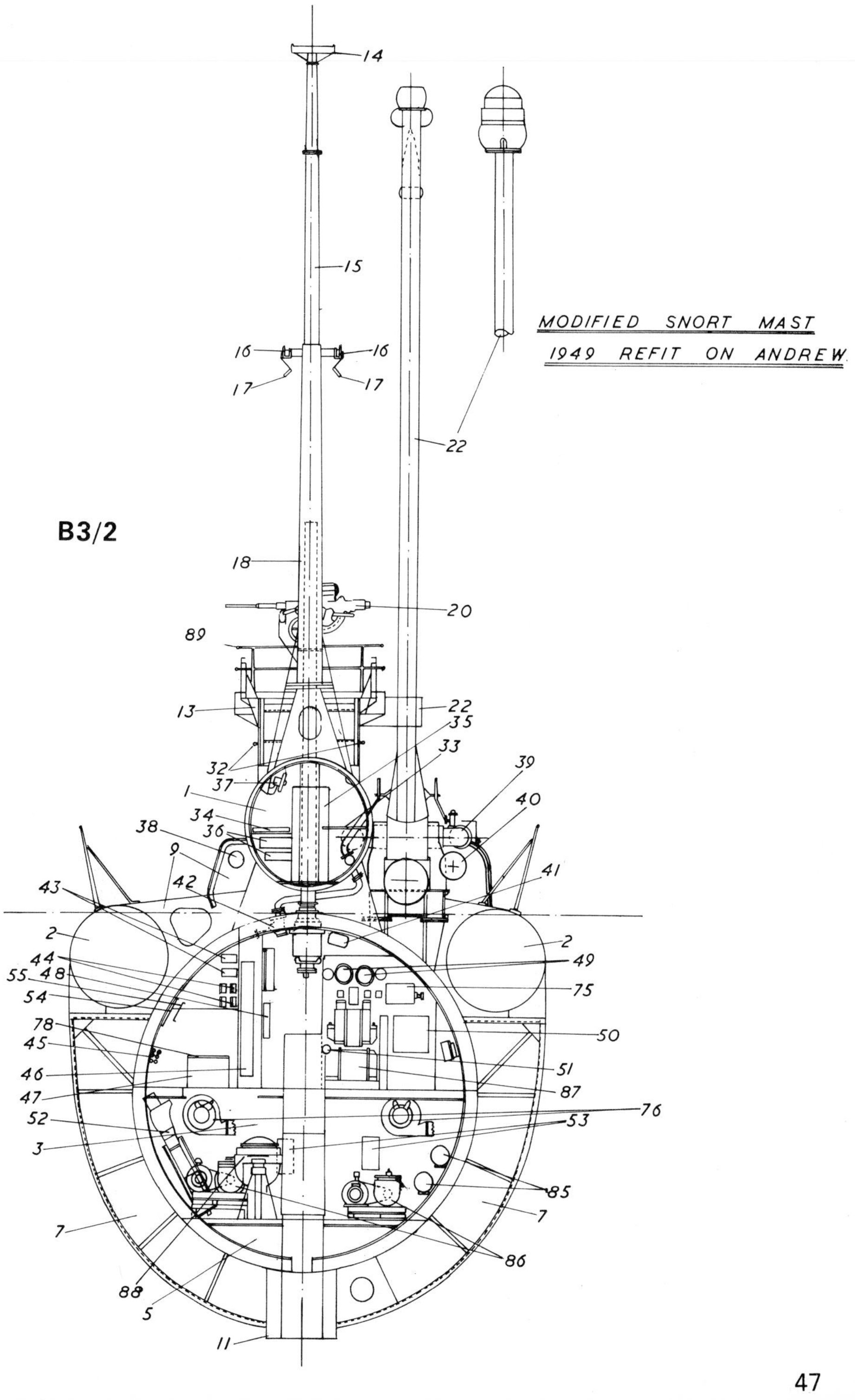

B General arrangements

B3/3 **Amphion, Astute and Auriga (Frame 76 looking forward)**

B3/4 **Amphion, Astute and Auriga (Frame 81 looking aft)**

B3/3

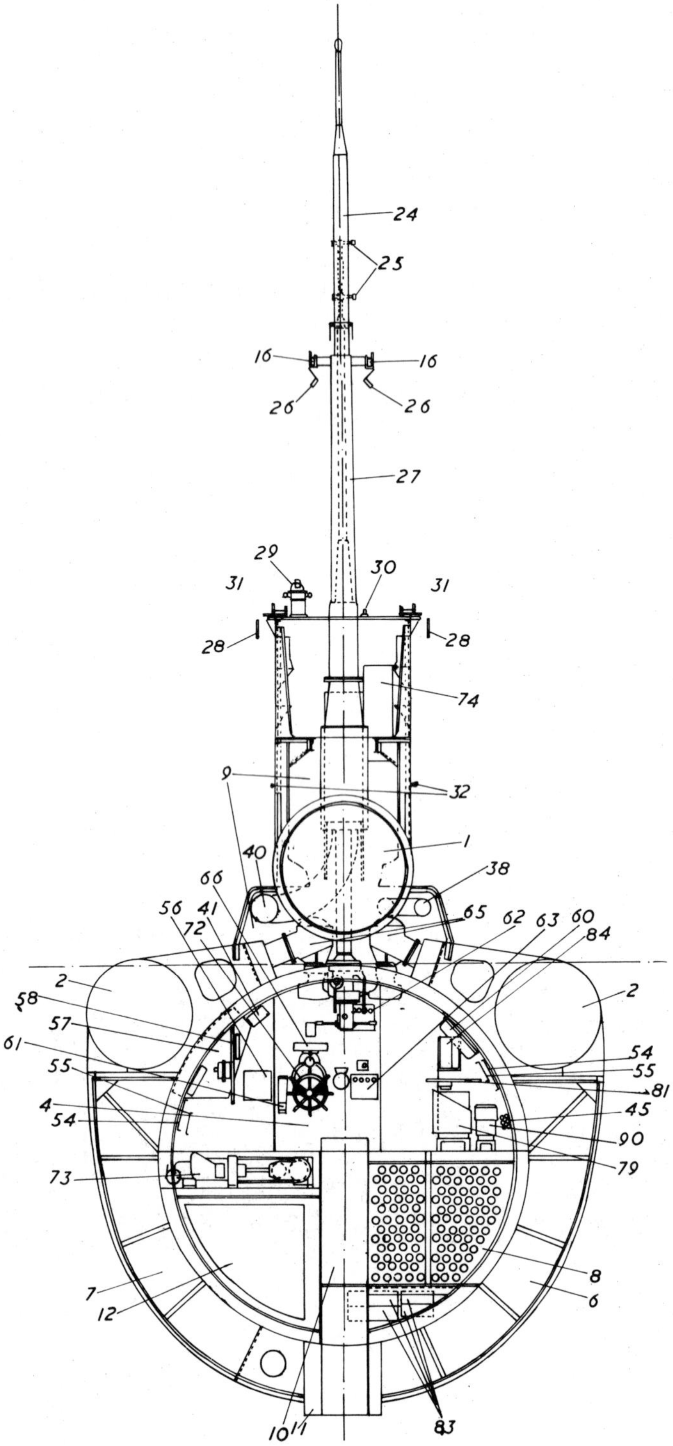

B3/4

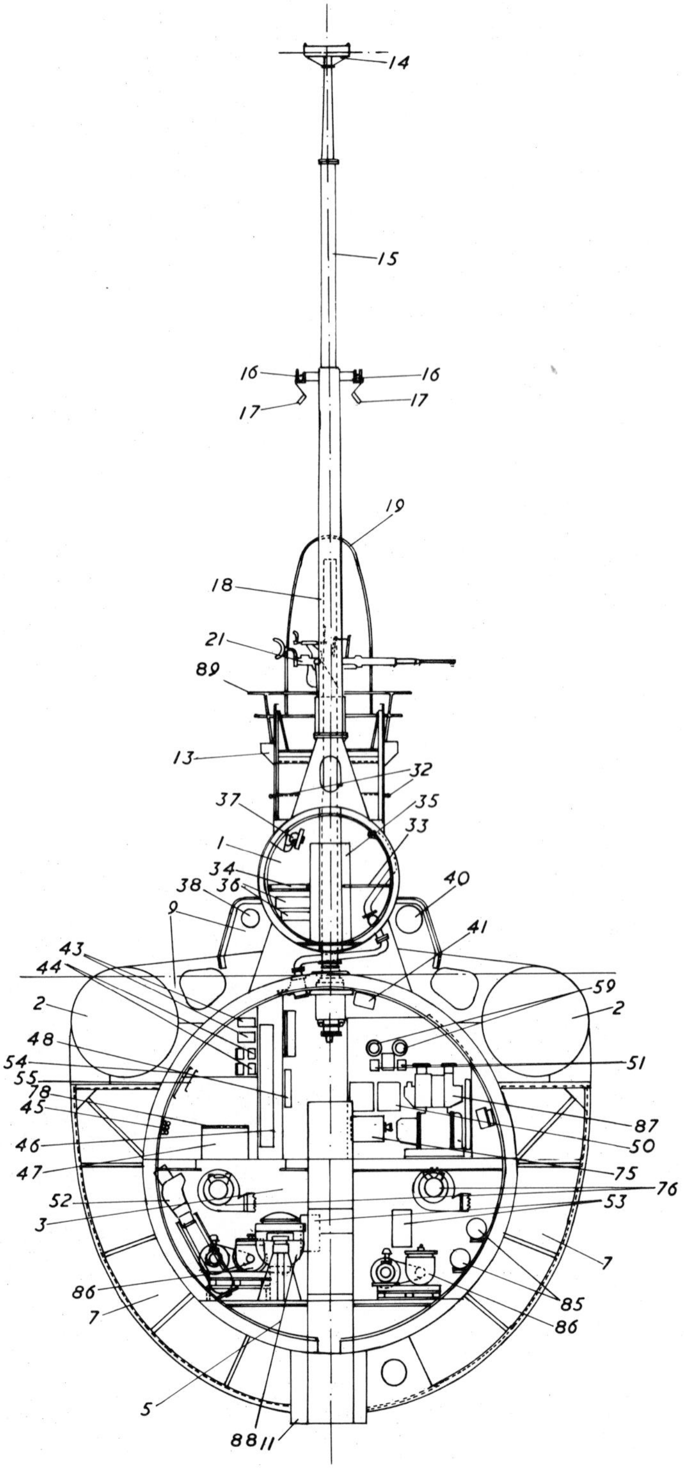

B4 **COMPARATIVE SECTIONS (Frame 63, looking forward; 1/96 scale)**

B4/1 **Auriga as fitted**

B4/2 **Andrew as fitted**

1 Bridge voice pipe
2 4in Mk XII gun on SI mounting, training 90° red
3 4in Mk XXIII gun on S2 mounting, training 90° red
4 Gun support
5 Position of oil fuel expansion tank
6 Walking platform
7 Battery ventilation trunk
8 Oil fuel tank No 2
9 Main tank No 2
10 Ballast keel
11 ERAs' mess
12 Tubular bunk
13 Ventilation trunk
14 15in auxiliary cable run
15 Curtain
16 Auxiliary cable run
17 Bed
18 Locker
19 Ready-use cool cupboard
20 Main cables
21 Echo sounder contactor unit
22 Second coxswain's store
23 Store
24 (2 off) air bottles
25 (3 off) air bottles
26 Battery fan
27 Bin
28 Shelves
29 Steel mesh portable bulkheads
30 Engineer's store forward side
31 Wood flat

B4/1

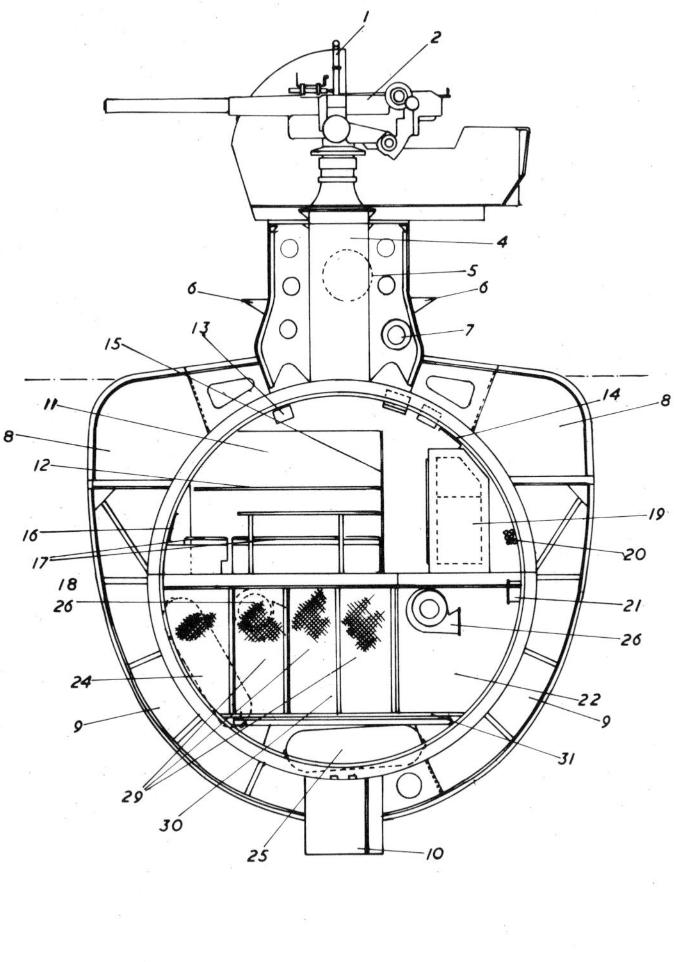

B4/2

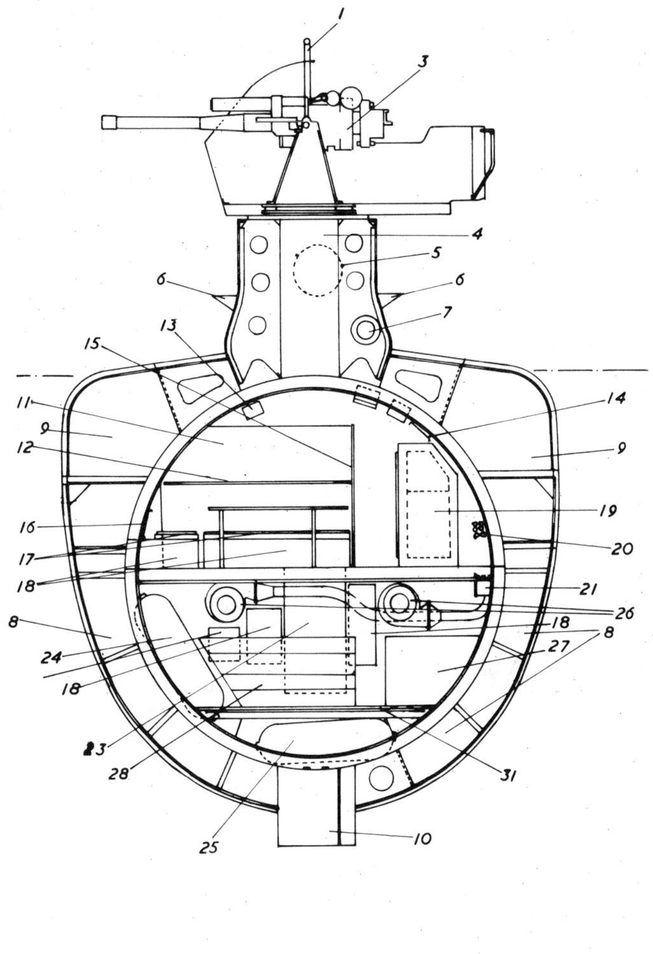

B5 **INTERNAL ARRANGMENTS OF 'A' CLASS WITH SNORT MAST (late 1950s; no scale)**

B5

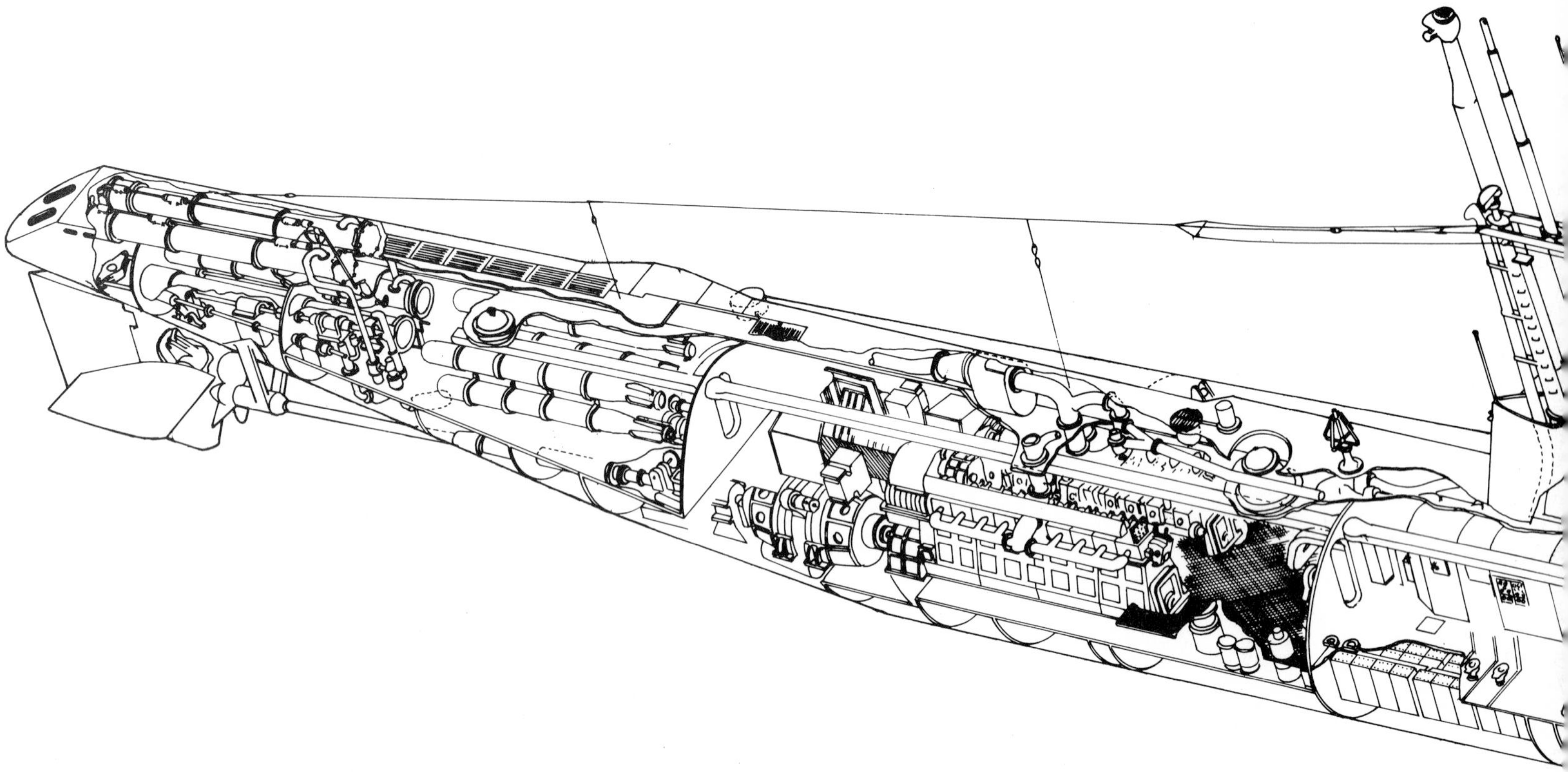

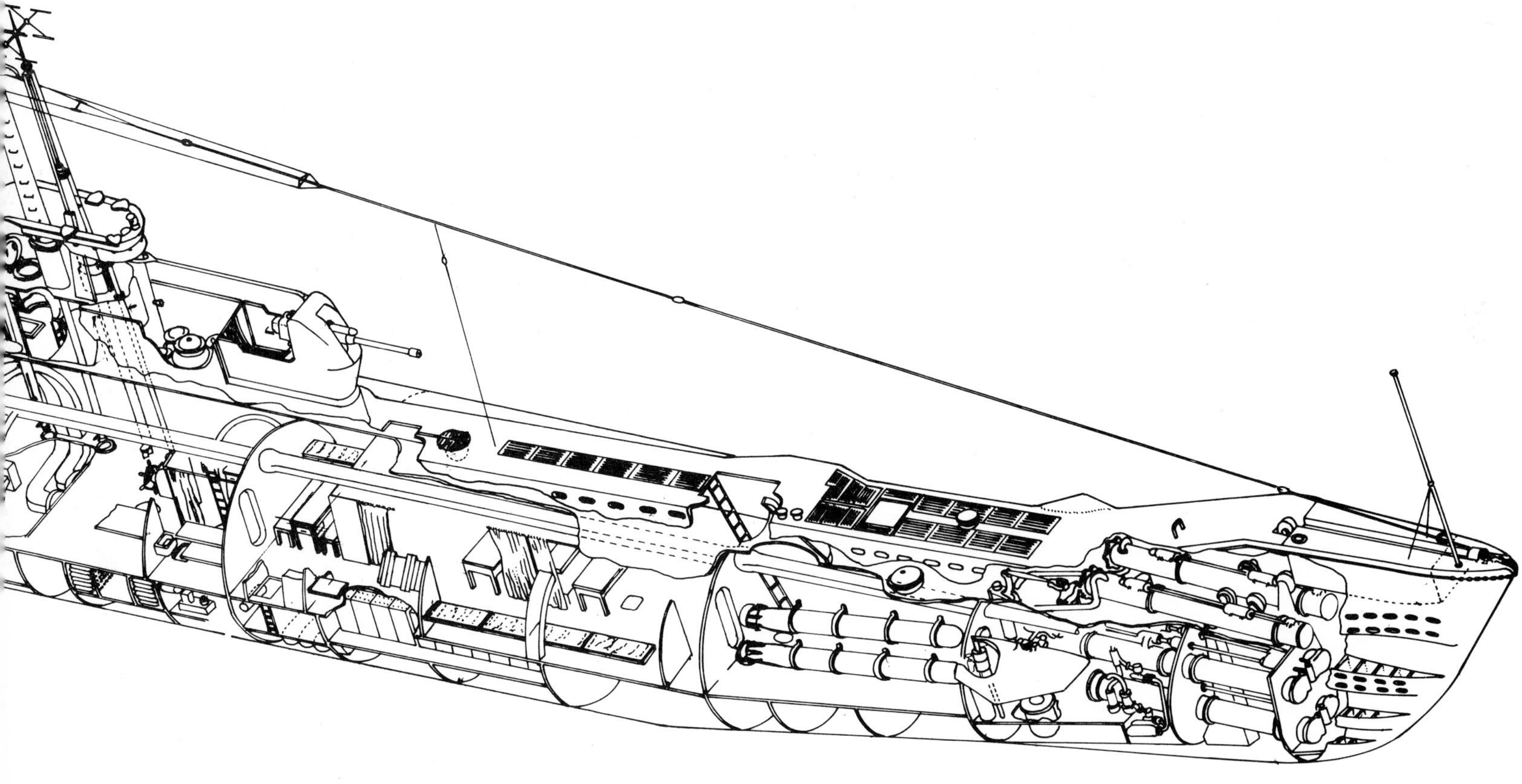

B General arrangements

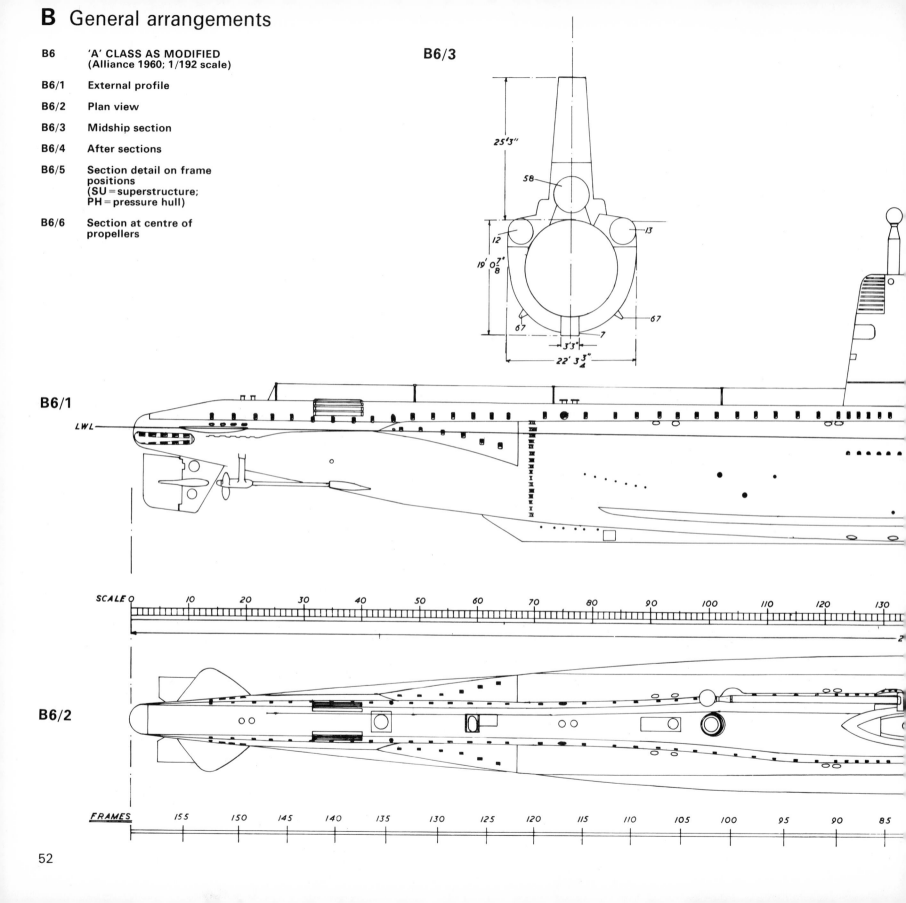

B6	**'A' CLASS AS MODIFIED (Alliance 1960; 1/192 scale)**
B6/1	**External profile**
B6/2	**Plan view**
B6/3	**Midship section**
B6/4	**After sections**
B6/5	**Section detail on frame positions (SU = superstructure; PH = pressure hull)**
B6/6	**Section at centre of propellers**

B6/3

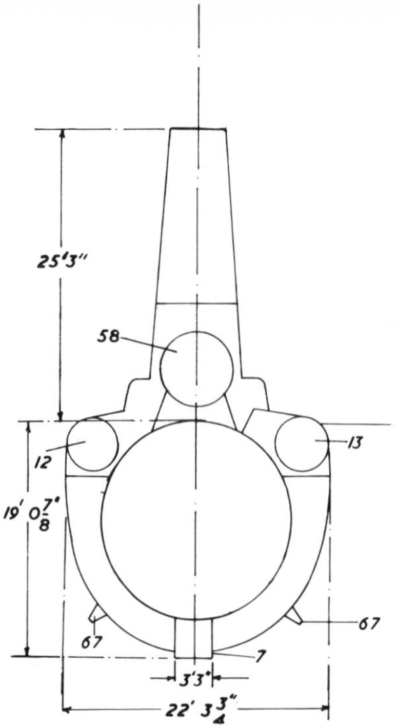

B6/1

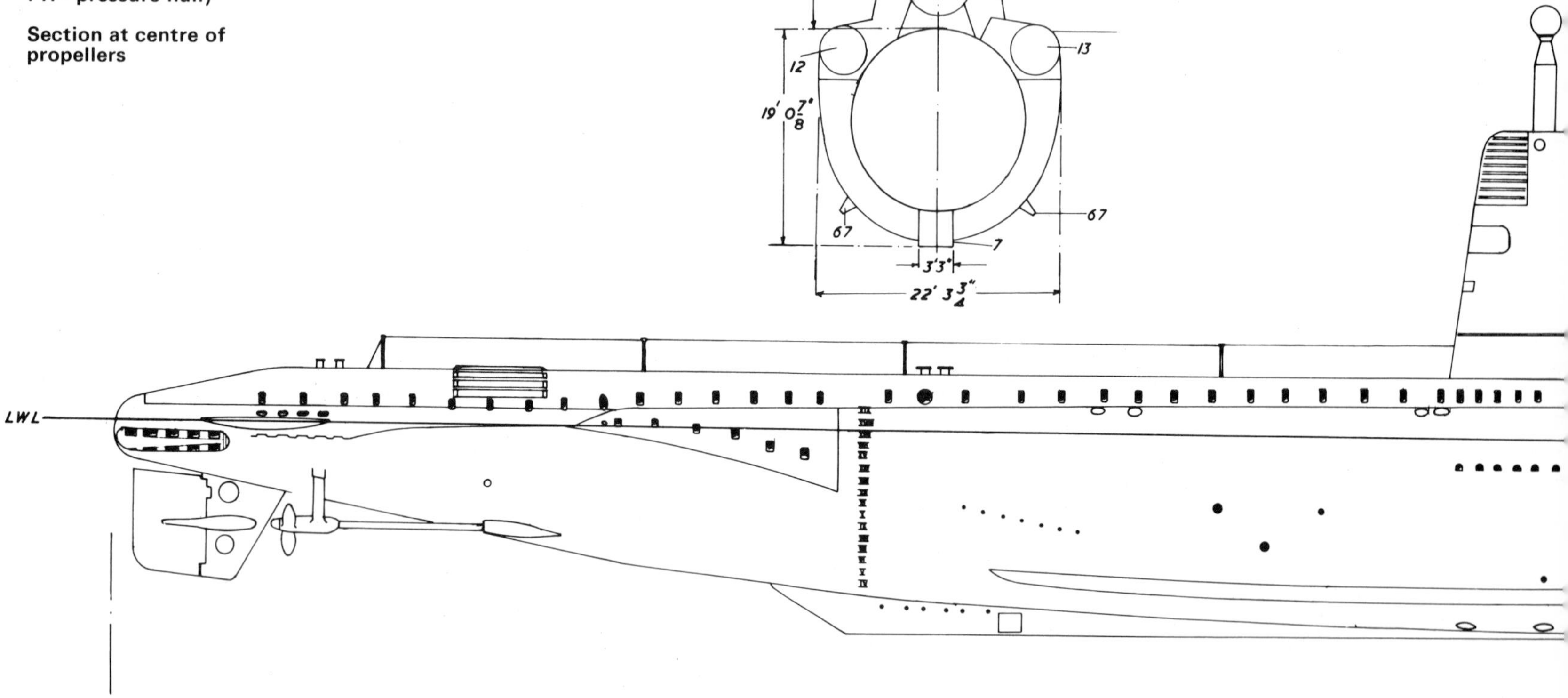

B6/2

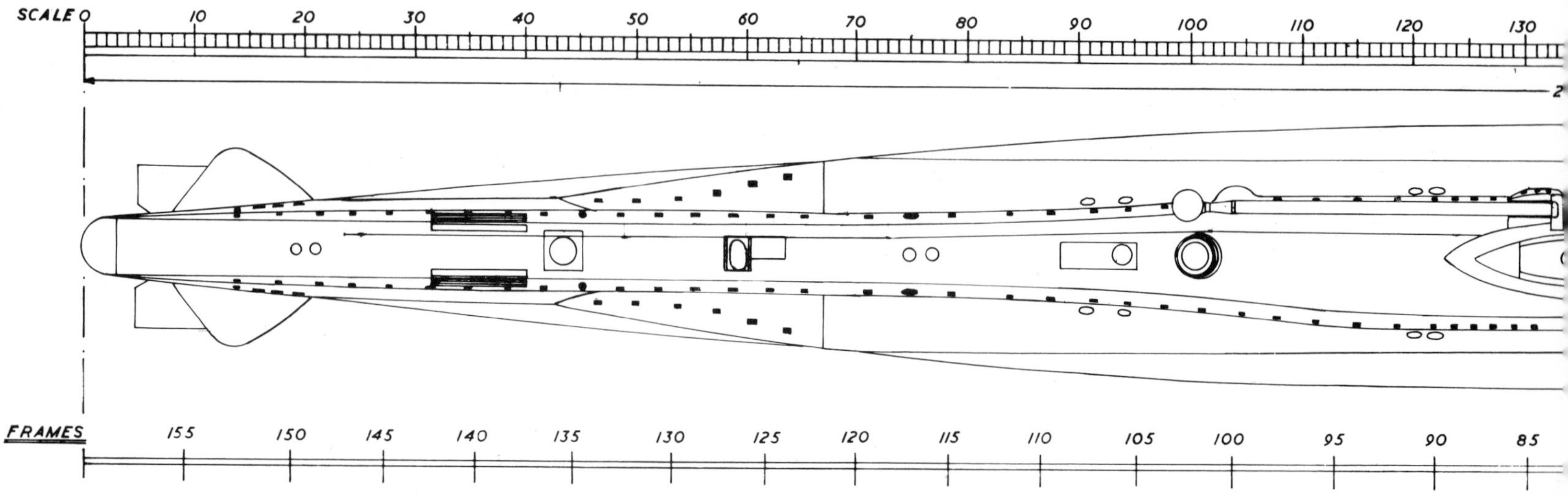

B6/4

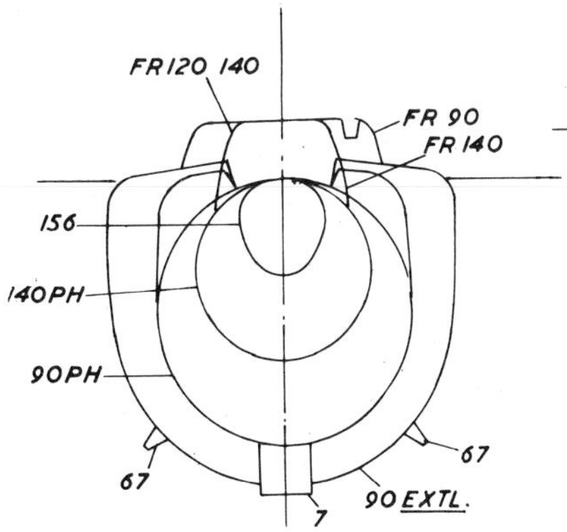

B6/5

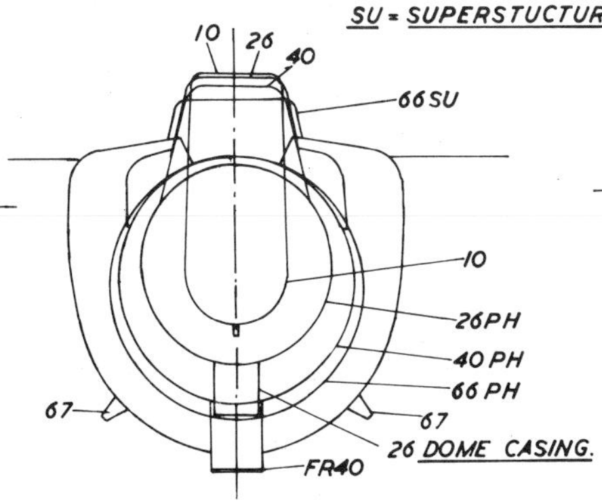

B6/6

SU = SUPERSTUCTURE. PH = PRESSURE HULL.

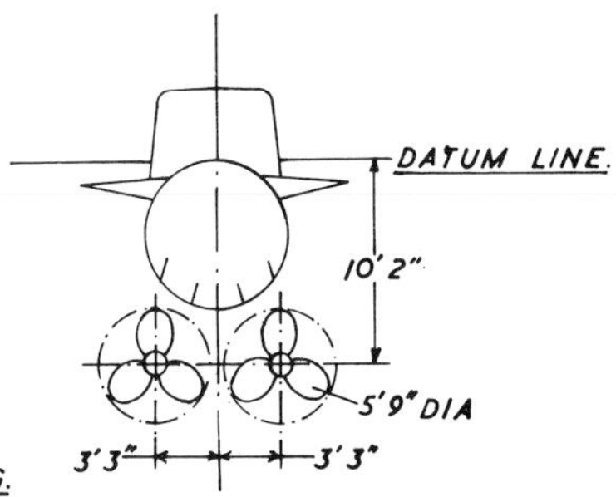

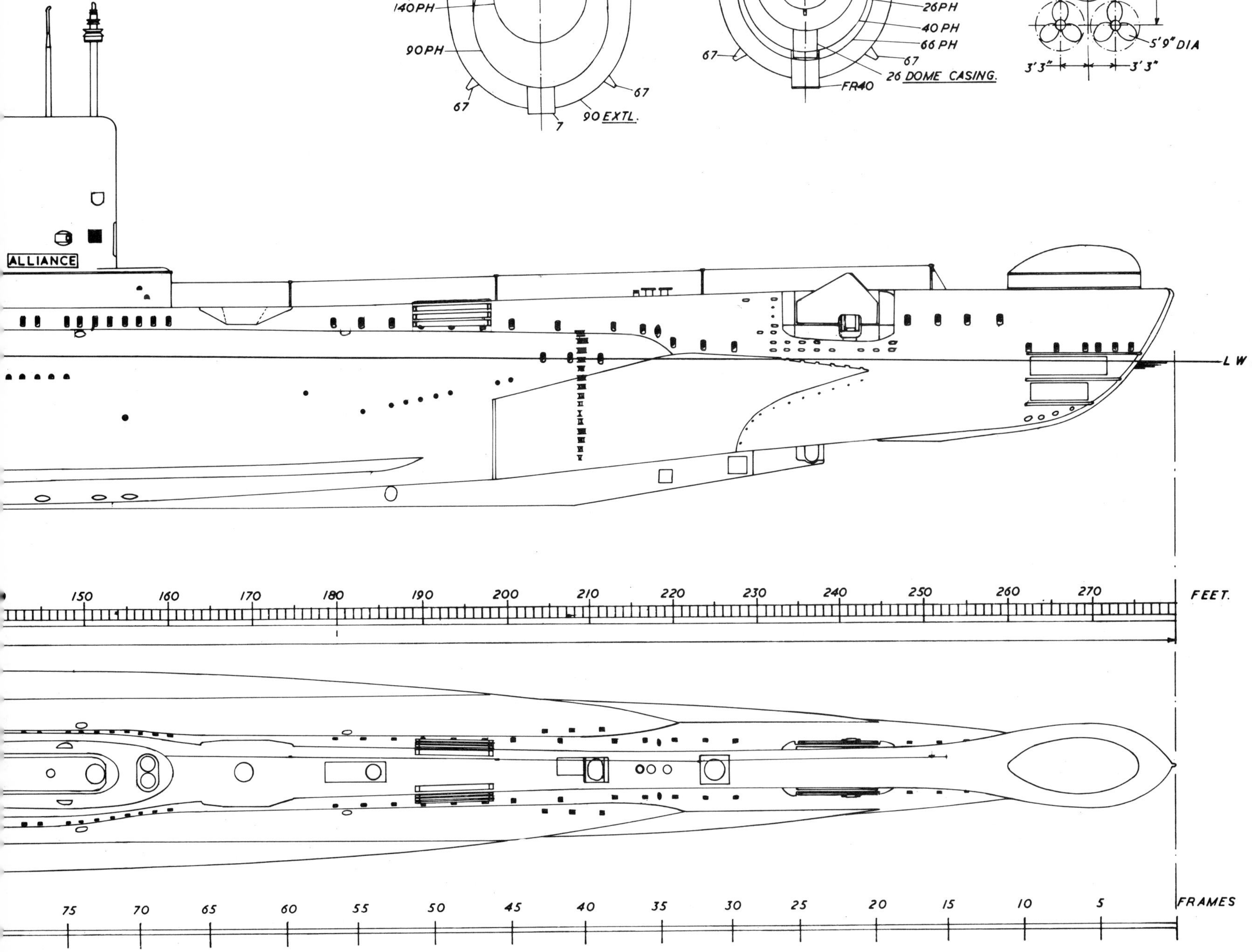

B General arrangements

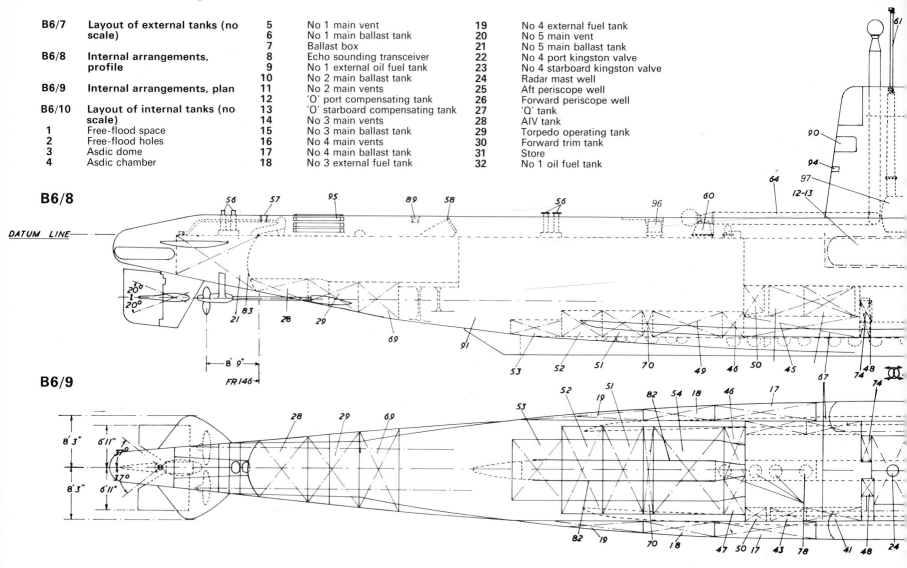

B6/7 **Layout of external tanks (no scale)**
B6/8 **Internal arrangements, profile**
B6/9 **Internal arrangements, plan**
B6/10 **Layout of internal tanks (no scale)**

1. Free-flood space
2. Free-flood holes
3. Asdic dome
4. Asdic chamber
5. No 1 main vent
6. No 1 main ballast tank
7. Ballast box
8. Echo sounding transceiver
9. No 1 external oil fuel tank
10. No 2 main ballast tank
11. No 2 main vents
12. 'O' port compensating tank
13. 'O' starboard compensating tank
14. No 3 main vents
15. No 3 main ballast tank
16. No 4 main vents
17. No 4 main ballast tank
18. No 3 external fuel tank
19. No 4 external fuel tank
20. No 5 main vent
21. No 5 main ballast tank
22. No 4 port kingston valve
23. No 4 starboard kingston valve
24. Radar mast well
25. Aft periscope well
26. Forward periscope well
27. 'Q' tank
28. AIV tank
29. Torpedo operating tank
30. Forward trim tank
31. Store
32. No 1 oil fuel tank

B6/8

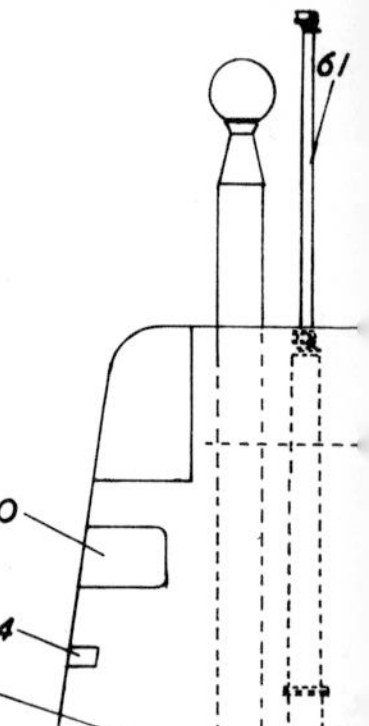
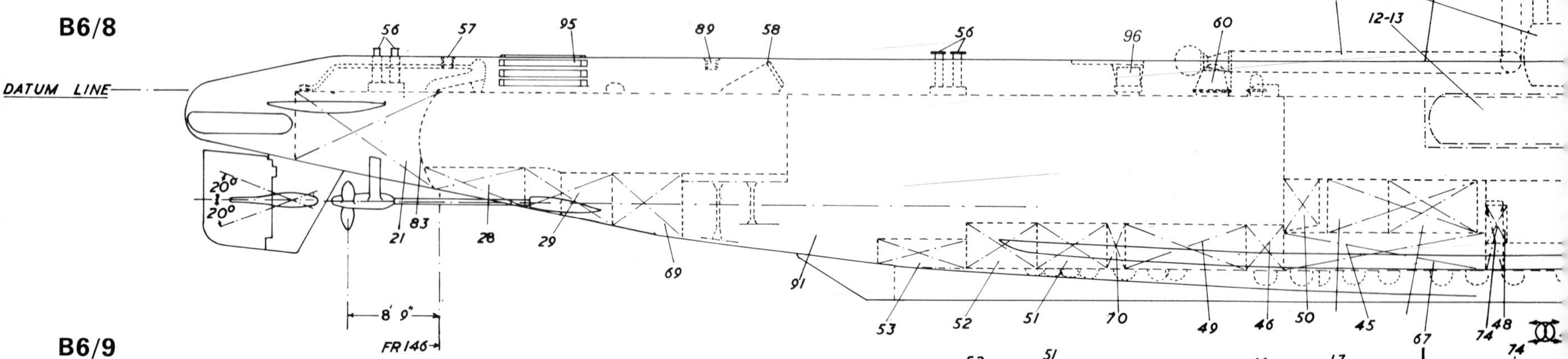

B6/9

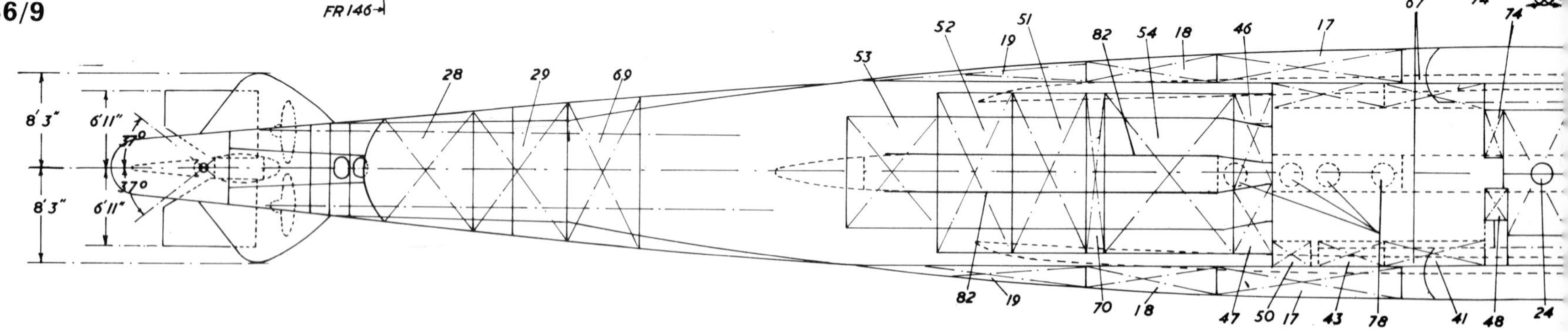

B6/7

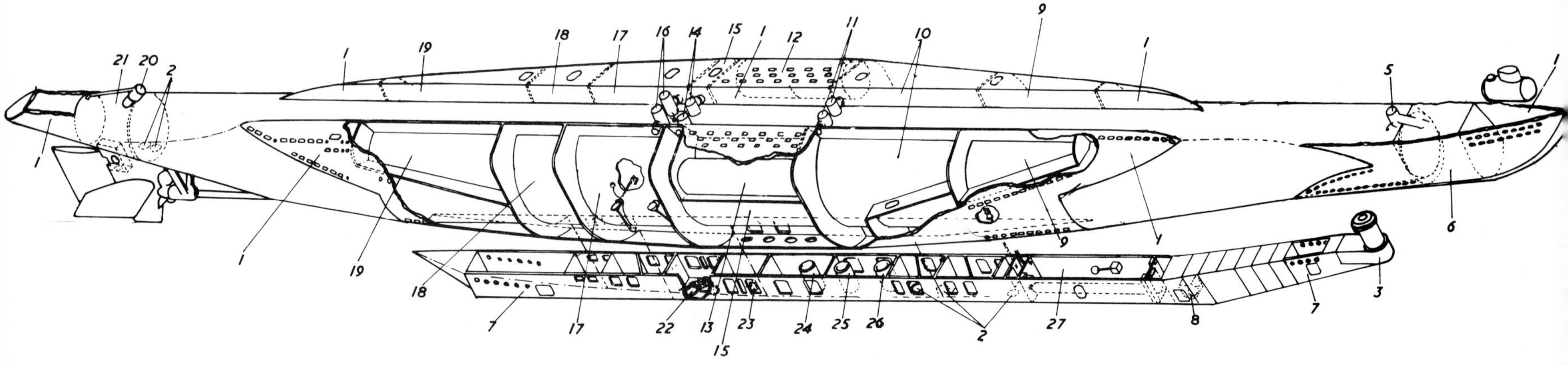

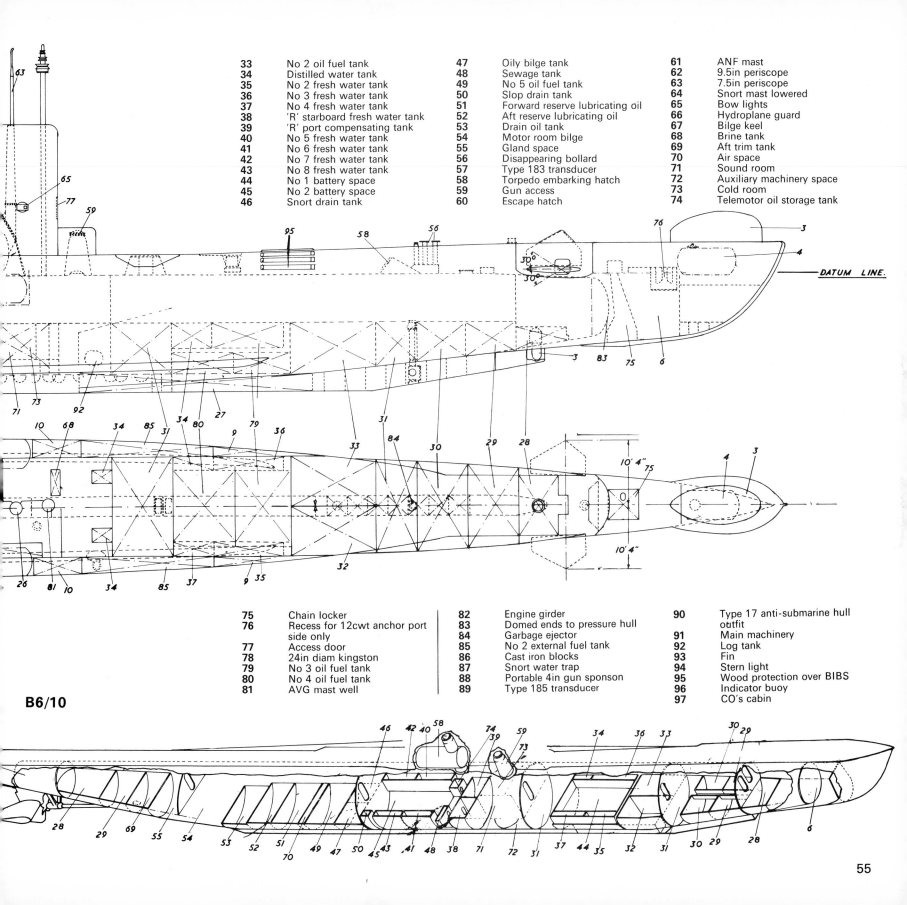

33 No 2 oil fuel tank
34 Distilled water tank
35 No 2 fresh water tank
36 No 3 fresh water tank
37 No 4 fresh water tank
38 'R' starboard fresh water tank
39 'R' port compensating tank
40 No 5 fresh water tank
41 No 6 fresh water tank
42 No 7 fresh water tank
43 No 8 fresh water tank
44 No 1 battery space
45 No 2 battery space
46 Snort drain tank
47 Oily bilge tank
48 Sewage tank
49 No 5 oil fuel tank
50 Slop drain tank
51 Forward reserve lubricating oil
52 Aft reserve lubricating oil
53 Drain oil tank
54 Motor room bilge
55 Gland space
56 Disappearing bollard
57 Type 183 transducer
58 Torpedo embarking hatch
59 Gun access
60 Escape hatch
61 ANF mast
62 9.5in periscope
63 7.5in periscope
64 Snort mast lowered
65 Bow lights
66 Hydroplane guard
67 Bilge keel
68 Brine tank
69 Aft trim tank
70 Air space
71 Sound room
72 Auxiliary machinery space
73 Cold room
74 Telemotor oil storage tank

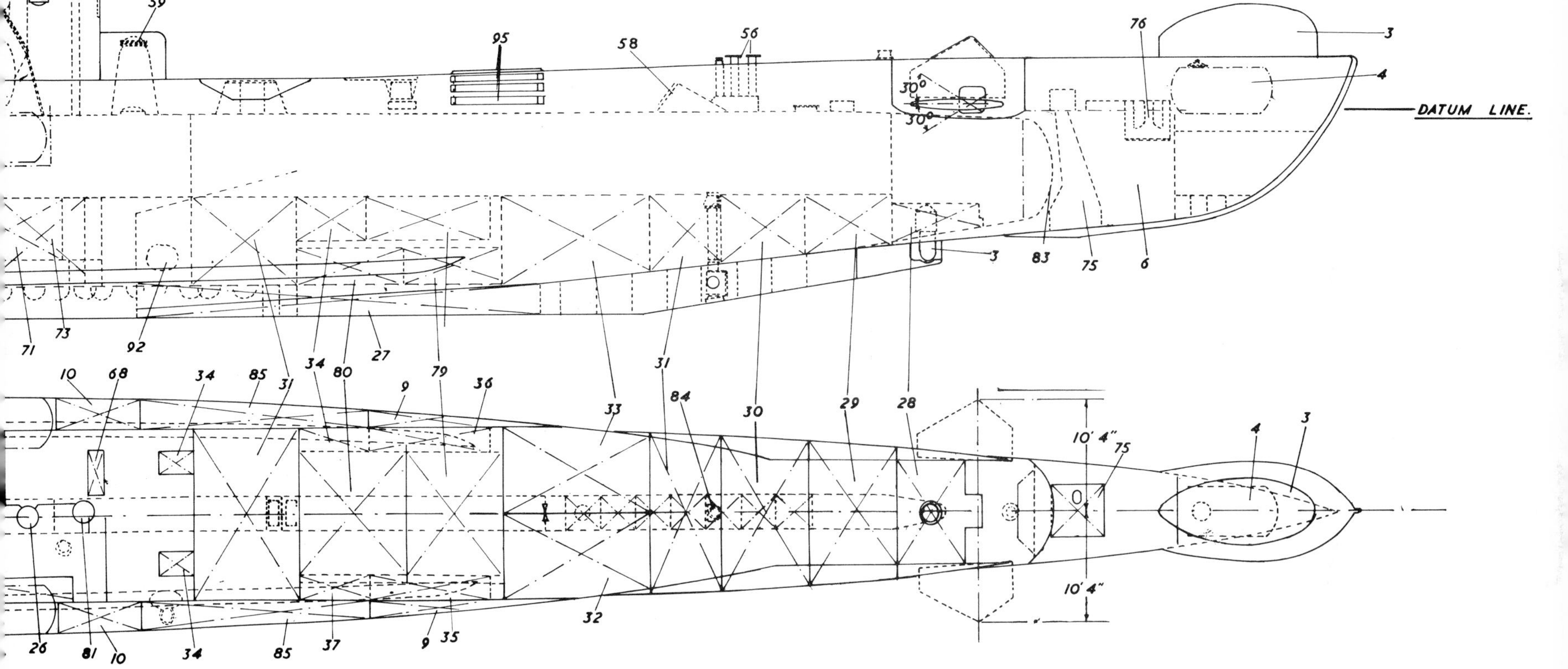

75 Chain locker
76 Recess for 12cwt anchor port side only
77 Access door
78 24in diam kingston
79 No 3 oil fuel tank
80 No 4 oil fuel tank
81 AVG mast well
82 Engine girder
83 Domed ends to pressure hull
84 Garbage ejector
85 No 2 external fuel tank
86 Cast iron blocks
87 Snort water trap
88 Portable 4in gun sponson
89 Type 185 transducer
90 Type 17 anti-submarine hull outfit
91 Main machinery
92 Log tank
93 Fin
94 Stern light
95 Wood protection over BIBS
96 Indicator buoy
97 CO's cabin

B6/10

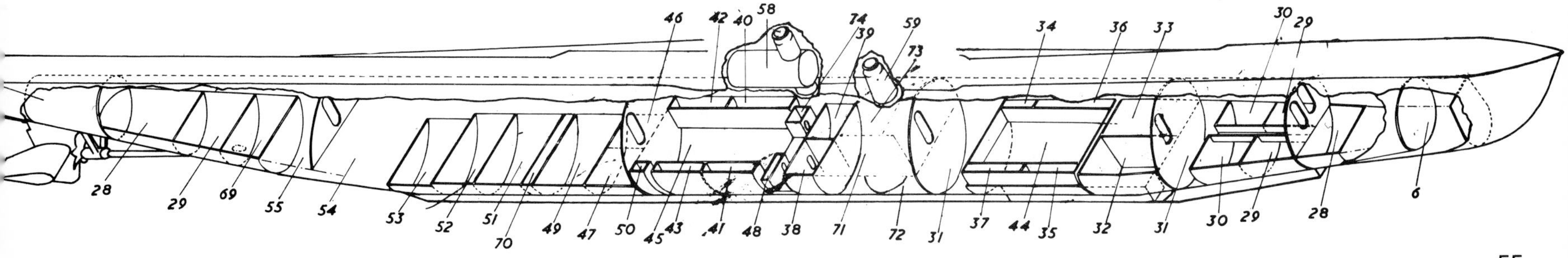

C Casing and superstructure

C1	BRIDGE DETAILS (Auriga as fitted 1946; 1/96 scale)	C1/3	Plan view of superstructure
C1/1	Internal profile (masts and periscopes raised)	C1/4	Section at Frame 74 (looking forward)
C1/2	Plan view of bridge	C1/5	External profile (masts and periscopes lowered)

C1/1

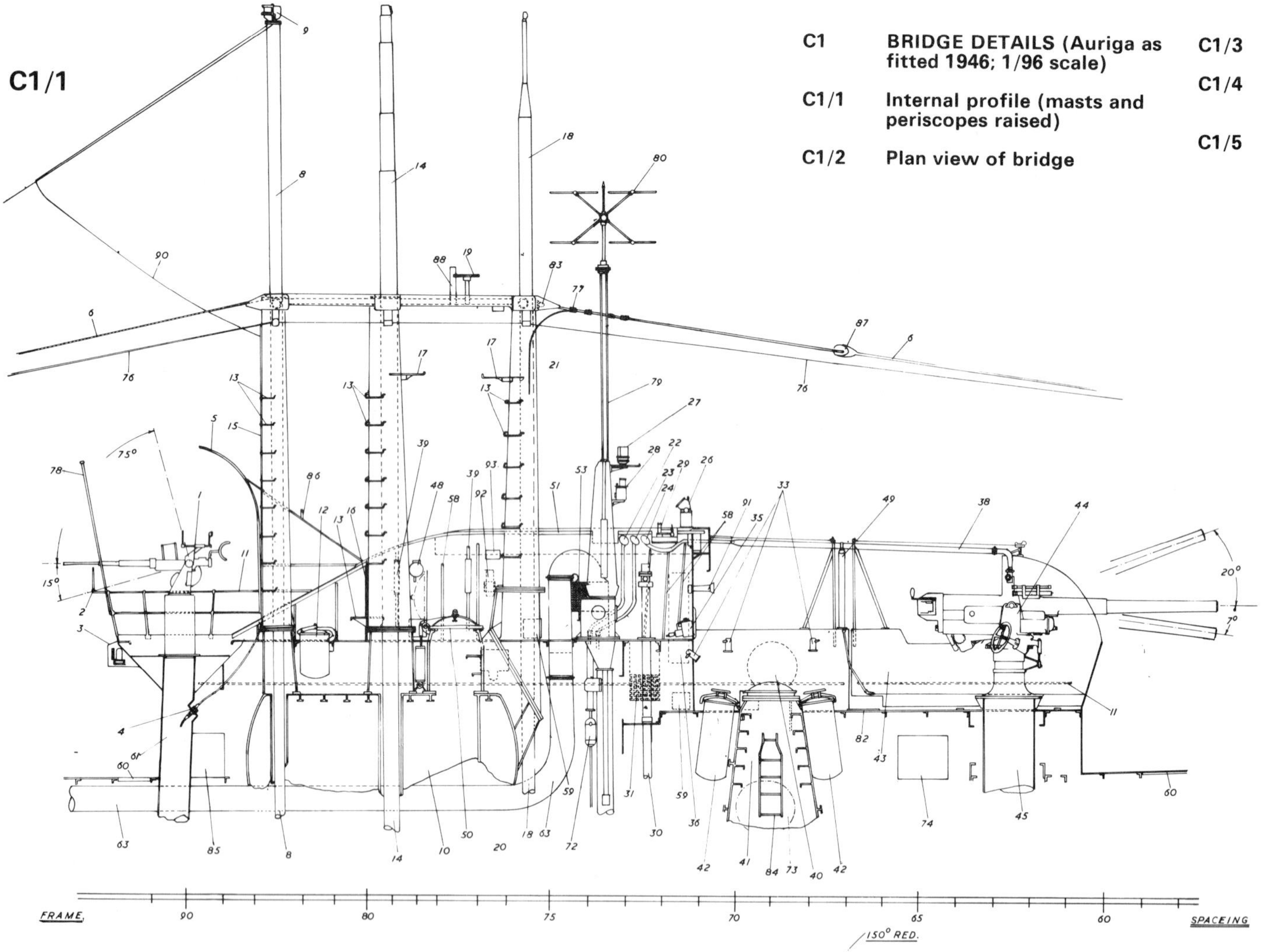

C1/2

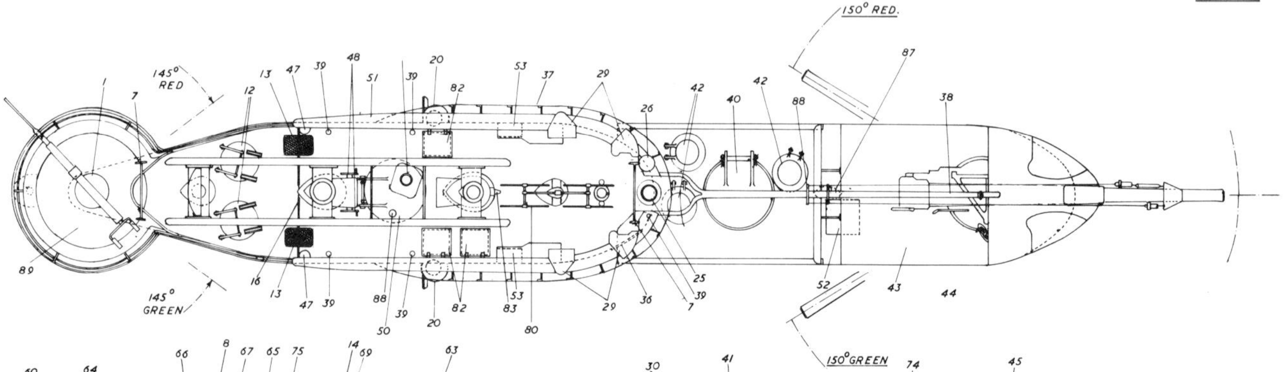

C1/3

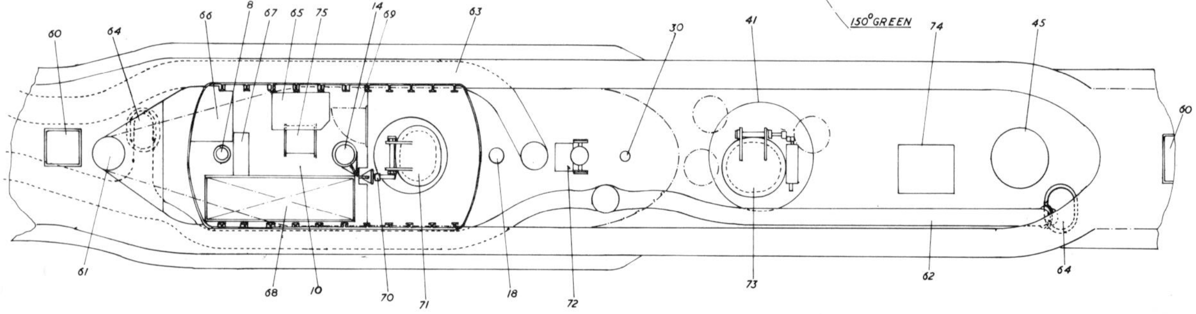

1 20mm Oerlikon on Mk VIIA mounting
2 Combined safety rail and muzzle clip
3 Overtaking and shaded stern light
4 Gland for main aerial lead in
5 Oerlikon safety rail
6 Jumping wire (3in bronze)
7 Spreader
8 ANF mast
9 Type 267 ANF aerial unit
10 CO's cabin
11 Handrail
12 Ready-use Oerlikon ammunition
13 Step
14 9.5in search periscope
15 Main and emergency aerials clamped to support bracket
16 Breakwater
17 Lookout platform
18 7.5in attack periscope
19 Type 253 radar array
20 Bowlight
21 Loop aerial (in conduit)
22 2in voice pipe to torpedo exactor and helm
23 2in voice pipe to radar and plot
24 2in voice pipe to 4in gun
25 Azimuth repeater
26 Standard compass
27 Steaming light
28 Emergency steaming light
29 Sub night sight (pattern 12041 port, pattern 12040 starboard)
30 Projector binnacle
31 Vent pocket (starboard)
32 Battery exhaust with rat-proof netting (starboard)
33 Ready-use locker light
34 Bridge deck
35 Rudder indicating recessed into bridge bulwark
36 Door in bridge front starboard
37 Wind deflector
38 3in voice pipe
39 Socket for Vickers .303in gas-operated gun
40 Gun access hatch
41 Gun access trunk
42 4in ready-use ammunition locker
43 Revolving gun platform
44 4in QF Mk XII gun on S1 mounting
45 Gun support
46 Step
47 Urinal
48 Engine room telegraph
49 Streamlined support
50 Conning tower hatch
51 Teak rail
52 Hinged cover
53 Engine induction
54 2in voice pipe stop cock
55 Gun deck
56 Baffle plate
57 Inlet
58 Bulwark stay
59 Freeing port
60 Grating
61 Water-tight deck tube and gun support
62 13in battery vent trunk
63 14in engine induction trunk
64 9in hull valve
65 Table
66 Wardrobe
67 Folding toilet
68 Bed with drawers (under)
69 Door
70 Hatch spring
71 Lower conning tower hatch
72 APT mast and hoist
73 Lower gun hatch
74 Oil fuel expansion tank
75 Chair
76 Main aerial
77 Loop aerial (taped to jumping wire)
78 Ensign staff
79 APT mast
80 Radar array
81 Pocket
82 Hatch
83 Unipol aerial
84 Ladder
85 Sanitary tank
86 Identification flare bracket
87 Insulator
88 Radar Type 86M
89 Gun platform
90 High frequency aerial
91 Klaxon
92 Emergency bowlight
93 Ready-use stowage for 6in signal lamp

C1/4

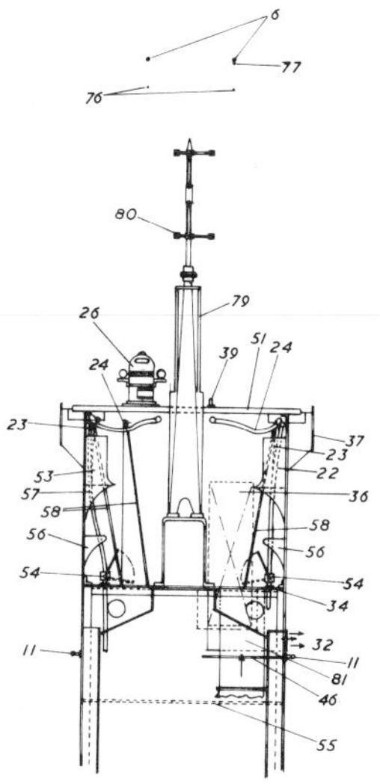

C1/5

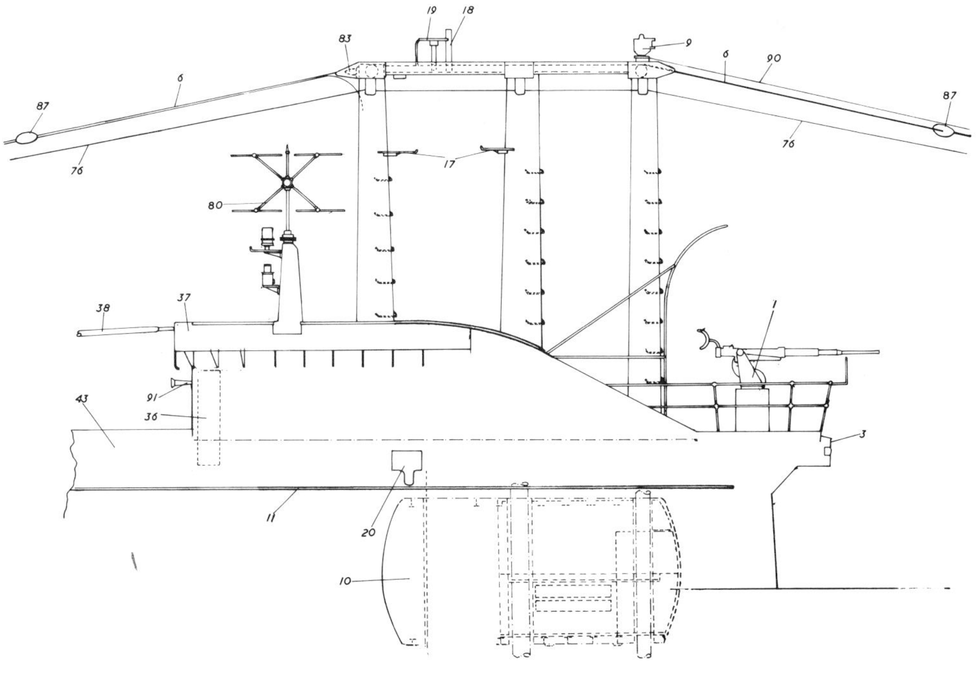

C Casing and superstructure

C2 FIN AND SNORT MODIFICATIONS 1961

C2/1 External profile (1/96 scale)

C2/2 Plan view of fin (1/96 scale)

1 3.75in wide wooden rail
2 Position for torpedo sight
3 Attack periscope
4 Search periscope
5 Snort mast
6 Towing slip eye
7 Towing wire cemented in position
8 Magnetic compass
9 Wood planking
10 Sliding bridge windows
11 Retractable emergency light
12 4in high combing
13 Weld 1in wide
14 Whip aerial
15 Wood grating
16 Anti-submarine hull outfit
17 Ladder
18 Gun access hatch
19 Handrail
20 2in diam drain holes
21 Steaming light
22 Battery vent cover (harbour use)
23 Access door
24 Overtaking and stern light

C2/1

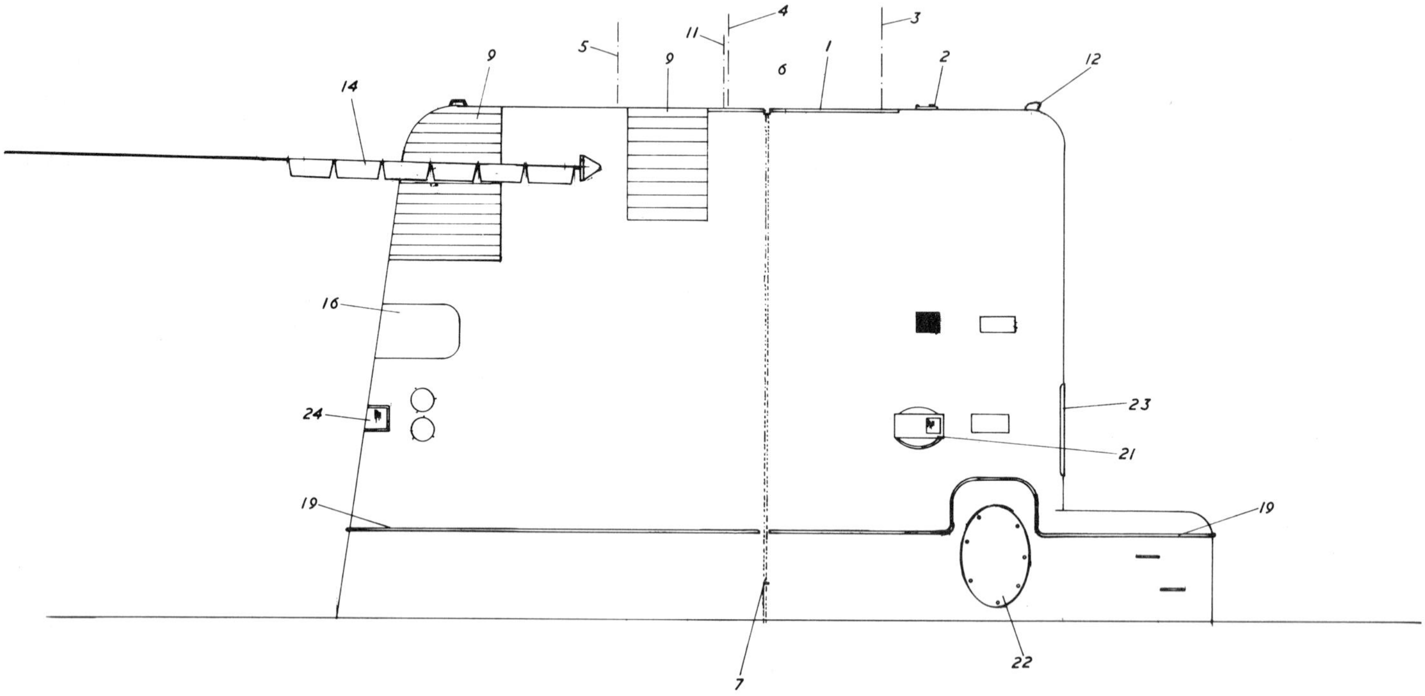

C2/2

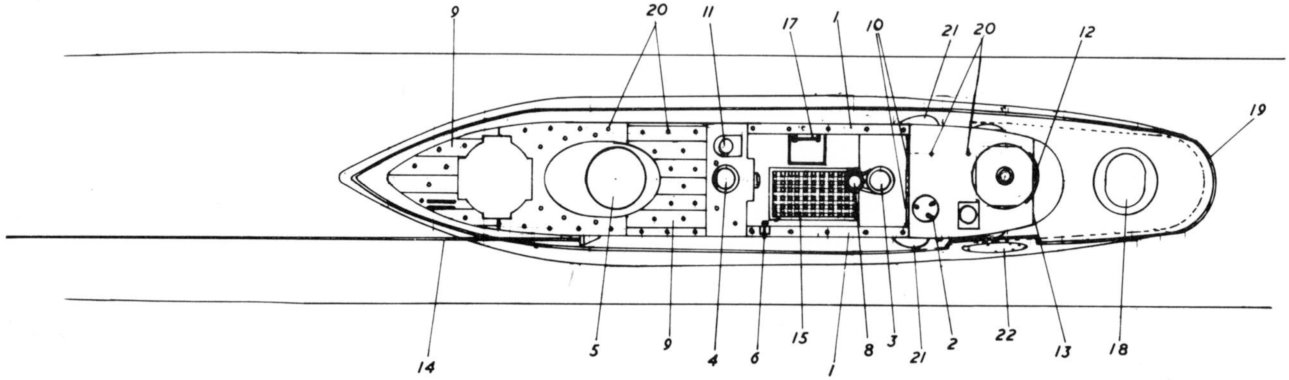

C2/3 Internal profile (1/96 scale)

C2/4 Plan of casing (1/96 scale)

1 Engine room hatch
2 Snort exhaust
3 Snort induction
4 Helix dryer
5 Opening door for anti-submarine hull outfit 17
6 Modified snort head valve
7 Loop aerial
8 Space for loop aerial and greenheart fairing
9 Bearing
10 Guide for ram
11 Cable tube
12 Snort mast hoist ram
13 Cable tensioning pully
14 CO's cabin
15 Engine induction valve
16 4in drain valve and piping (existing)
17 Galley
18 4in shut-off valve
19 Drain from engine induction hood
20 Wireless telegraphy (W/T) machinery space
21 No 4 MT vent
22 No 3 MT vent
23 Drain from helix dryer
24 W/T office
25 2in drain valve
26 Inboard vent pipe
27 4in drain valve and piping (existing)
28 To visible tundish
29 Projected corner of superstructure
30 10.75in outside diameter .25in thick snort exhaust
31 6in outboard drain
32 6in outboard flood and drain valve
33 14.5in in outside diameter .25in thick snort induction
34 Strum
35 6in master valve locked open
36 MT vent
37 Longitudinal cutting line with pressure hull
38 Longitudinal cutting line with external tank
39 No 4 main tank vents to be trunked to superstructure or top

C2/3

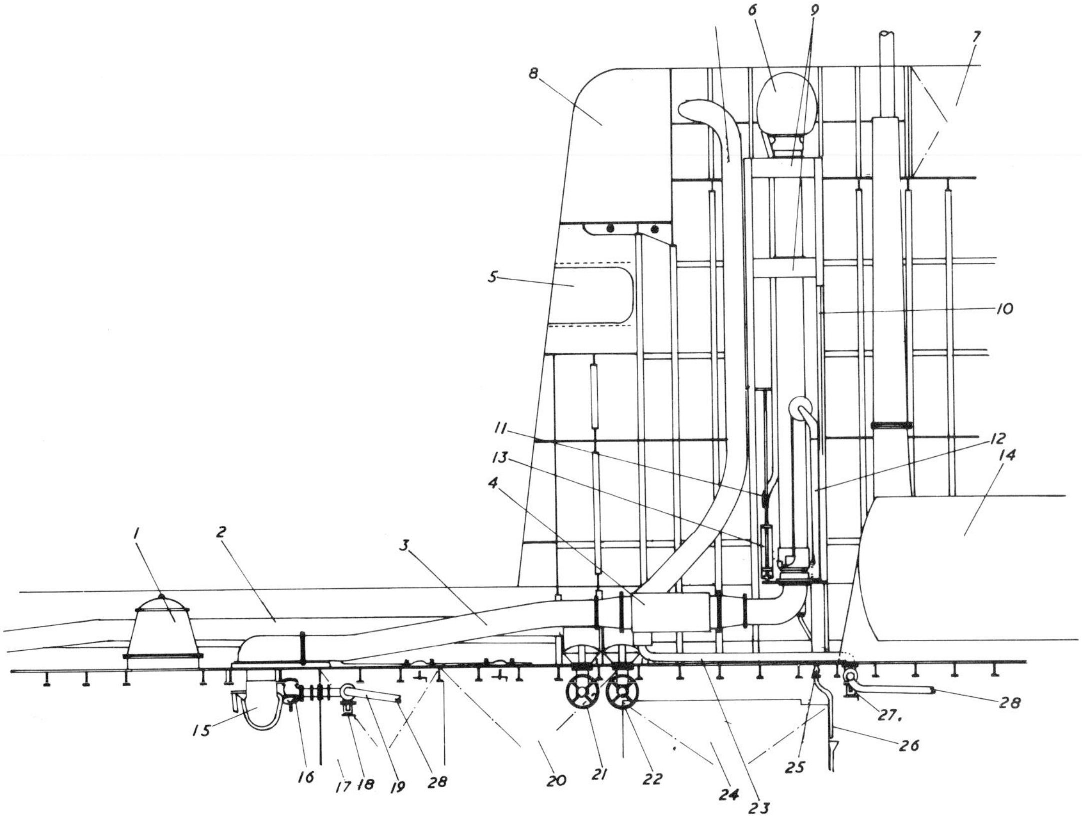

C2/4

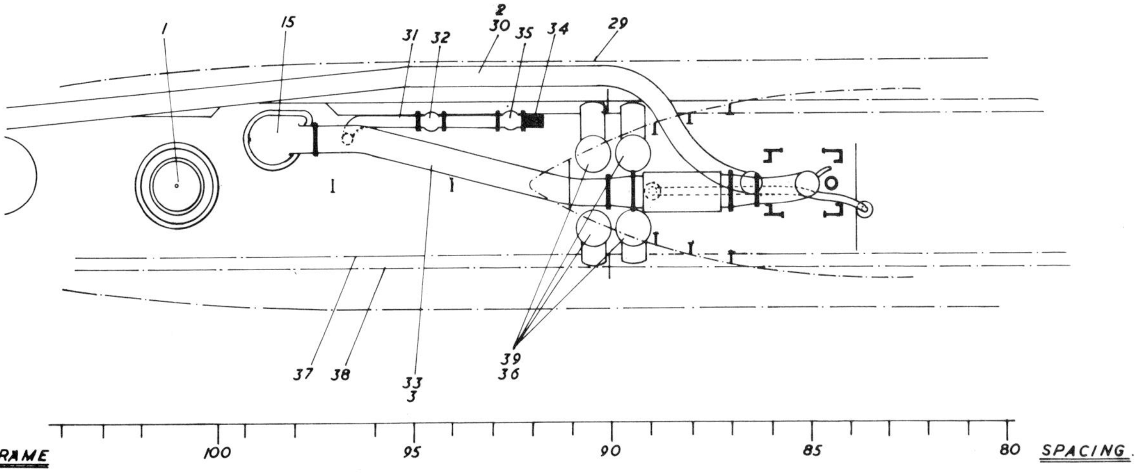

C Casing and superstructure

C3	**EXTERNAL DETAILS (Alliance as modified; no scale)**
C3/1	Asdic dome
C3/2	View forward
C3/3	Starboard bow showing flare
C3/4	Port bow showing anchor
C3/5	Admiralty standard stockless anchor
C3/6	Forward torpedo hatch (open)

C3/1

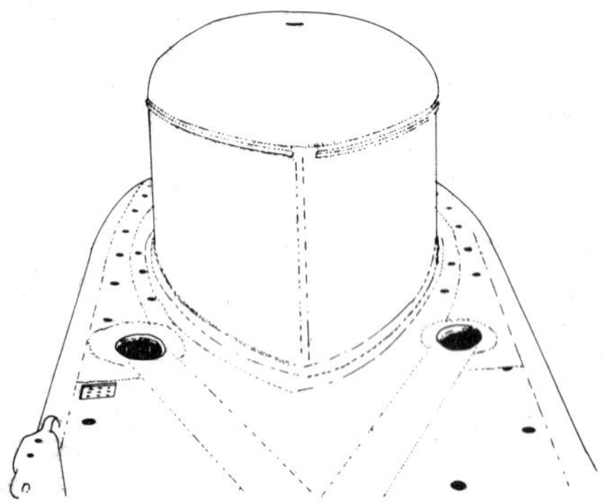

C3/2

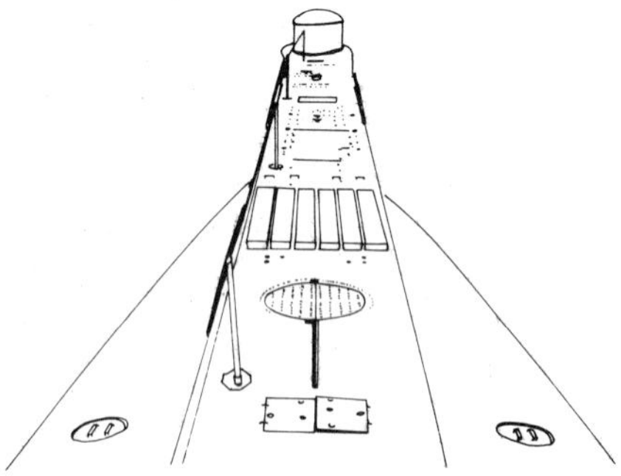

C3/3

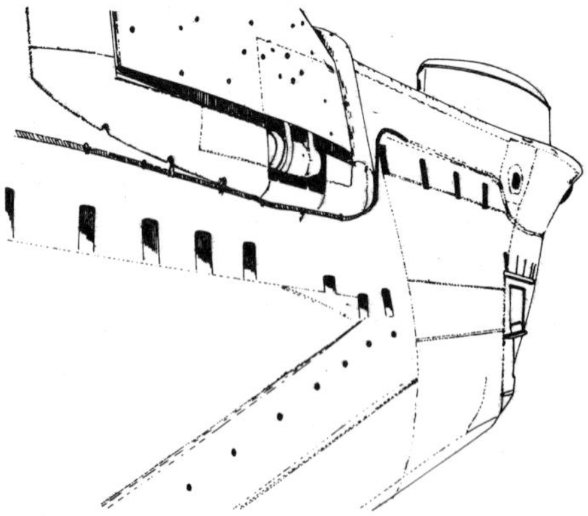

C3/4

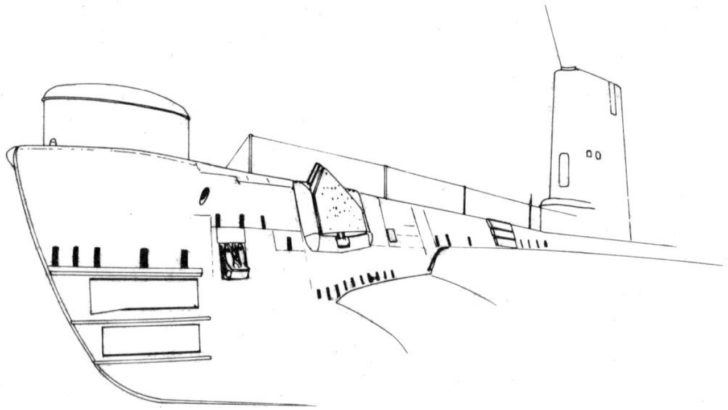

C3/5

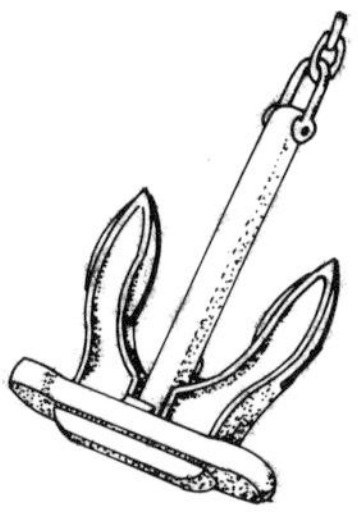

C3/6

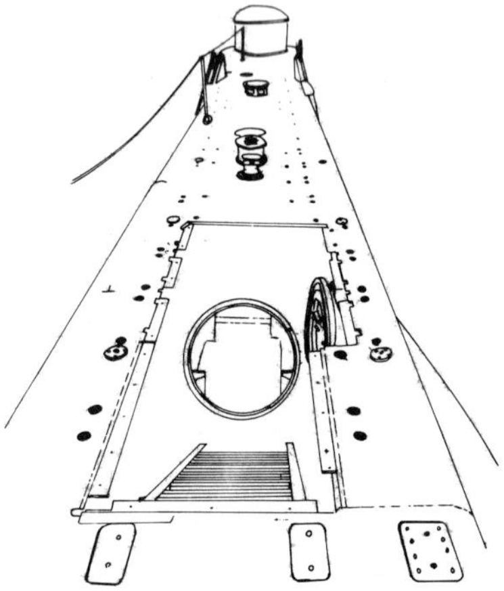

C3/7 Fin, starboard side

C3/8 Fin, from forward

C3/9 Fin, from aft

C3/10 Top of fin, showing aerial fairing

C3/11 After casing looking aft

C3/8

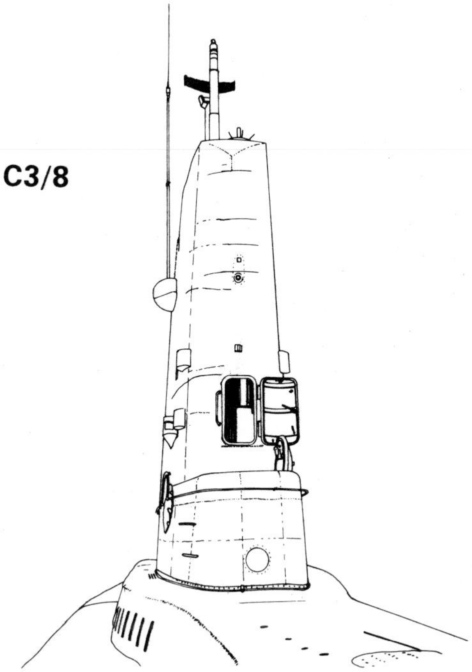

C3/7

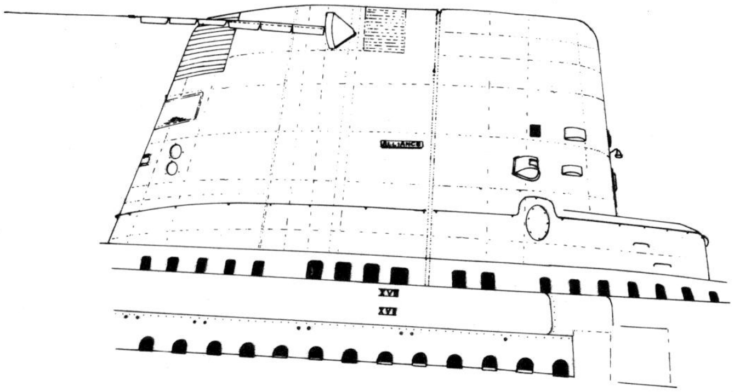

C3/9

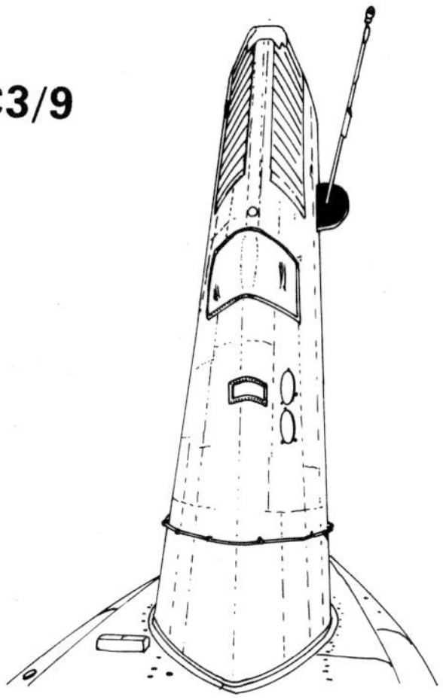

C3/10

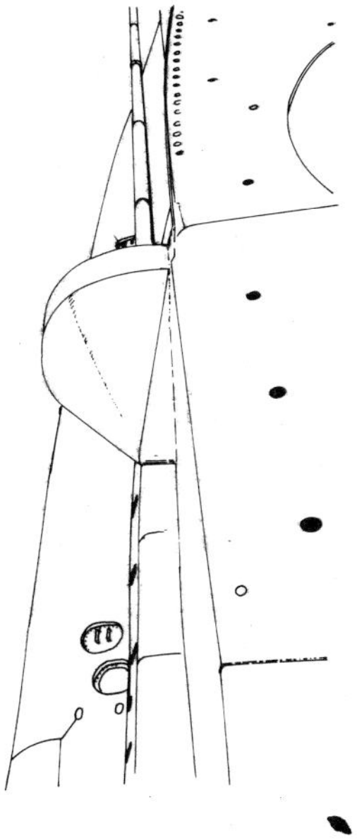

C3/11

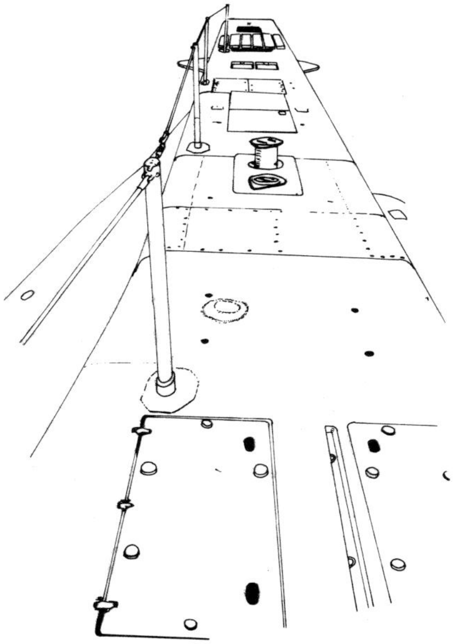

C Casing and superstructure

C3/12	After casing looking forward
C3/13	After torpedo loading hatch (open)
C3/14	View of hull looking forward
C3/15	Starboard quarter view
C3/16	Propellers, rudder and after hydroplanes
C3/17	Typical guardrail stanchion

C3/12

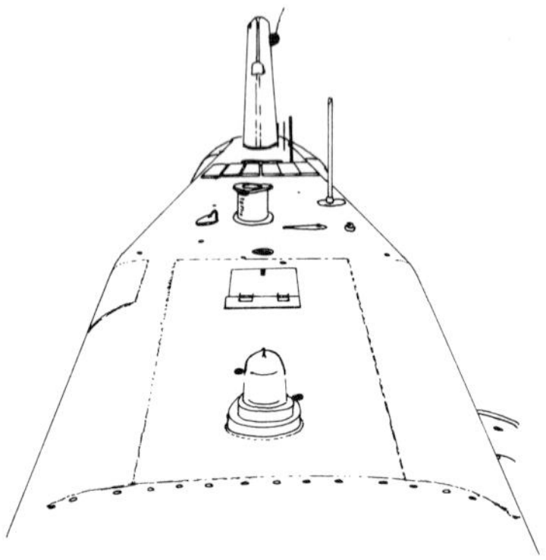

C3/13

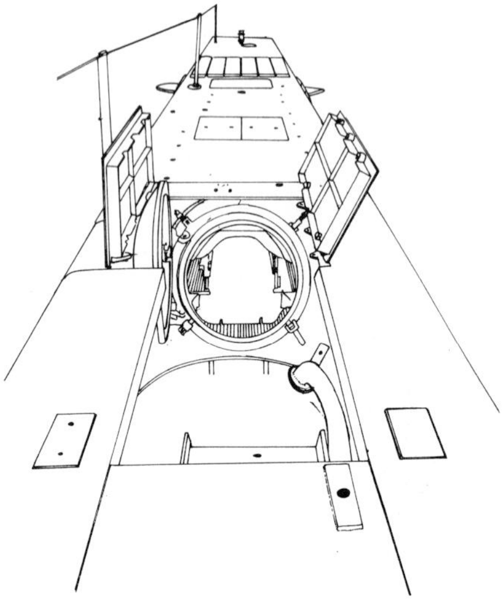

C3/14

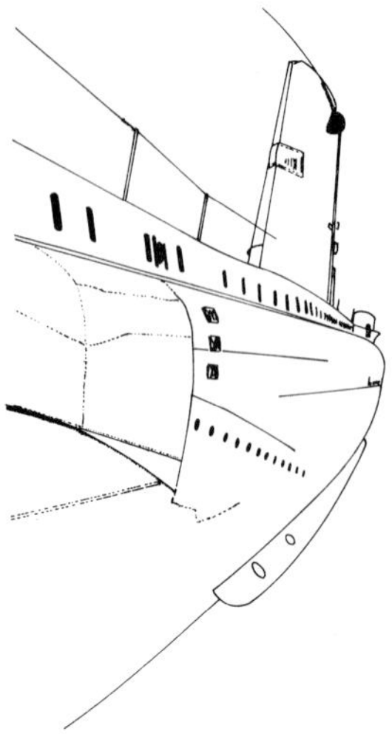

C3/15

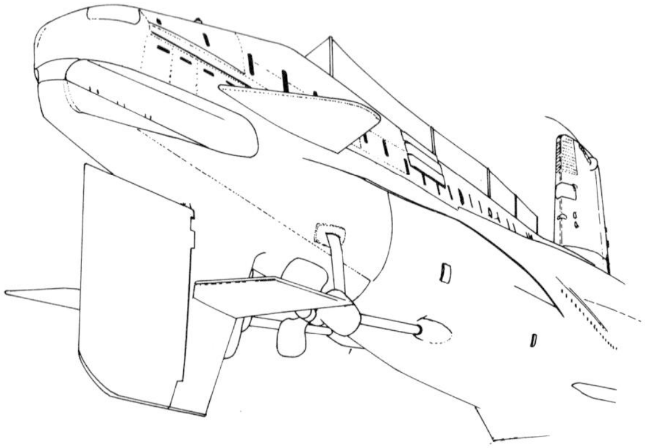

C3/16

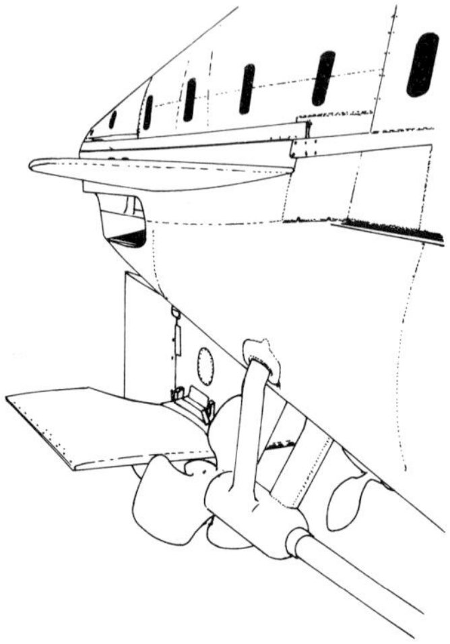

C3/17

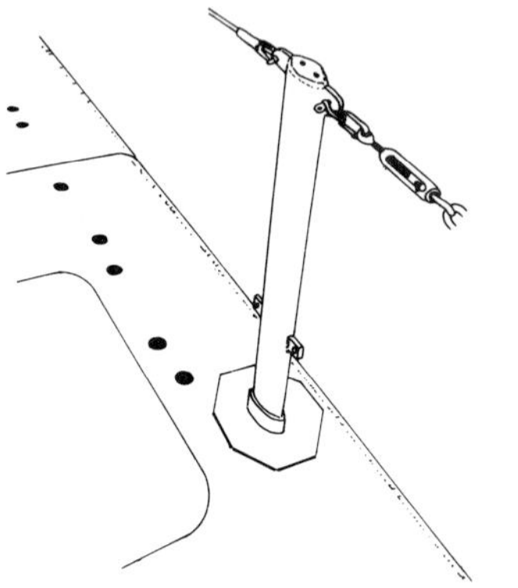

D Internal arrangements

D1 HULLS, TANKS AND SYSTEMS (as during 1950s: no scale)

D1/1 Layout of internal tanks

1 No 1 main ballast tank
2 Air inboard vent (AIV) tank – 982 gallons
3 Torpedo operating tank – 2240 gallons
4 Forward trim tank – 3026 gallons
5 Store
6 No 1 oil fuel tank – 4465 gallons
7 No 2 oil fuel tank – 4465 gallons
8 No 3 oil fuel tank – 1795 gallons
9 No 4 oil fuel tank – 1948 gallons
10 No 1 battery tank
11 No 2 battery tank
12 No 2 fresh water tank – 421 gallons
13 No 3 fresh water tank – 578 gallons
14 No 4 fresh water tank – 435 gallons
15 'Q' tank – 1248 gallons
16 Distilled water tank – 315 gallons
17 Auxiliary machinery space
18 Magazine
19 'R' port compensating tank – 1965 gallons
20 'R' starboard compensating tank – 2140 gallons
21 Cold cupboards
22 Sewage tank – 236 gallons
23 Telemotor storage tank – 219 gallons
24 No 5 fresh water tank – 484 gallons
25 No 6 fresh water tank – 450 gallons
26 No 7 fresh water tank – 500 gallons
27 No 8 fresh water tank – 318 gallons
28 Slop drain tank – 168 gallons
29 No 5 oil fuel tank – 4024 gallons
30 Air space
31 Forward reserve lubricating oil tank – 1730 gallons
32 After reserve lubricating oil tank – 1730 gallons
33 Drain oil tank – 1132 gallons
34 Motor room bilge
35 Gland space
36 After trim tank – 2203 gallons
37 Torpedo operating tank – 1764 gallons
38 Air inboard vent tank – 835 gallons
39 No 5 main ballast tank
40 Washing water tank – 626 gallons

D1/2 Layout of external tanks

1 Bow buoyancy vents
2 Bow buoyancy tank
3 Free-flood space
4 Free-flood holes
5 No 1 main vent
6 No 1 main ballast
7 Grease connections
8 'Q' kingston operating ram
9 'Q' kingston compartment
10 'Q' tank
11 Simmonds gauge float
12 Echo sounding transceiver
13 'Q' tank syphon compartment
14 Ballast box
15 Dome casting
16 Asdic dome
17 No 1 external oil fuel
18 No 2 external fuel
19 No 2 main ballast
20 Forward periscope well
21 After periscope well
22 Radar mast well
23 No 4 starboard kingstons
24 No 4 port kingstons
25 Kingston operating gear
26 'O' starboard compensating tank – 2388 gallons
27 No 3 main vents
28 No 3 main ballast
29 Cast iron ballast
30 No 4 main vents
31 No 4 main ballast
32 Free-flooding pocket
33 No 3 external oil
34 Cast iron block
35 No 4 external oil
36 No 5 main vent
37 No 5 main ballast
38 Gearing for hand-operated bow buoyancy vent
39 No 2 main vents
40 'O' port compensating tank

D1/1

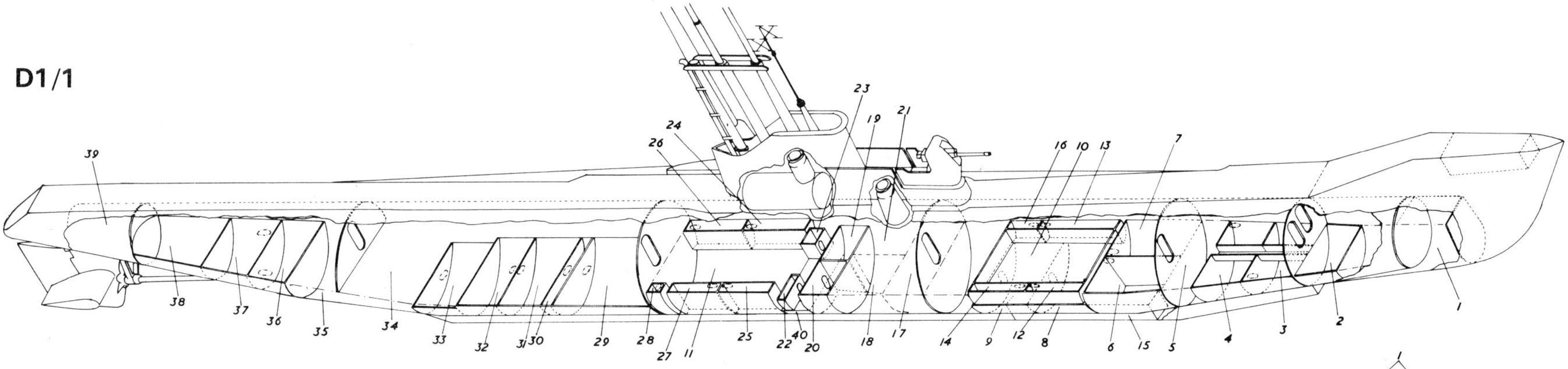

D1/2

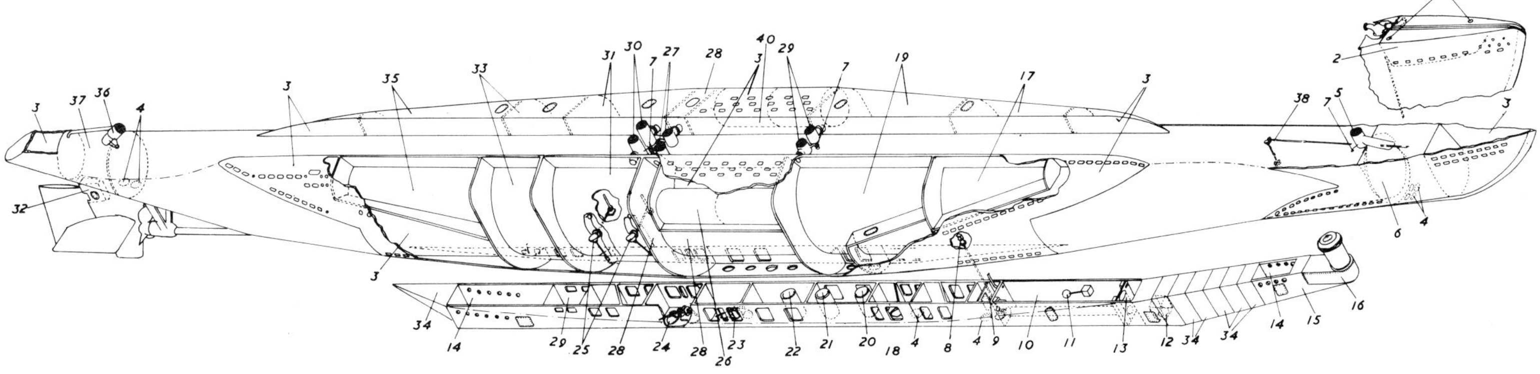

D Internal arrangements

D1/3 LP airline and HP direct blowing system

1 Main ballast high pressure (HP) and low pressure (LP) tanksides
2 Voice pipe
3 Blanks for compartment testing
4 'Q' tank
5 Pipe for joining LP line and voice pipe in position
6 Motor
7 Drain cock
8 HP blow hull valve
9 LP blower
10 Blower shut off
11 Flexible pipe connection
12 No 2 main ballast starboard HP and LP tanksides
13 No 2 main ballast port HP and LP tanksides
14 Relief
15 No 1 and 2 LP master blows
16 Sea connection
17 Differential gauge
18 Blowing valve HP to LP
19 Sea relief (10lb per sq in)
20 Quick blow to 'Q' tank
21 Direct HP blowing panel
22 No 3 main ballast port HP and LP tankside
23 No 3 main ballast starboard HP and LP tankside
24 No 4 main ballast port HP and LP tankside
25 No 4 main ballast starboard HP and LP tankside
26 Split HP blow to 3 main ballast
27 No 3, 4 and 5 LR master blows
28 No 5 main ballast HP and LP tankside

D1/4 Ship's ventilation and air purification

1 Bulkhead flap valve
2 Portable trunking
3 CO_2 absorption unit
4 Oxygen generator
5 Coxswain's store shut-off valve
6 Auxiliary machinery space shut-off valve
7 Air conditioning coolers
8 10in x 6in fan
9 10in x 3in fan
10 Portable trunking connection
11 Heating elements
12 Deodoriser
13 CO's cabin shut-off valve
14 Natural supply from snort induction
15 $7\frac{1}{2}$in fan
16 Gland space shut-off valve
17 Bulkhead flap (to be kept shut except when $7\frac{1}{2}$in fan is running)

D1/5 Hull detail

The pressure hull is constructed of $\frac{7}{8}$in plate welded over internal frames 21in apart. It has a circular cross-section throughout

D1/6 Layout of bathrooms and WCs

1 Flushing water supply from sanitary tank
2 Hull valve
3 Reducing valve
4 Intermediate valve
5 Slop drain tank
6 Inlet valve
7 Connections to flushing line
8 From main circulator
9 Soil pipe flushing line
10 Deodoriser
11 Domestic water heater
12 Supply to galley range
13 Outboard vent
14 Non-return valve
15 Combined vent and blow for sewage and slop drain tank
16 Sewage tank
17 Flushing water to accommodation space heads
18 Supply from fresh water system
19 Hot water to wardroom sink
20 Supply from washing water tank
21 Soil pipe
22 Drain from wardroom sink

D1/7 Auxiliary circulating water system

1 Hull valve and reducing valve for WC flushing water
2 From main circulator
3 From auxiliary circulator
4 Cross-connecting valve
5 Soil pipe flushing valve
6 Sanitary tank
7 Sewage tank
8 Air conditioning plant coolers
9 Discharge overboard
10 'R' port compensating tank
11 Hull valve
12 Discharge to sanitary tank
13 Pump
14 Alternative circulating water supply and return from 'R' port tank
15 Discharge overboard
16 Sea suction
17 To sub-pressure pump
18 Strainers
19 Refrigerating plant cooler
20 HP air compressor

D1/8 Fresh and distilled water systems

1 Domestic hot water heater
2 Vent and blow

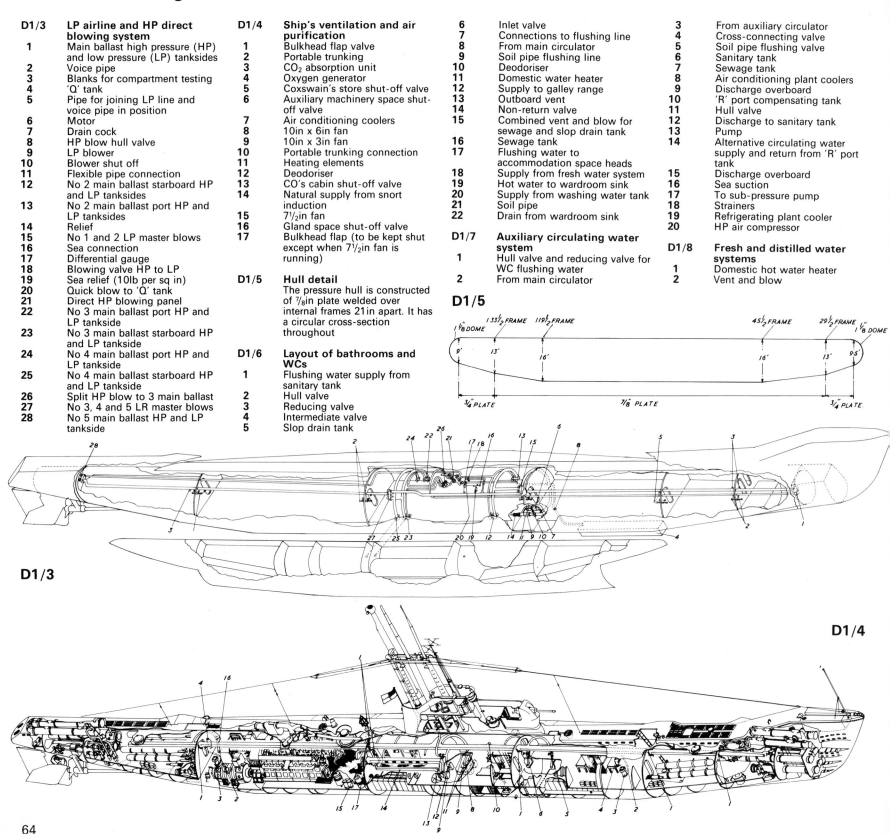

D1/5

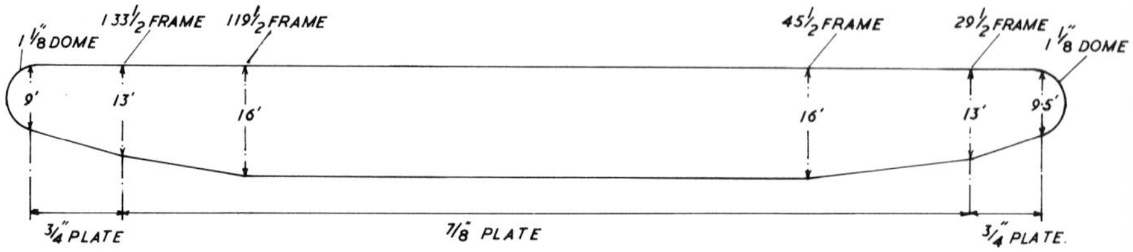

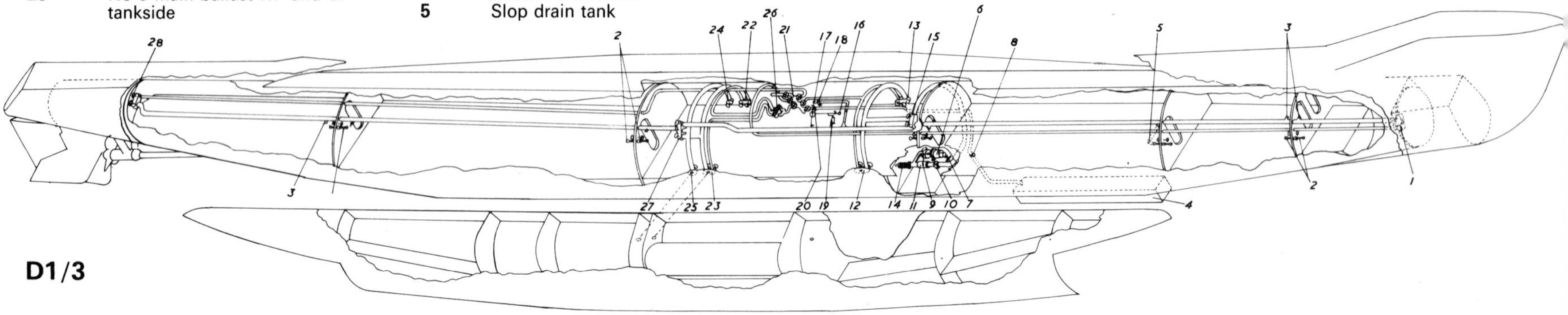

D1/3

D1/4

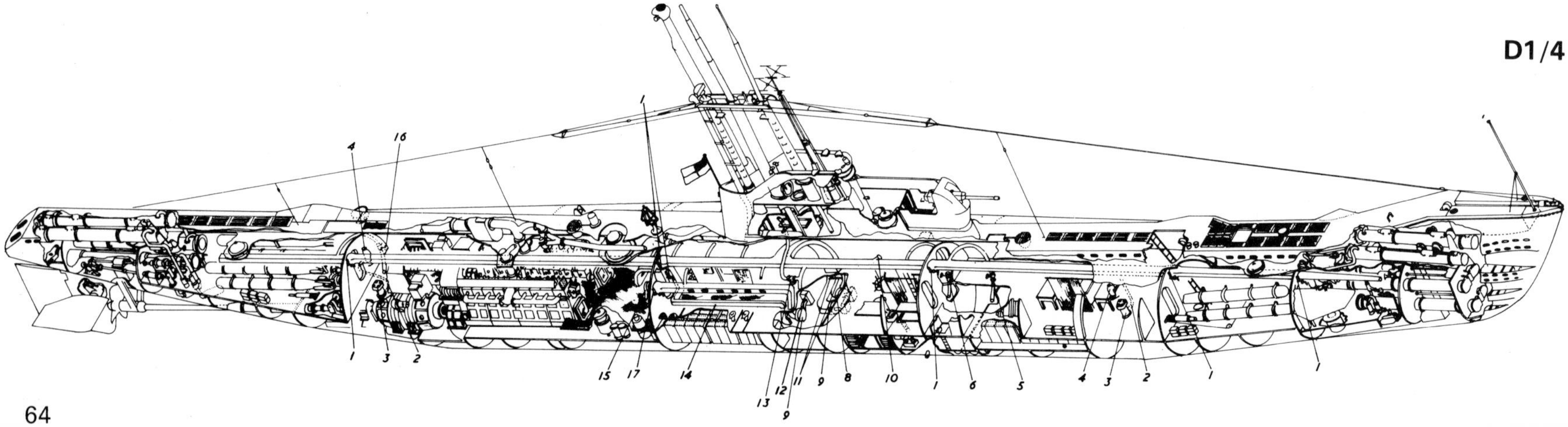

3 No 7 fresh water tank
4 No 8 fresh water tank
5 Topping-up hose for No 1 battery space
6 Topping-up hose for No 2 battery space
7 Vent
8 Syphon pipe
9 Drain
10 Strainer
11 No 5 fresh water tank
12 No 6 fresh water tank
13 To fresh water supply aft
14 Water to basins and showers
15 Washing water tank
16 Hose connection
17 Distilled water filling connection
18 Supply to Nos 5 and 6 fresh water tanks from distiller
19 Distilled water hand pump
20 10lb per sq in relief valve
21 Hand pump supply from distillers
22 No 2 fresh water tank
23 No 3 fresh water tank
24 No 4 fresh water tank
25 Supply to forward taps and urns
26 Distilled water tank
27 Upper deck filling connection
28 Hull valve

D1/9 HP and LP tankside valves

D1/10 'Q' tank and services

1 Differential gauge
2 HP air blow
3 Sea connection
4 25lb per sq in sea relief valves
5 Mainline suction
6 Telemotor panel
7 Quick-acting blow
8 Simmonds gauge
9 Hand-operated inboard vent
10 Kingston
11 'Q' tank
12 Syphon compartment
13 Telemotor-operated vent
14 Hand-operated outboard vent
15 Kingston-operated ram
16 Simmonds gauge float

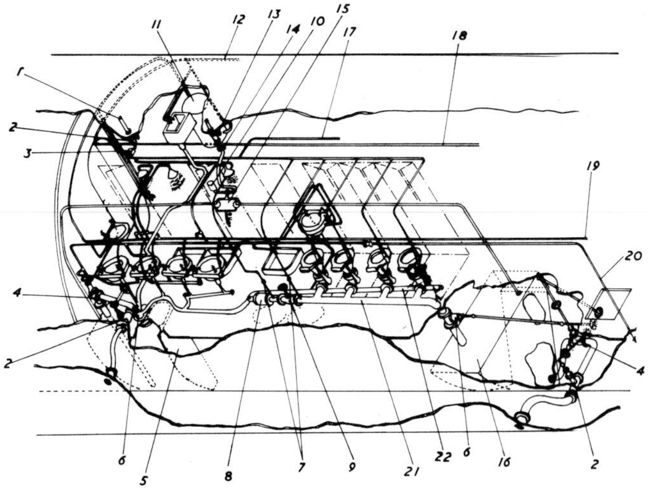

D1/6

D1/7

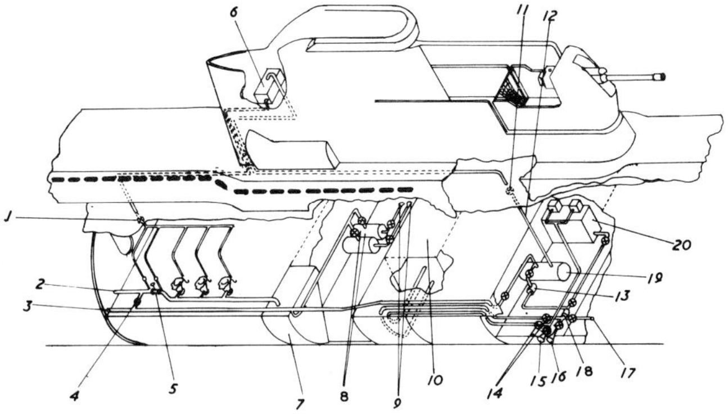

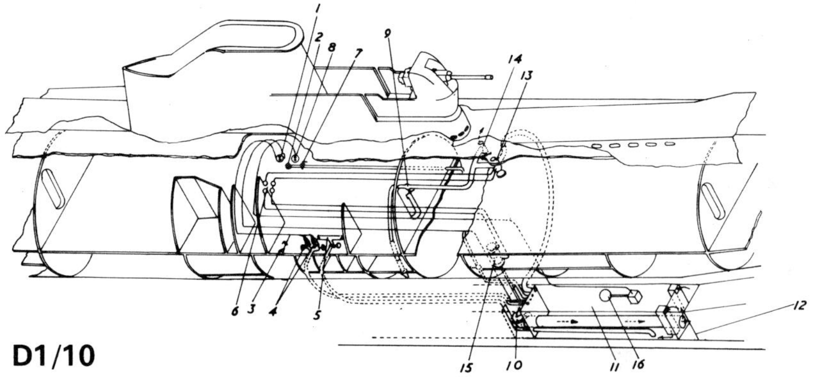

D1/10

D1/8

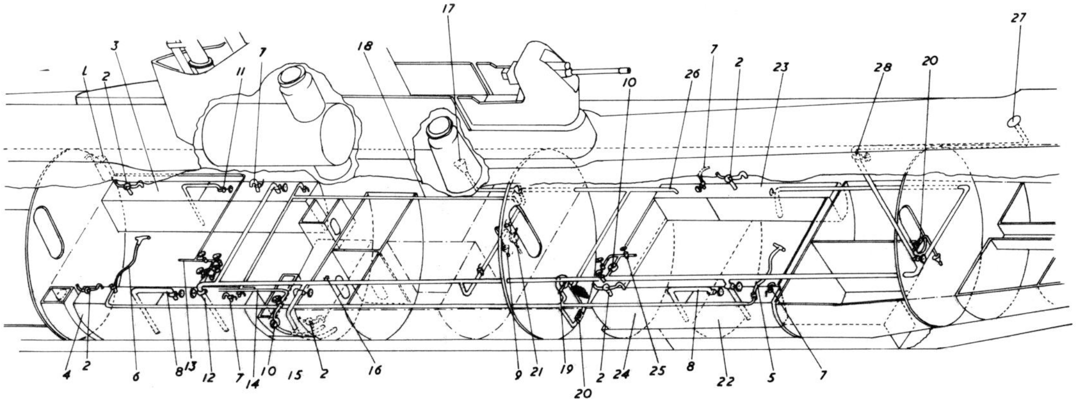

D1/9

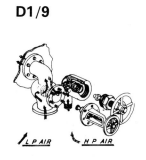

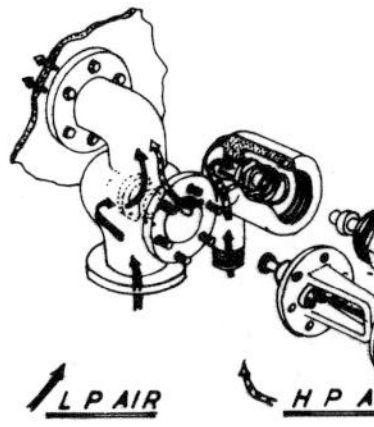

D Internal arrangements

D2 CONTROL ROOM ARRANGEMENTS (1/96 scale)

D2/1 Elevation looking to port

D2/2 Elevation looking to starboard (reversed)

D2/3 Frame 96 (looking aft)

D2/4 Frame 90 (looking aft)

D2/5 Frame 84 (looking aft)

1 Galley range control panel
2 LP M/G regulator
3 DP switch for galley range
4 Control panel for 10-gallon heater
5 Battery air intake trunk
6 10-gallon water heater
7 OF subs filling line
8 Main cables
9 LP M/G control panel
10 LP M/G starter
11 LP blow No 4 main tank
12 12in TO vent valve No 4 main tank
13 Screen transformer
14 No 2 battery fuse panel
15 Imo telemotor pump
16 Water-tight supply panels
17 Trimming line
18 Inboard vent No 5 main tank
19 18in auxiliary cable plate
20 Inboard vent No 3 tank
21 Aft telemotor pump starter
22 12in TO vent valve No 5 main tank
23 Combined HP and LP blow No 3 main tank
24 12in auxiliary cable plate
25 220v JB No 22
26 Trimming pump
27 Trimming pump starter
28 Forward telemotor pump starter
29 Sea valve for trimming
30 Main motor speed indicator
31 HP air pressure gauges
32 Engine telegraphs
33 10in depth gauge
34 Grouper telegraph transfers
35 Revolution telegraph
36 Measuring gauge for 'O' compensating tank
37 Control cock for trimming
38 Flow meter for trimming
39 Valve chest 'O' compensating tank
40 Valve chest vent and blow for trimming
41 Valve group inboard vent for Nos 1, 3 and 5 main tanks
42 After trim pressure gauge
43 DP and C pressure gauges
44 Trim blow pressure gauge
45 HP air valve chest
46 Radar Type 267MW ANF mast
47 9.5in diam search periscope
48 HP air blow direct to panel
49 Pressure gauge 'Q' tank indicator
50 LP air pressure gauge
51 Bathythermograph
52 Pressure gauge 'Q' tank blow
53 Telepump accumulator indicator
54 Telepump accumulator buzzer
55 Telepump motor isolating switch
56 Telepump motor selector switch
57 Hydroplane stop indicators
58 Klaxon push
59 Hydroplane control panel
60 Pump and flood order transfer receiver
61 Conning tower drain
62 Klaxon isolating switch
63 Telemotor chest for periscope and radar masts
64 Telemotor chest main line pressure and return
65 Strainer hydroplane panel
66 Control valve for oleo unit
67 Bridge bell
68 Fudge resistance box
69 HP air valve group
70 7.5in attack periscope
71 LP blow for No 2 main tank
72 Telephone control box
73 Telemotor service and semi-rotary hand pump for transferring from reserve to replenishing tank
74 Evershed telegraph steering gear
75 Steering motor running indicator
76 Steering pedestal
77 Dimmer for shaded stern light
78 Helmsman's call bell
79 Exactor torpedo firing order panels
80 Protection compass resistance
81 Navigation light switch box
82 Fire and stop orders transfer, aft tubes
83 Gyro steering repeater
84 Loran OP switch
85 Switch for rudder indicator
86 Fire and stop orders transmitter, forward tubes
87 Replenishing tank for oleo unit
88 15in auxiliary cable plate
89 Voice pipe bridge to helm
90 Voice pipe branch to torpedo data computer
91 HP air, shore charging
92 HP air group
93 Ventilation trunk
94 Distilled water filling line
95 HP air blow
96 HP air ring main
97 Drain from gun access trunk
98 LP blower main line
99 Inboard vent No 1 main tank
100 Main cable glands
101 Main cables
102 Circulating water discharge from refrigerators to sanitary tank
103 HP air whistle valve
104 Water service main line
105 Circulating water to auxiliary machinery space
106 Torpedo data computer
107 Chernikeef log distance receiver (not if torpedo data computer is fitted)
108 Iswas repeater
109 Automatic plotter
110 Aldis resistance box
111 Range receiver

D2/1

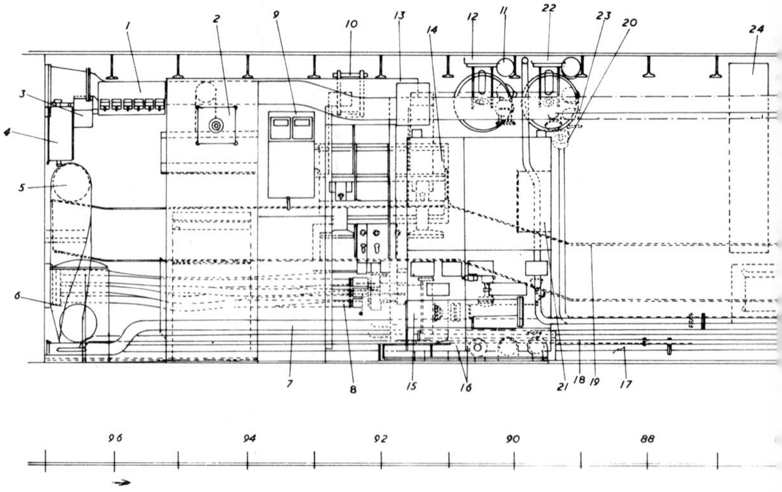

D2/2

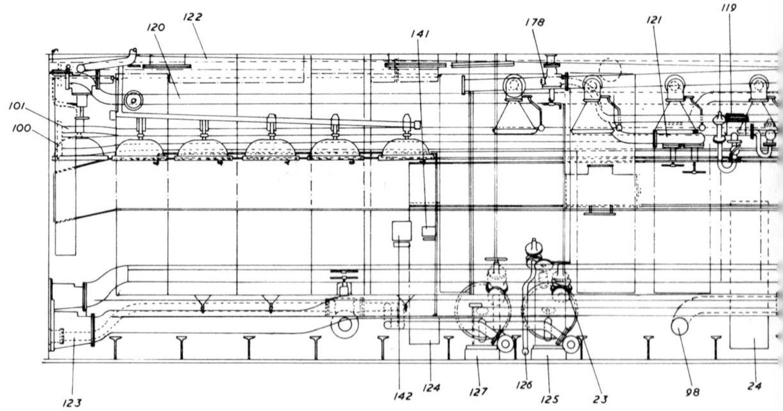

D2/3

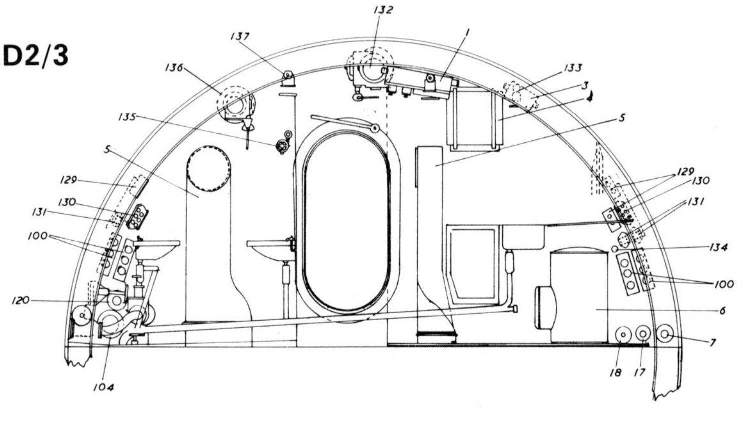

D2/4

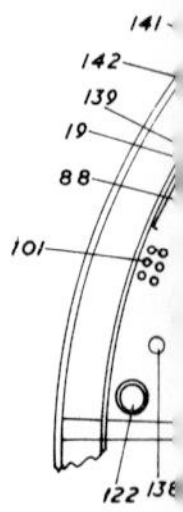

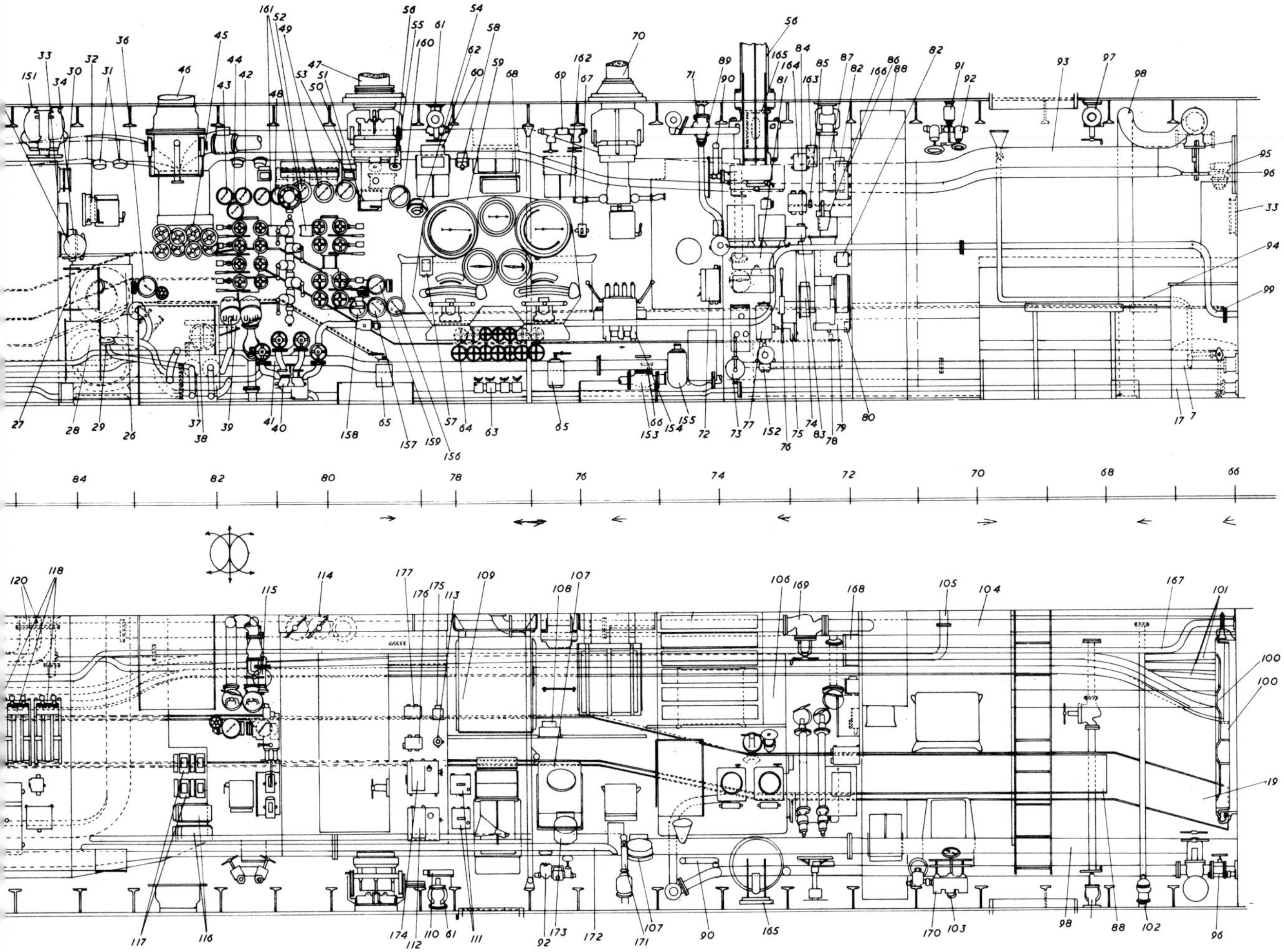

D2/5

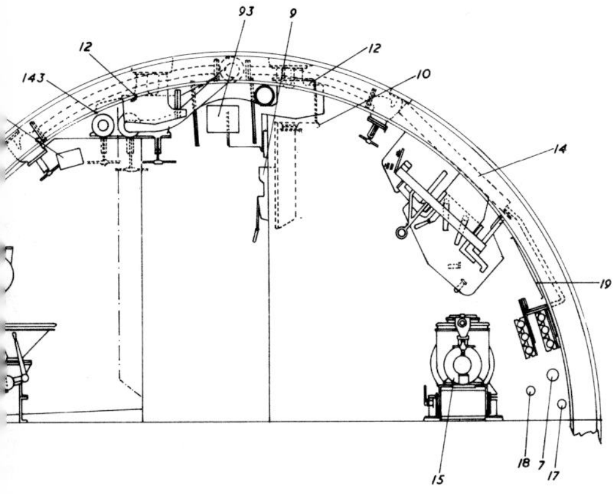

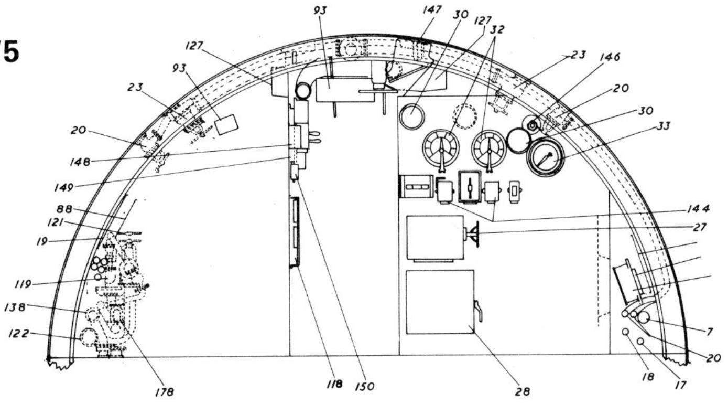

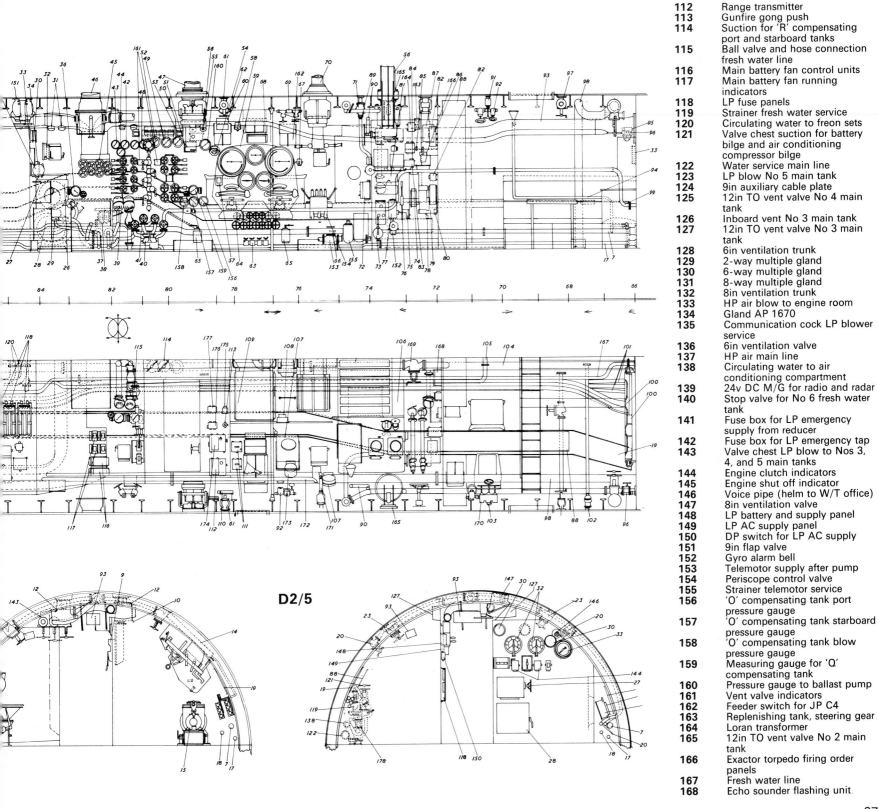

112	Range transmitter
113	Gunfire gong push
114	Suction for 'R' compensating port and starboard tanks
115	Ball valve and hose connection fresh water line
116	Main battery fan control units
117	Main battery fan running indicators
118	LP fuse panels
119	Strainer fresh water service
120	Circulating water to freon sets
121	Valve chest suction for battery bilge and air conditioning compressor bilge
122	Water service main line
123	LP blow No 5 main tank
124	9in auxiliary cable plate
125	12in TO vent valve No 4 main tank
126	Inboard vent No 3 main tank
127	12in TO vent valve No 3 main tank
128	6in ventilation trunk
129	2-way multiple gland
130	6-way multiple gland
131	8-way multiple gland
132	8in ventilation trunk
133	HP air blow to engine room
134	Gland AP 1670
135	Communication cock LP blower service
136	6in ventilation valve
137	HP air main line
138	Circulating water to air conditioning compartment
139	24v DC M/G for radio and radar
140	Stop valve for No 6 fresh water tank
141	Fuse box for LP emergency supply from reducer
142	Fuse box for LP emergency tap
143	Valve chest LP blow to Nos 3, 4, and 5 main tanks
144	Engine clutch indicators
145	Engine shut off indicator
146	Voice pipe (helm to W/T office)
147	8in ventilation valve
148	LP battery and supply panel
149	LP AC supply panel
150	DP switch for LP AC supply
151	9in flap valve
152	Gyro alarm bell
153	Telemotor supply after pump
154	Periscope control valve
155	Strainer telemotor service
156	'O' compensating tank port pressure gauge
157	'O' compensating tank starboard pressure gauge
158	'O' compensating tank blow pressure gauge
159	Measuring gauge for 'O' compensating tank
160	Pressure gauge to ballast pump
161	Vent valve indicators
162	Feeder switch for JP C4
163	Replenishing tank, steering gear
164	Loran transformer
165	12in TO vent valve No 2 main tank
166	Exactor torpedo firing order panels
167	Fresh water line
168	Echo sounder flashing unit

D Internal arrangements

D2/6 **Frame 82½ (looking aft)**
D2/7 **Frame 79½ (looking aft)**
D2/8 **Frame 77 (looking forward)**
D2/9 **Frame 77 (looking aft)**
D2/10 **Frame 75½ (looking forward)**
D2/11 **Frame 73 (looking forward)**
D2/12 **Frame 67½ (looking forward)**
D2/13 **Frame 66 (looking forward)**
D2/14 **Frame 70 (looking aft)**

169 Periscope hoist recess suction
170 HP air No 4 group
171 Voice pipe to radar office
172 Voice pipe (chart table to radar office)
173 Chernikeef log master speed indicator (not fitted if torpedo data computer is)
174 Deflection transmitter
175 Illumination switch
176 Range receiver switch
177 Range and deflection transfer switch
178 Stop valve for No 6 fresh water tank
179 Transformer for torpedo angling calculator
180 Gyro Iswas repeater
181 Voice pipe plot and chart table to radar office
182 LP junction box No 9
183 Chernikeef log master speed indicator
184 Chernikeef long distance recorder
185 Voice pipe bridge to plot and chart table
186 Projector binnacle
187 Projector compass resistance
188 Indicator outfit
189 Receiver outfit
190 Klaxton available indicator
191 'Q' tank suction
192 Sea relief valves 'Q' tank
193 Valve chest for sea relief 'Q' tank
194 Torpedo orders, forward tubes
195 Torpedo orders, aft tubes
196 Echo sounder power unit
197 Echo sounder junction box
198 Echo sounder fuse board
199 Distribution box C3E
200 Air heaters on indicators
201 Distribution box C3D
202 BAS vibrator unit
203 BAS amplifier
204 BAS resistance unit
205 Feeder switch for JP V3
206 JP V3
207 LP junction box No 10
208 Stowage box for telephone Mk X
209 Echo sounder amplifier
210 LP junction box No 3
211 Voice pipe branch for range settings
212 JP V2
213 Blower telegraph transfer receiver
214 9in bulkhead ventilation valve
215 LP blow No 1 main tank
216 Torpedo director (if fitted)
217 Gyro angling transmitter
218 Chernikeef log switch box
219 Junction box C3A
220 Combined HP and LP valve blow to No 2 main tank
221 LP junction box No 7
222 4-way multible gland
223 Communication cock LP blower service
224 Compensating water to oil fuel system
225 Automatic plotter
226 PPI (plan position indicator)
227 Loran receiver
228 Loran indicator
229 Distribution box C4C
230 Flowmeter for trimming
231 Telemotor blow panel
232 Telemotor system valve chest
233 Telemotor replenishing tank
234 'Lolos' strainer telemotor service
235 Stowage box for signal lantern
236 Navigation lights switch boxes
237 Dimmer for navigation lights
238 Dimmer for shaded stern light
239 Suction from periscope hoist recess
240 Telemotor accumulator indicator
241 Pressure gauge for trimming service
242 Gauge for 'O' compensating tank port and starboard and 'O' compensating blow
243 Teleflex hydroplane indicator
244 LP junction box No 11
245 JP C4
246 Feeder switch for JP V2
247 Ballast pump pressure gauge
248 Telemotor accumulator buzzer
249 Voice pipe radar to bridge
250 Feeder switch for JP C3

D2/6

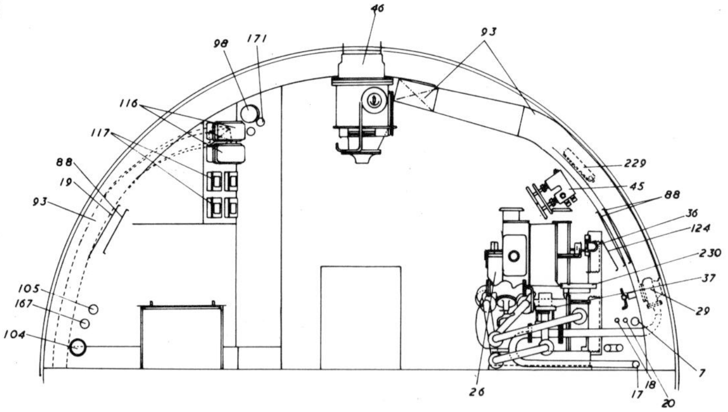

D2/7

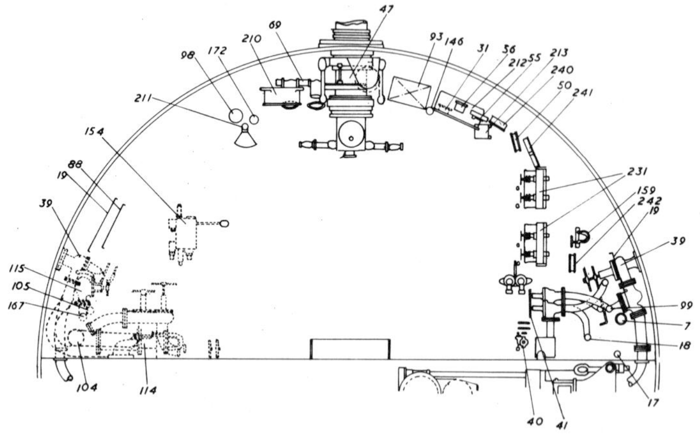

D2/8

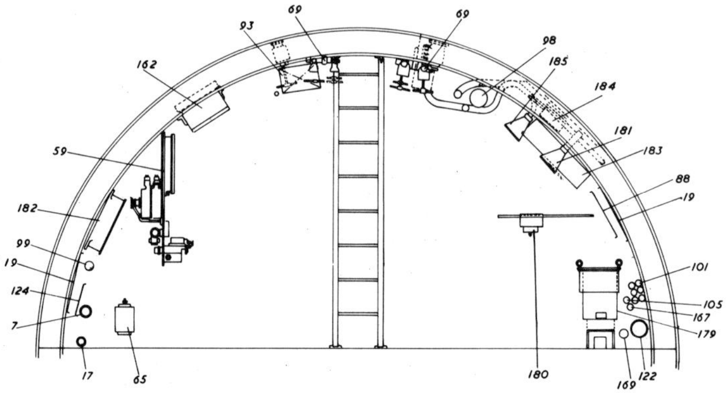

D2/9

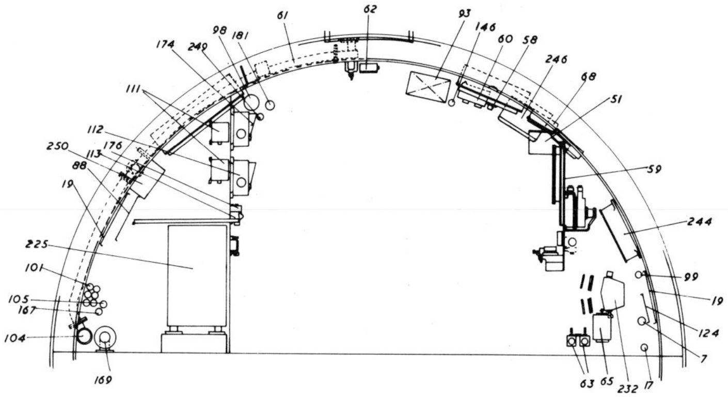

D2/12

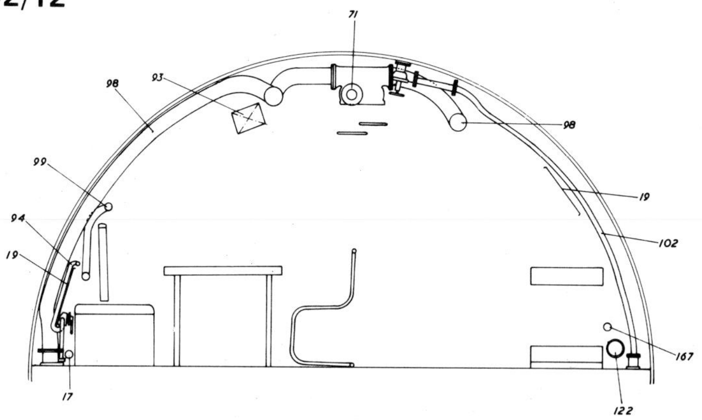

D2/10

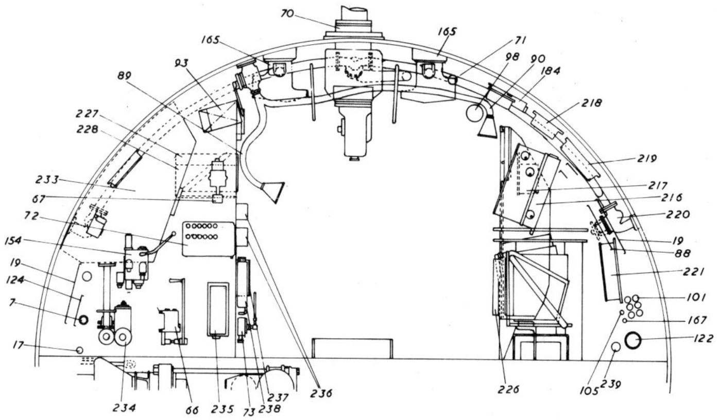

D2/13

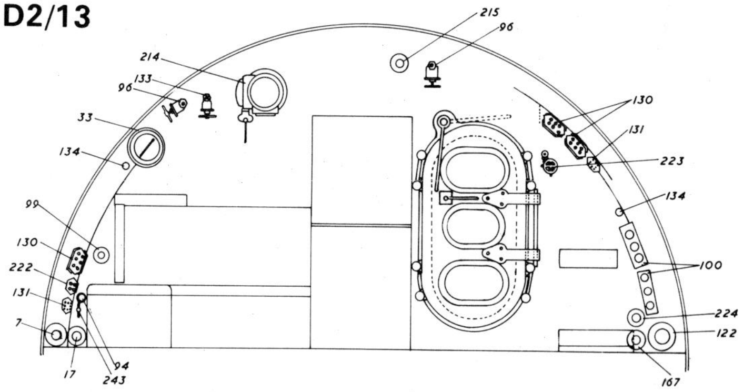

D2/11

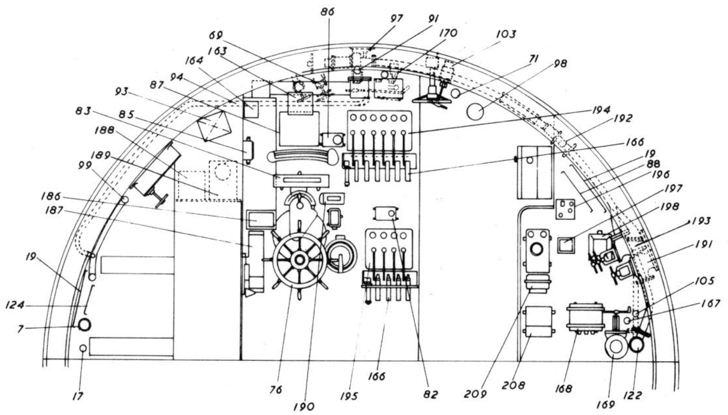

D2/14

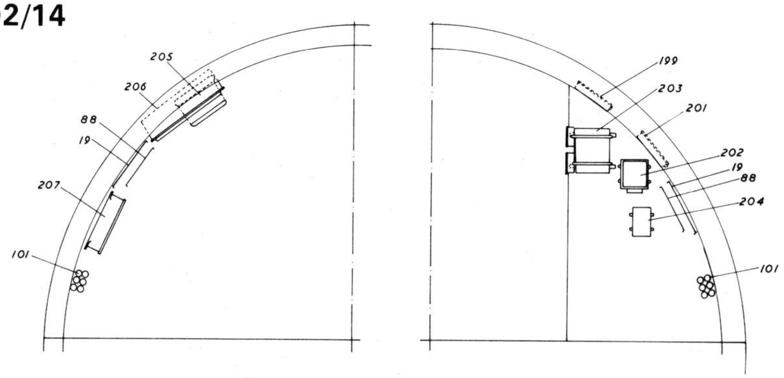

D Internal arrangements

D3 CAPSTAN AND CABLE HOLDER (no scale)

1 Drain
2 After worm
3 Telemotor control valve
4 VSG 'B' end water-tight dome
5 Two-speed gearbox
6 Expansion coupling
7 Pressure hull
8 Warping barrel
9 Oldhams coupling
10 Expansion coupling
11 Cable indicator
12 Clutch operating shaft
13 Brake band operating shaft
14 Dog clutch
15 Lay shaft
16 Combined four snug cable holder and brake drum
17 Cable locker
18 Anchor cable
19 Casing

D4 HYDROPLANES (no scale)

D4/1 Schematic arrangement of interlocks for forward hydroplanes

1 Port hydroplane
2 Starboard hydroplane
3 Pivot shaft lever
4 Pivot shaft
5 Trunnion block
6 Shut-off valve
7 By-pass
8 Tilting piston and cylinder
9 Handgear rack and pinion
10 Interlock 'A'
11 Interlock 'B'
12 Interlock 'C'
13 Housing control valves
14 Handgear clutch
15 Housing control lever
16 Handgear lever
17 Handgear clutch lever
18 Housing piston
19 Housing lever
20 Power-operated stops
21 Housing shaft
22 Tongue and groove
23 Tilting shaft
24 Toggle shaft
25 Toggle lever
26 Main shaft
27 Connecting rod
28 Tilting control valve
29 Return
30 Pressure

D4/2 General arrangement of aft hydroplane

1 Rudder
2 Fin
3 Starboard after hydroplane
4 Hydroplane shaft
5 Tilting lever
6 Lower connecting rod
7 Hydroplane nut
8 Fulcrum pin
9 Bell crank lever
10 Upper connecting rod
11 Crosshead
12 Crosshead guide
13 Gudgeon pin
14 Crosshead rod
15 Split coupling
16 Bulkhead gland
17 Piston rod
18 Tilting piston
19 Tilting cylinder
20 Differential pressure gauge
21 Locking bolt bracket
22 Handgear clutch
23 Worm gear
24 Interlock and by-pass valves
25 Rack
26 Pedestal
27 Clutch handlever
28 Handgear handlever

D4/3 Forward hydroplanes

1 Block and flexible pipes
2 Pivot shaft
3 Tilting shaft
4 Pivot lever
5 Trunnion block
6 Pressure hull
7 Hydroplane pin
8 Main bearing
9 Main hydroplane shaft
10 Centre bearing
11 Connecting rod
12 Toggle lever
13 Toggle shaft

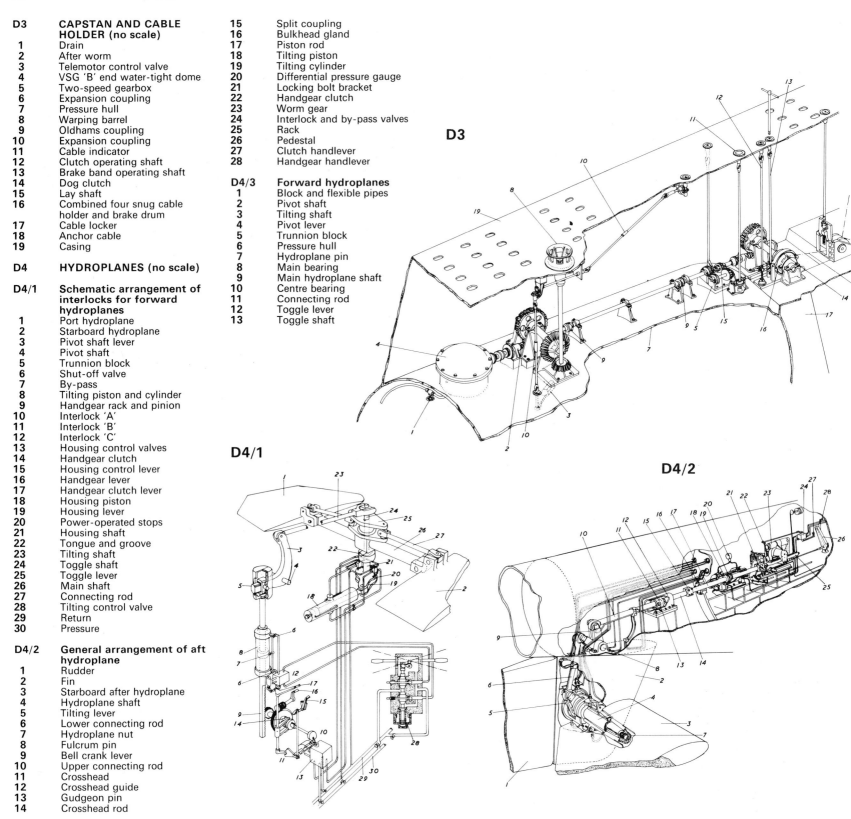

D3

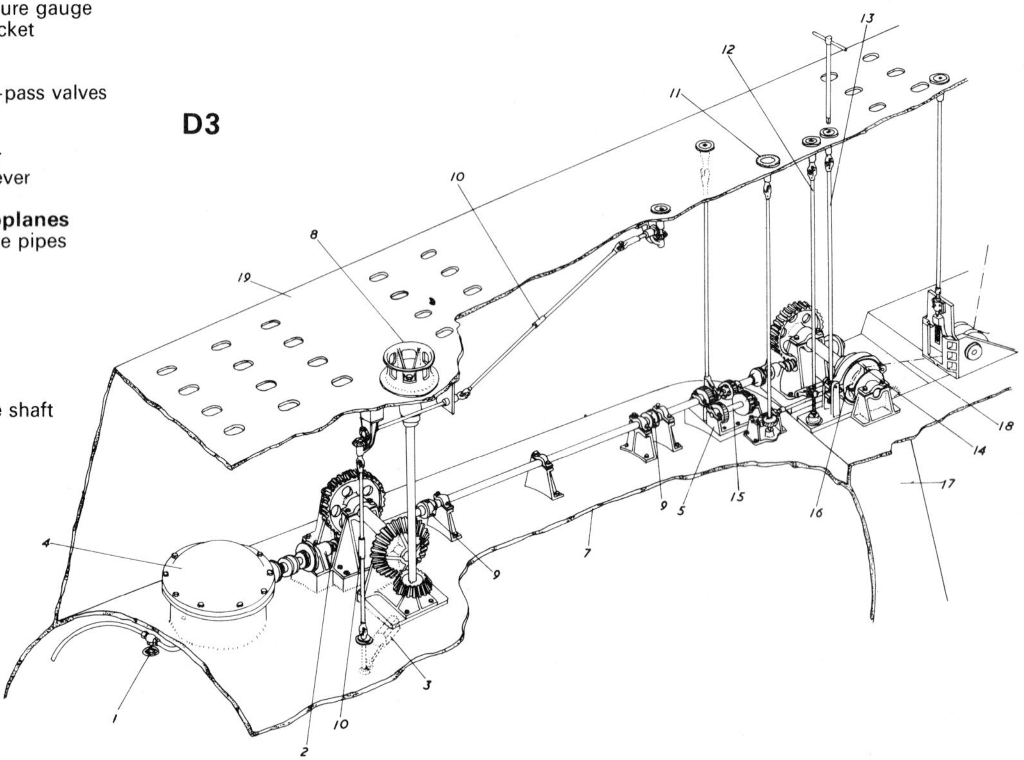

D4/1

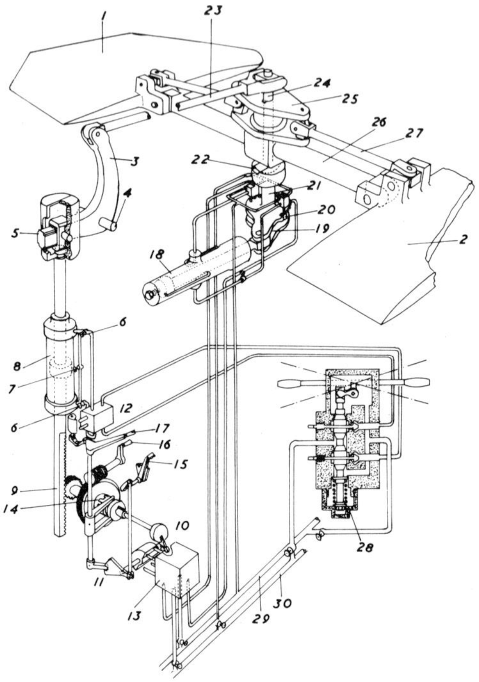

D4/2

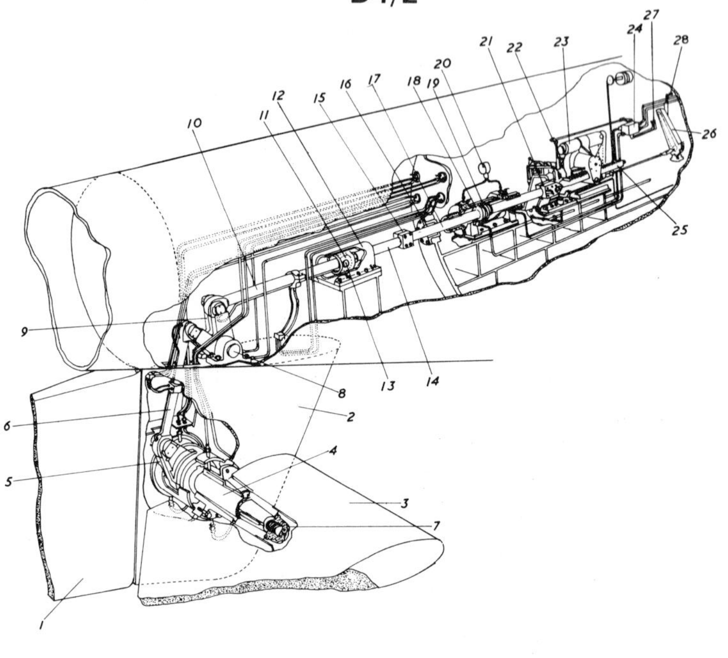

D4/3

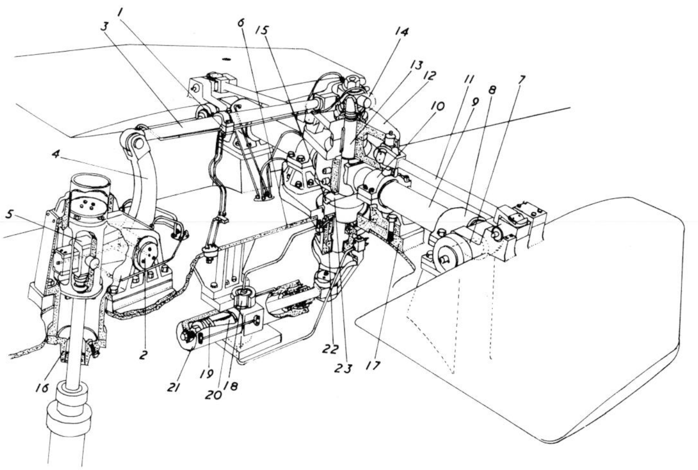

D4/4

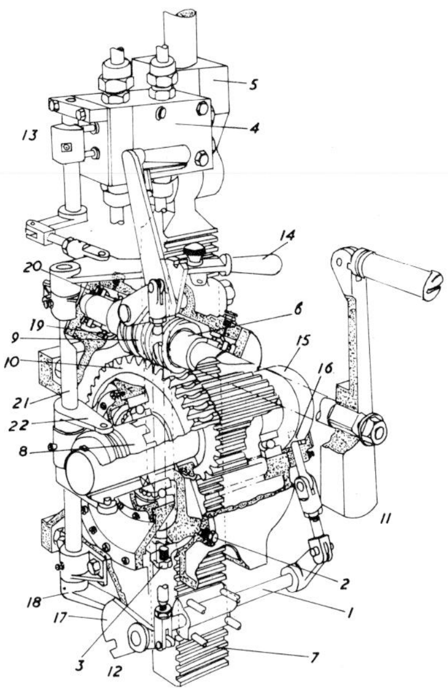

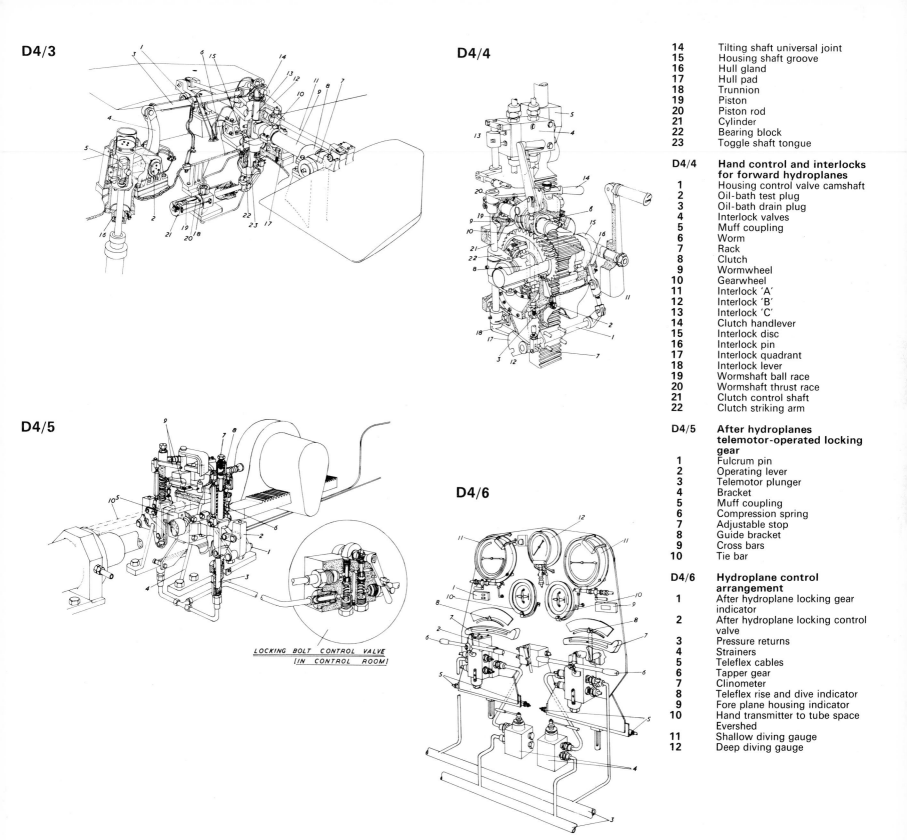

14	Tilting shaft universal joint
15	Housing shaft groove
16	Hull gland
17	Hull pad
18	Trunnion
19	Piston
20	Piston rod
21	Cylinder
22	Bearing block
23	Toggle shaft tongue

D4/4 Hand control and interlocks for forward hydroplanes

1	Housing control valve camshaft
2	Oil-bath test plug
3	Oil-bath drain plug
4	Interlock valves
5	Muff coupling
6	Worm
7	Rack
8	Clutch
9	Wormwheel
10	Gearwheel
11	Interlock 'A'
12	Interlock 'B'
13	Interlock 'C'
14	Clutch handlever
15	Interlock disc
16	Interlock pin
17	Interlock quadrant
18	Interlock lever
19	Wormshaft ball race
20	Wormshaft thrust race
21	Clutch control shaft
22	Clutch striking arm

D4/5 After hydroplanes telemotor-operated locking gear

1	Fulcrum pin
2	Operating lever
3	Telemotor plunger
4	Bracket
5	Muff coupling
6	Compression spring
7	Adjustable stop
8	Guide bracket
9	Cross bars
10	Tie bar

D4/6 Hydroplane control arrangement

1	After hydroplane locking gear indicator
2	After hydroplane locking control valve
3	Pressure returns
4	Strainers
5	Teleflex cables
6	Tapper gear
7	Clinometer
8	Teleflex rise and dive indicator
9	Fore plane housing indicator
10	Hand transmitter to tube space Evershed
11	Shallow diving gauge
12	Deep diving gauge

D4/5

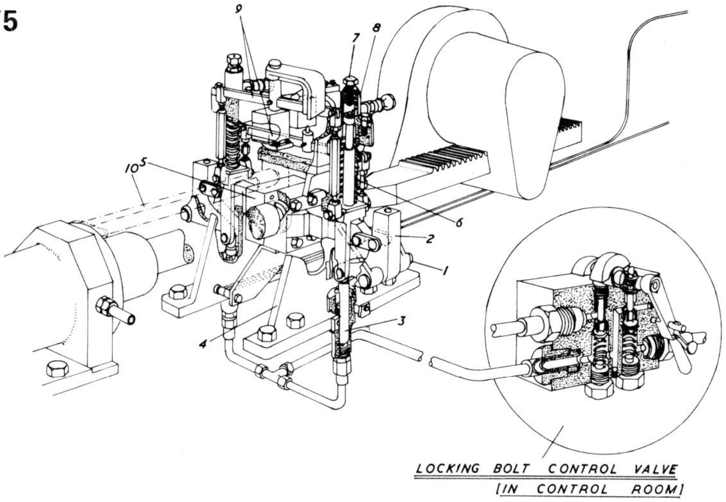

D4/6

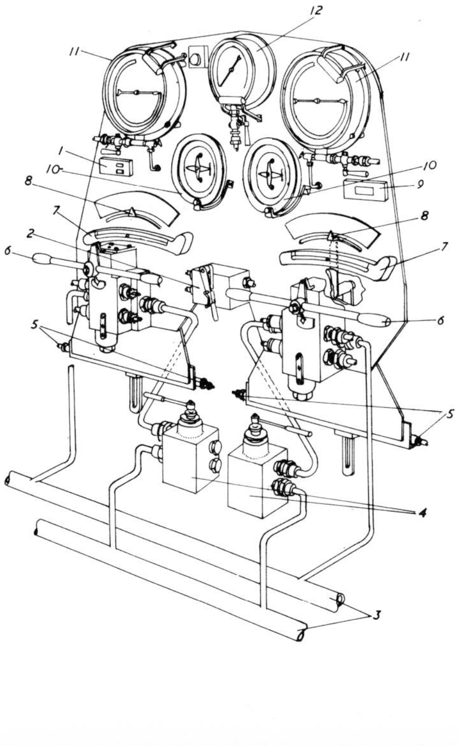

D Internal arrangements

D5 STEERING GEAR (no scale)
A Rudder operating oil system
B Ship's telemotor pressure system
C Ship's telemotor return system
D Brown's telemotor system
E Hunting gear telemotor system
F VSG (variable delivery pump) oil system

D5/1 General arrangement of steering gear
1 Rudder
2 Rudder pintle
3 Evershed transmitter
4 Spring-loaded accumulator
5 Brown's telemotor transmitter in the control room
6 Change-over valve block
7 Brown's telemotor receiver
8 VSG 'A' end
9 Hunting gear receiver
10 Telemotor control valve
11 Charging and circuit valve block
12 Shaft space
13 Torpedo stowage compartment
14 Actuating lever
15 Hunting gear transmitter
16 Power cylinder
17 No 5 main tank
18 Crosshead
19 Connecting rods
20 Rudder crosshead

D5/2 Steering gear power unit
1 To change-over valve block
2 Trunnion lever link
3 To VSG replenishing tank
4 To Brown's transmitter
5 To Hunting gear transmitter
6 To ship's telemotor return line
7 From ship's telemotor return line
8 Spring-loaded link
9 Hunting gear receiver
10 Telemotor control valve
11 Screwshaft
12 Weighshaft
13 Floating lever
14 Vent plug
15 Operating rod
16 Swinging link
17 Screwed sleeve
18 Ram
19 Bracket
20 Handwheel
21 Main crosshead
22 Spring crosshead
23 To power cylinder
24 Cylinder
25 Operating rod sleeve
26 Piston rod
27 Cylinder liner
28 Piston valve
29 Handwheel sleeve
30 Guide rod
31 Screw block
32 Guide rod sleeve

D5/3 The Brown's transmitter
1 Evershed transmitter and repeater
2 Mechanical pointer
3 Replenishing tank
4 To receiver
5 Rack
6 Pinion
7 By-pass valve
8 Vent plug
9 Relief valve
10 Piston
11 Pinion shaft
12 Replenishing valve
13 Gear wheel
14 Steering wheel shaft
15 Ship's wheel
16 Spur wheel
17 Gear case
18 Cut-out valve

D5/1

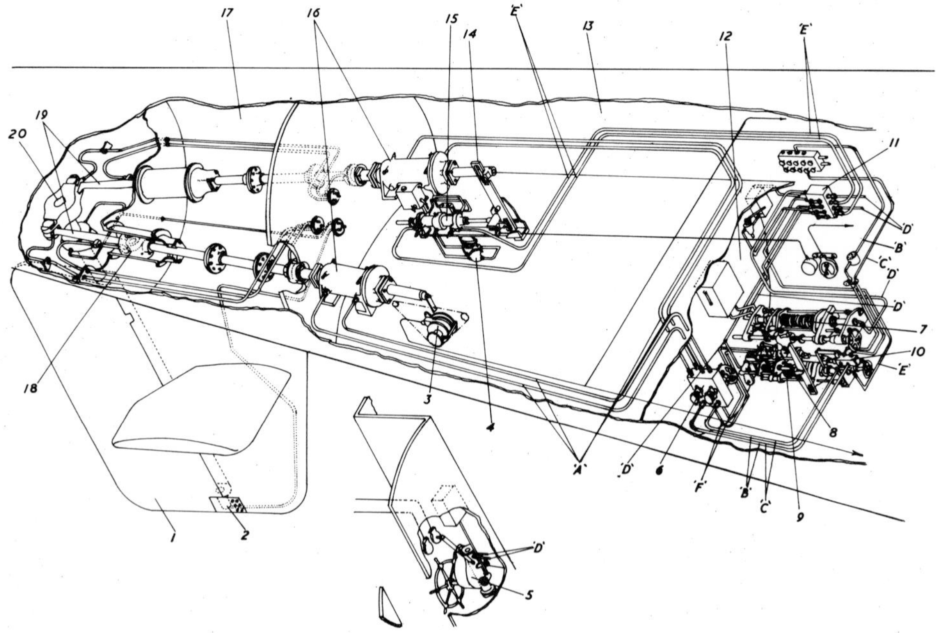

D5/2

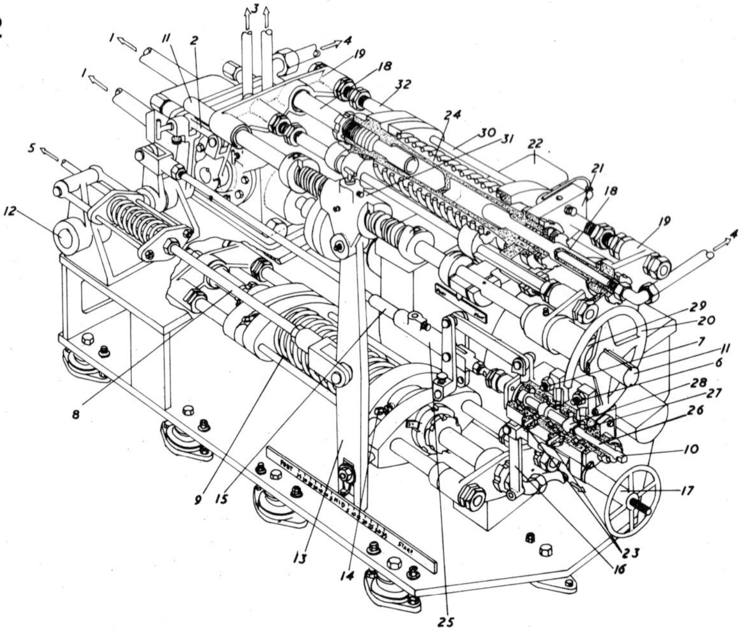

D5/3

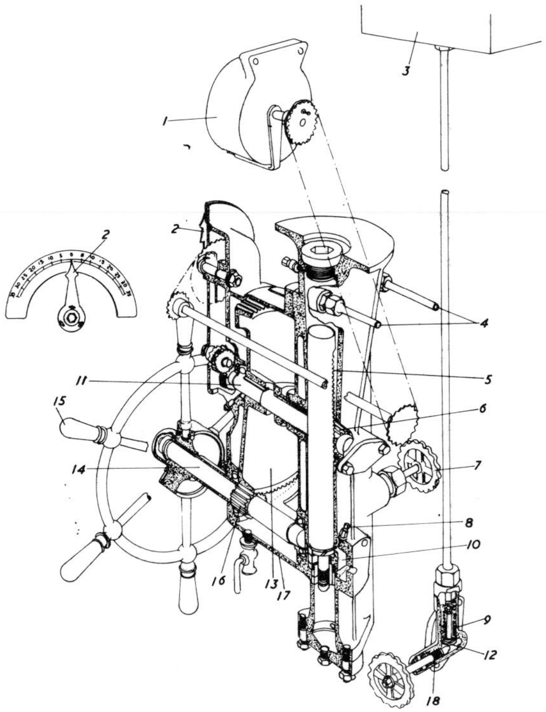

D6	AIR-LOADED ACCUMULATOR
1	Indicator cap
2	Indicator coils
3	Air connection
4	Air strainer
5	Accumulator body
6	Indicator rod
7	Securing ring lip
8	Top securing ring
9	Piston
10	Fabric ring
11	Spring-loaded non-return valve
12	Oil test plug
13	Oil passage
14	Air test plug
15	Bottom cover
16	Oil connection to contact pressure gauge
17	Crown metal seat
18	Oil connection to telemotor pressure line
19	Shut-off valve
20	Bottom securing ring

D7	VALVES (no scale)
D7/1	**Main vent valve**
1	Wire hood
2	12in diameter valve
3	Screwed valve seat ring
4	Valve body
5	Guide bush
6	Valve spindle
7	Gland packing
8	Pressure hull
9	Valve spindle links
10	Operating lever
11	By-pass valve
12	Handgear crosshead
13	Handwheel
14	Handwheel clutch
15	Position indicator
16	Four start thread
17	Handgear link
18	Locking cotter holes
19	Fulcrum pin
20	Gland nut
21	Neck ring
22	Packing ring
23	Operating ram
24	Pressure to shut
25	Pressure to open
26	Operating cylinder
27	From internal greasing point
28	From main ballast tank
29	Dexine seat ring

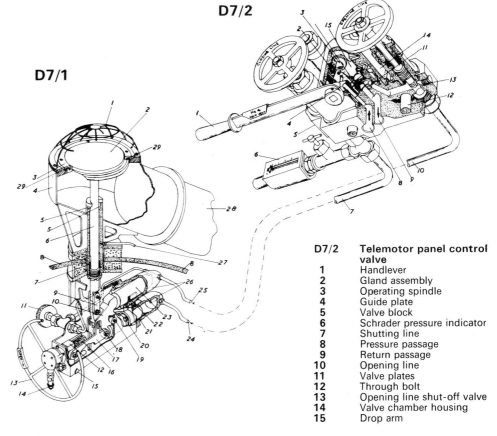

D6

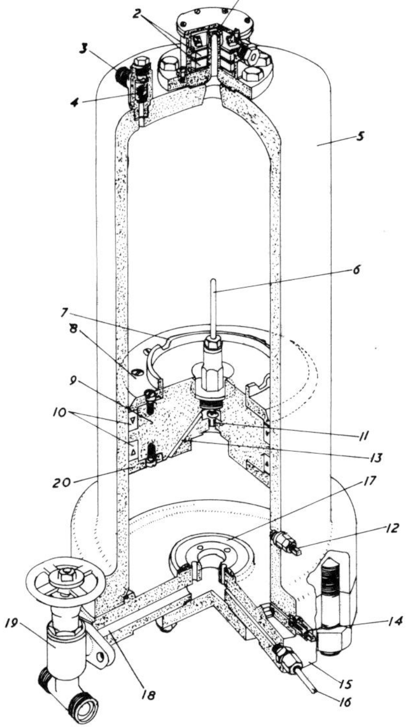

D7/1

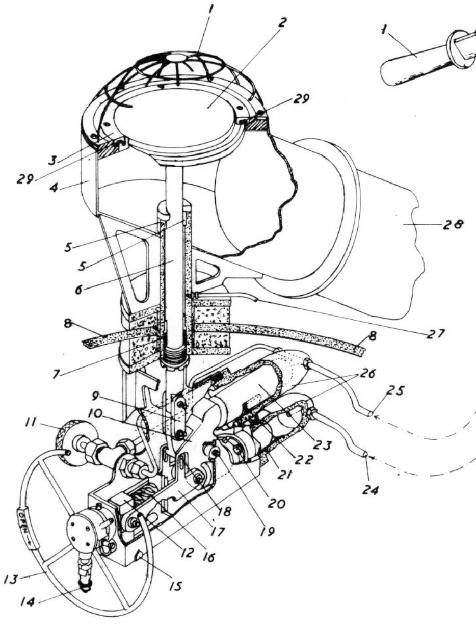

D7/2

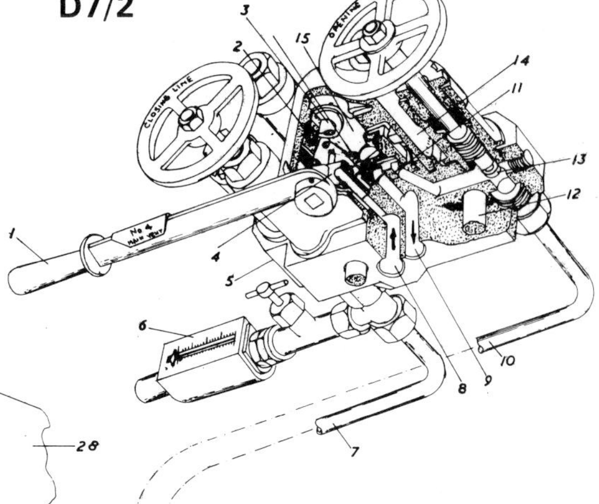

D7/2	Telemotor panel control valve
1	Handlever
2	Gland assembly
3	Operating spindle
4	Guide plate
5	Valve block
6	Schrader pressure indicator
7	Shutting line
8	Pressure passage
9	Return passage
10	Opening line
11	Valve plates
12	Through bolt
13	Opening line shut-off valve
14	Valve chamber housing
15	Drop arm

D7/3 'Q' kingston valve
1 Pressure to open
2 Opening ram
3 Crosshead
4 Pressure to shut
5 Shutting rams
6 Retaining ring
7 Main body casting
8 Hull gland
9 Pressure hull
10 'Q' tank
11 Free-flood holes
12 Valve seat casting
13 Pipe to syphon compartment
14 Bottom keel plate
15 Kingston valve
16 Portable access plate
17 Guide bearing plate
18 Valve spindle link block
19 Link pins
20 Fulcrum pin
21 Crank lever
22 Operating shaft link block
23 Lock nuts
24 Operating shaft

D7/4 Hand-operated kingstons
1 Three greasing points
2 Hand ratchet lever
3 Open/shut indicator
4 Hull gland
5 Felt grease seals
6 Securing plates
7 First bevel gearbox
8 Universal expansion joint
9 Second bevel gearbox
10 Bottom keel plate
11 Kingston valve
12 Bushes
13 Limit stop
14 Dexine seat ring (not shown)
15 Connecting links
16 No 4 port main ballast tank
17 Pressure hull
18 Link plate
19 Left-hand thread
20 Air escape groove
21 Gearcase
22 Screwed sleeve
23 Right-hand thread

D8 DUPLEX CONTROL VALVE (Both coolers in use)
The Duplex control valve is situated in the main engine lubricating oil system between the two Serck oil coolers. The control valve directs the oil through either or both coolers or by-passes both coolers. All lubricating oil piping inside the boat is of steel, tested at 100lb per sq in
1 To port cooler
2 Supply from pumps via Lolos strainers
3 To starboard cooler
4 Discharge to engines
5 From starboard cooler
6 Drain
7 Spring-loaded locking bar
8 From port cooler

D7/3

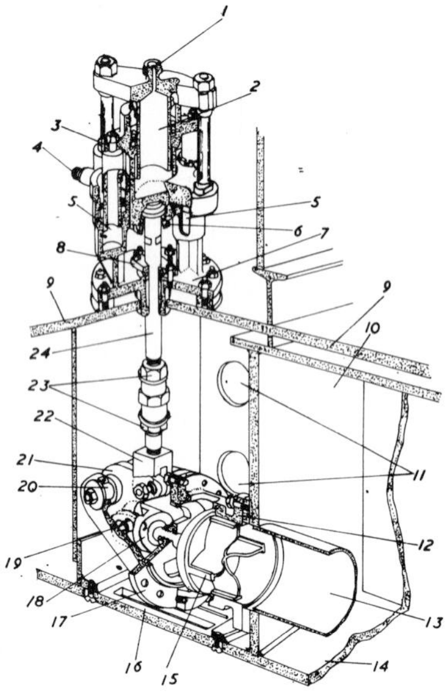

D7/4

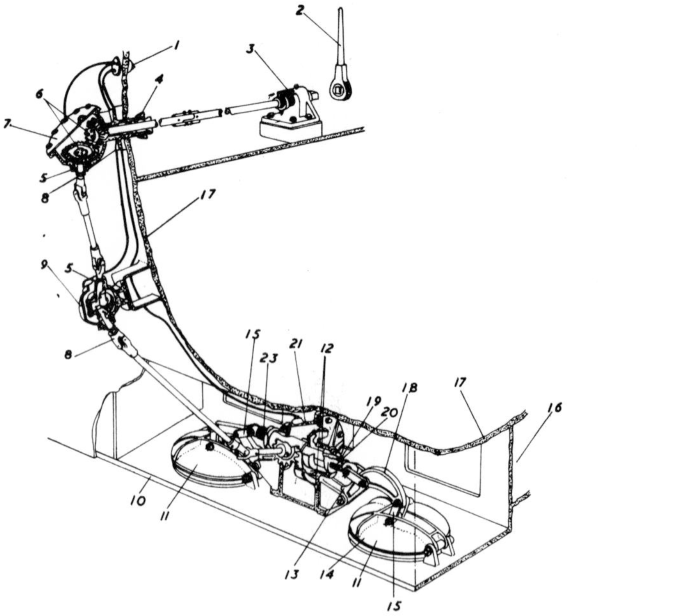

D8

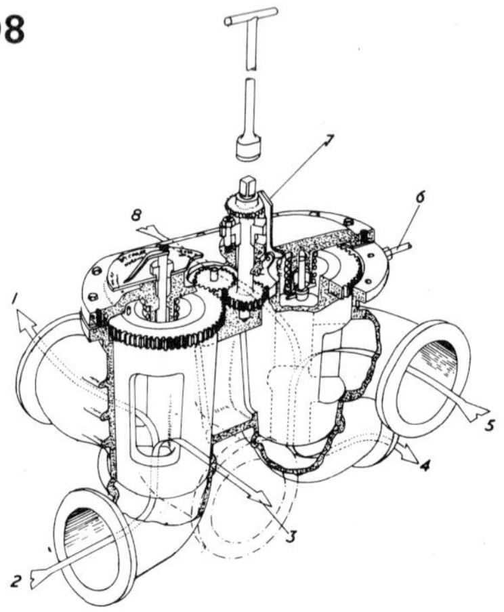

D9 SNORT INDUCTION SYSTEM (no scale)

D9/1 General arrangement
1 Engine room
2 Water trap
3 Mast trunnion bearings
4 Pin for locking mast in raised position
5 Control box for raising mast
6 Crutch for supporting mast in raised position
7 Telemotor-operated ram for raising and lowering mast
8 Vertical exhaust pipe rigidly attached to ANF mast standard
9 Pad piece for holding float valve open when mast is lowered
10 Crutch for supporting mast in lowered position
11 Hull valve on drain for induction valve dome
12 Telemotor-operated snort induction hull valve
13 Snort drain 2 intermediate valve
14 Port main ballast tank
15 Group exhaust hull valve from starboard engine
16 Bridge induction line valve
17 Snort induction line valve
18 Bridge induction outboard drain valve
19 Both drains discharge into 'R' port
20 Tundish with sight glass
21 Shut-off valve
22 Control room
23 Induction tube
24 Pressure hull
25 Starboard surface exhaust muffler tank
26 Port surface exhaust muffler tank
27 Port snort muffler valve
28 Starboard snort muffler valve
29 Inboard drain from port snort muff
30 Snort exhaust outboard drain valve
31 Snort exhaust inboard drain
32 Handwheels for working line valves
33 Hull valve on drain from water trap
34 Telemotor system leads
35 Snort mast in raised position
36 Float-controlled head valve
37 Bridge superstructure
38 Mast position indicator
39 Bridge induction trunking
40 Locking pin operating gear
41 Strengthening plate
42 Air inlet

D9/2 General arrangement of snort mast raising gear
When raised and lowered the mast pivots in its trunnion bearings, the leverage being applied to a forked crank arm welded to the mast base. In its raised position the mast comes to rest in a housing crutch welded to the after bridge superstructure; in the fully raised position the mast is not quite vertical
1 Branch pipe leading from the induction tube to water trap
2 Mast crutch welded to side of bridge structure

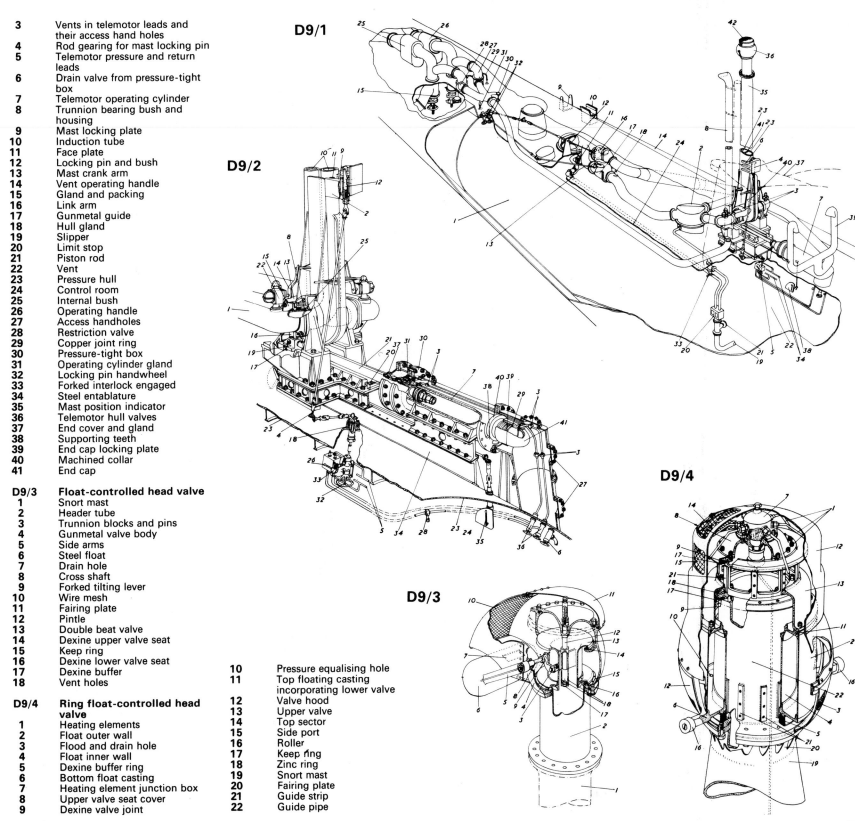

3 Vents in telemotor leads and their access hand holes
4 Rod gearing for mast locking pin
5 Telemotor pressure and return leads
6 Drain valve from pressure-tight box
7 Telemotor operating cylinder
8 Trunnion bearing bush and housing
9 Mast locking plate
10 Induction tube
11 Face plate
12 Locking pin and bush
13 Mast crank arm
14 Vent operating handle
15 Gland and packing
16 Link arm
17 Gunmetal guide
18 Hull gland
19 Slipper
20 Limit stop
21 Piston rod
22 Vent
23 Pressure hull
24 Control room
25 Internal bush
26 Operating handle
27 Access handholes
28 Restriction valve
29 Copper joint ring
30 Pressure-tight box
31 Operating cylinder gland
32 Locking pin handwheel
33 Forked interlock engaged
34 Steel entablature
35 Mast position indicator
36 Telemotor hull valves
37 End cover and gland
38 Supporting teeth
39 End cap locking plate
40 Machined collar
41 End cap

D9/3 Float-controlled head valve

1 Snort mast
2 Header tube
3 Trunnion blocks and pins
4 Gunmetal valve body
5 Side arms
6 Steel float
7 Drain hole
8 Cross shaft
9 Forked tilting lever
10 Wire mesh
11 Fairing plate
12 Pintle
13 Double beat valve
14 Dexine upper valve seat
15 Keep ring
16 Dexine lower valve seat
17 Dexine buffer
18 Vent holes

D9/4 Ring float-controlled head valve

1 Heating elements
2 Float outer wall
3 Flood and drain hole
4 Float inner wall
5 Dexine buffer ring
6 Bottom float casting
7 Heating element junction box
8 Upper valve seat cover
9 Dexine valve joint
10 Pressure equalising hole
11 Top floating casting incorporating lower valve
12 Valve hood
13 Upper valve
14 Top sector
15 Side port
16 Roller
17 Keep ring
18 Zinc ring
19 Snort mast
20 Fairing plate
21 Guide strip
22 Guide pipe

D9/1

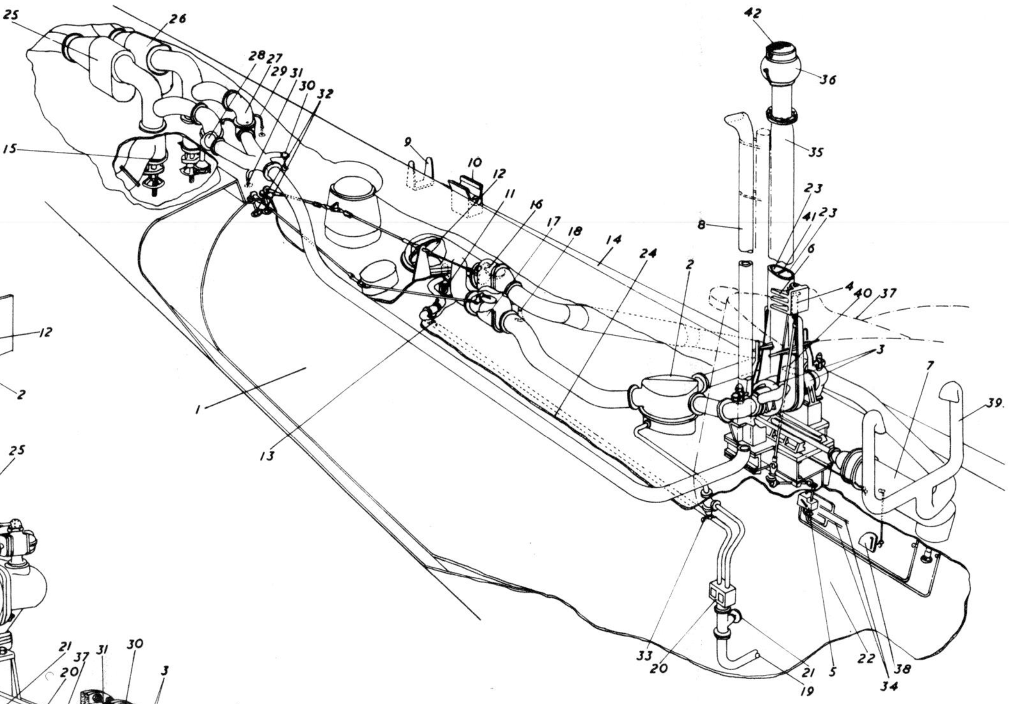

D9/2

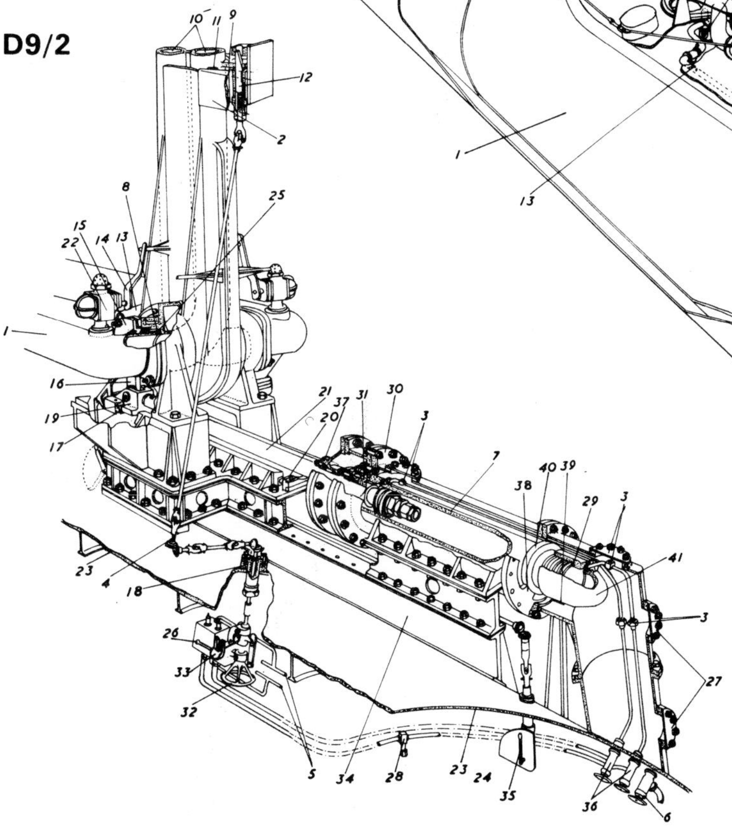

D9/3

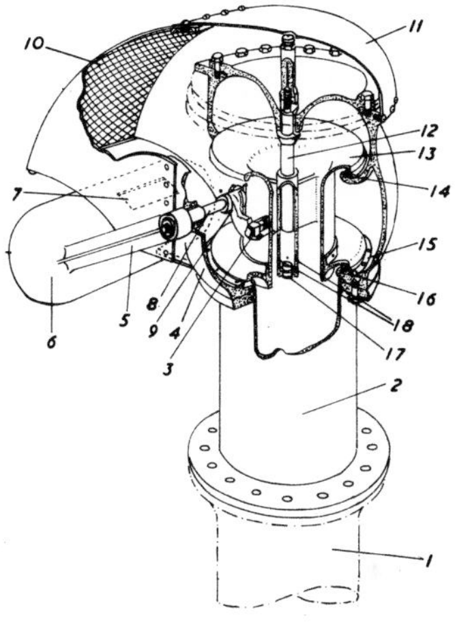

D9/4

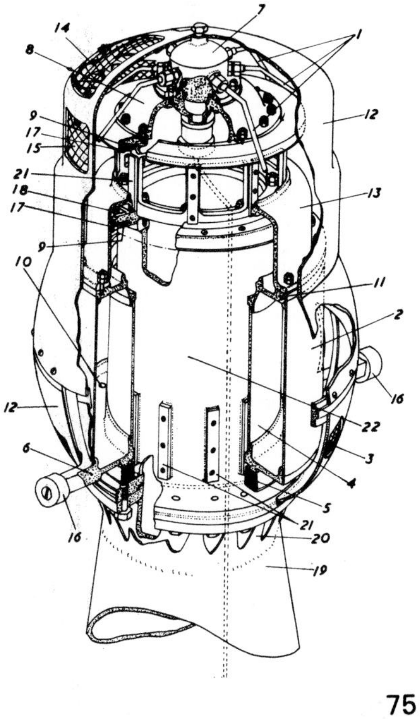

D9/5 Air induction system

1 Relief valve
2 Supercharger
3 Return to suction
4 Air inlet valve
5 Air inlet manifold

D9/6 Snort muffler valve

1 Circulating water pipes
2 Discharge from group exhaust valve
3 HP air blow to starboard muffler valve
4 Discharge to exhaust mast
5 4in bore outboard drain
6 Discharge from starboard valve
7 Connection to exhaust back pressure gauge
8 1.5in bore inboard drain
9 Operating gear spur wheel
10 Valve grinding handwheel
11 Valve operating lever
12 Operating shaft driving worm
13 Grinding shaft bevel wheel
14 Valve operating gear handwheel
15 HP air blow
16 Water jacket
17 Lower valve body
18 End cover
19 Valve body feet
20 Stuffing box
21 Hull gland
22 Pressure hull
23 Operating spindle links
24 Grinding shaft
25 Operating shaft
26 Grub screw

D9/7 Snort muffler valve (screw down type)

1 Discharge from group exhaust valve
2 Water-jacketed exhaust pipe bend
3 Gearbox bottom casting
4 To exhaust mast
5 Gearbox top casting
6 Operating handwheel
7 Grinding handwheel
8 Valve indicator
9 Stellited face
10 Valve seat
11 Valve spindle
12 Valve lid
13 Pressure hull
14 Driving spur gear
15 Idler spur gear
16 Spindle cover
17 Damper handwheel
18 Keyway
19 Wormshaft
20 Valve box
21 Gland
22 Hull pad
23 Gland bush
24 Grease nipples
25 Double thrust ball race
26 Gearbox support

D9/8 Telemotor-operated induction hull valve

1 'Y' piece
2 Air from snort mast
3 Pressure-tight dome
4 Valve seat
5 Upper valve body
6 Lower valve body
7 Fulcrum lever
8 Operating cylinder
9 Fixed hollow ram
10 Operating handle
11 Induction hull valve
12 Air from bridge induction system
13 Dexine seat secured by brass keep rings
14 Tecalemit grease connection
15 Telemotor pressure or return from control box
16 Emergency flap valve
17 Hull valve to drain from dome space
18 To 'R' compensating tank
19 Snort drain 2 intermediate valve
20 Gland nut
21 Links
22 Operating rod
23 Cotter
24 Raised buffer
25 Drain cock
26 Gland
27 To flap valve, which admits air to engine room bilges or ship's ventilation system or both

D9/9 Group exhaust valve

1 Slot for withdrawing valve seat
2 Square end of spindle
3 Valve position indicator
4 Tecalemit grease nipple
5 Circular rack gear
6 Valve handwheel
7 Steel key
8 Keyway
9 Valve guide
10 Bridge piece
11 Rotating handle
12 Gland
13 Valve cover
14 Setscrew
15 Water jacket
16 Drain connection
17 Valve seat
18 Pad piece
19 Rotating collar
20 Steel valve
21 Valve spindle

D9/10 Exhaust muffler tank

1 Vent and vacuum breaker valve
2 Manganese bronze ring
3 Heat resistant steel ring
4 Dexine seat ring
5 Thrust collars
6 Bushed bearing
7 Square stud
8 Locking lever
9 Muffler valve
10 Operating lever
11 Weir
12 Spray cone
13 Muffler tank
14 Jacket
15 Baffle plate
16 Vent hole
17 Wormwheel
18 Inspection and cleaning door
19 Water jacket and spray
20 Zinc anti-corrosion slab
21 Non-return flap shock valve

D9/5

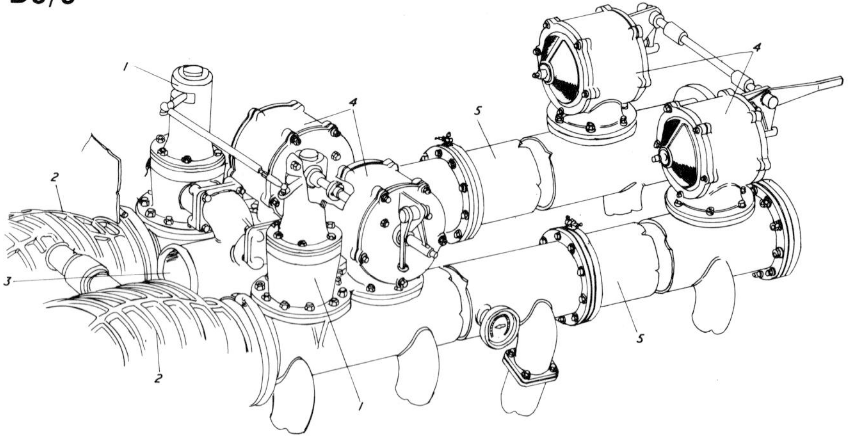

D9/6

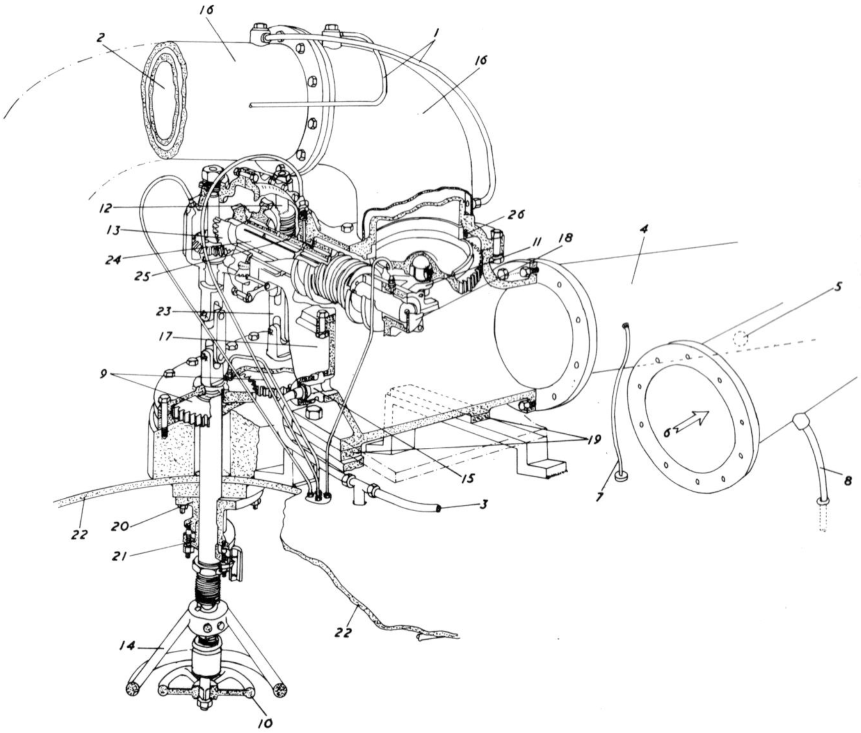

D9/7

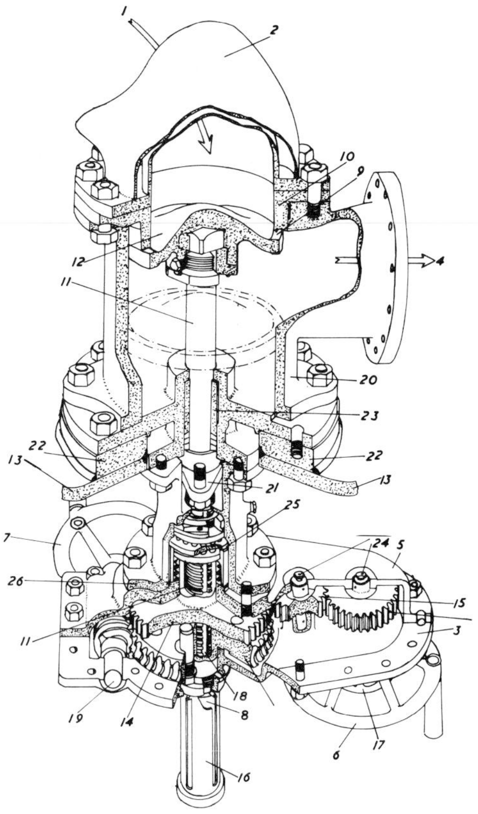

D9/8

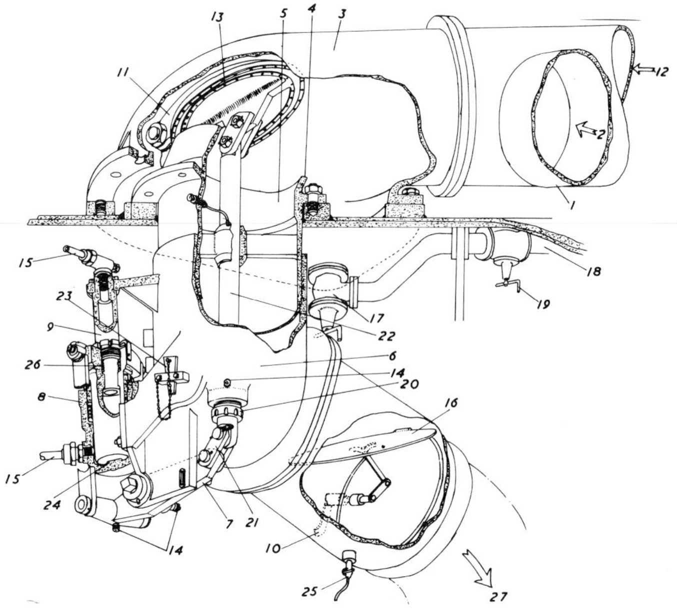

D9/10

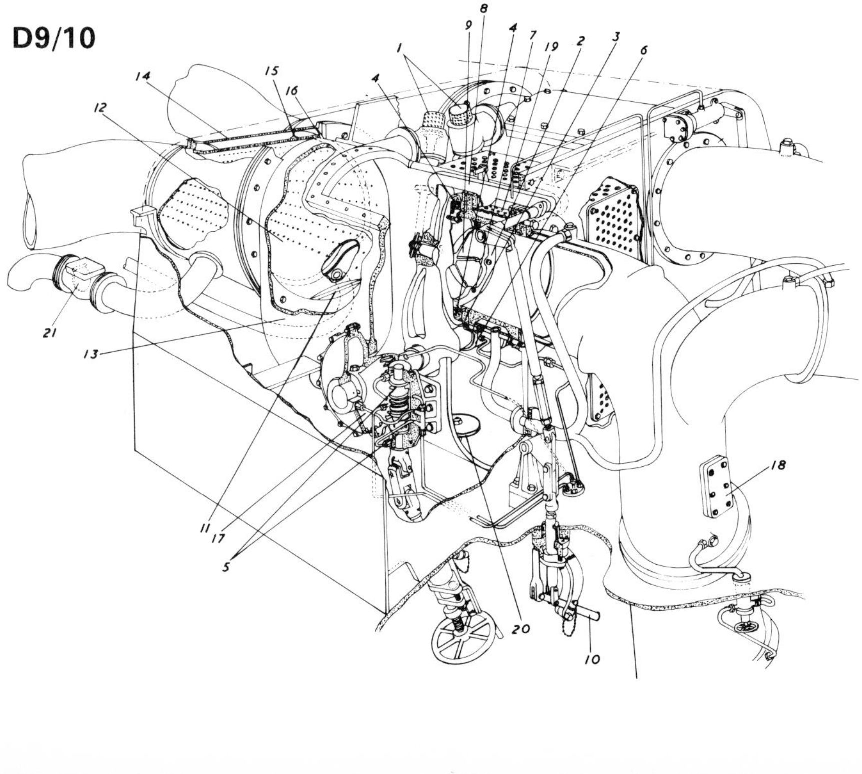

D9/9

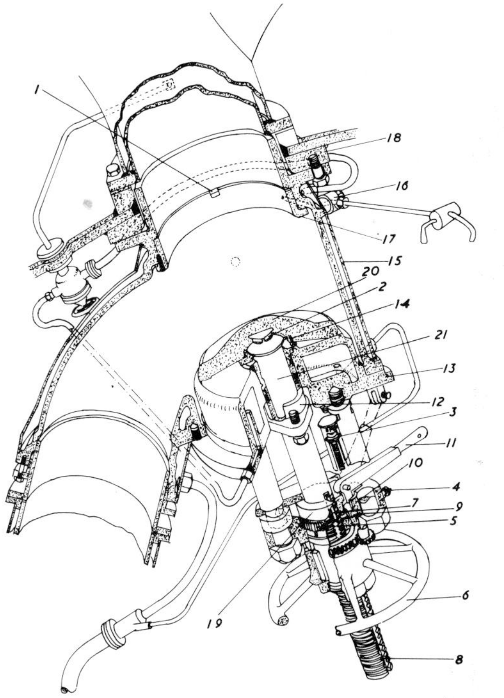

D Internal arrangements

D10 PERISCOPES (no scale)

D10/1 Type CK14 general arrangement

1 Head
2 Top prisms
3 Change power telescope
4 First objective
5 Combined graticules and deviating prisms
6 Top forging
7 Upper main tube
8 Upper main objective
9 Lower main objective
10 Lower main tube
11 Range estimator and converging lenses
12 Crosshead
13 Bottom prism
14 Face plate

D10/2 Type CK14 optical system

1 Top prisms
2 Negative change power lenses
3 Positive change power lenses
4 HP first objective lenses
5 Combined graticules and deviating prisms
6 Upper main objective
7 Lower main objective
8 Range estimator prisms
9 Converging lenses
10 Bottom prisms
11 Colour filter discs
12 Interocular adjusting prisms
13 Collector lenses
14 Eye lenses

D10/3 Type CK14 intermediate sections

1 End piece of middle frame tube
2 Lower end of middle frame tube
3 Upper frame tube
4 Upper main tube
5 Middle frame tube
6 Screwed coupling ring
7 Upper main objective
8 Lower main objective
9 Lower frame tube
10 Lower main tube
11 Desiccator pipe
12 Top forging
13 Registering key
14 Lens holder

D10/4 Type CK14 sealed frame assembly

1 Combined graticule and deviating prisms
2 Stray light baffle
3 Desiccator pipe
4 Top forging
5 HP first ojectives
6 Sealed frame
7 Microflex pipe
8 Upper frame tube
9 Guide tubes for operating wires

D10/1

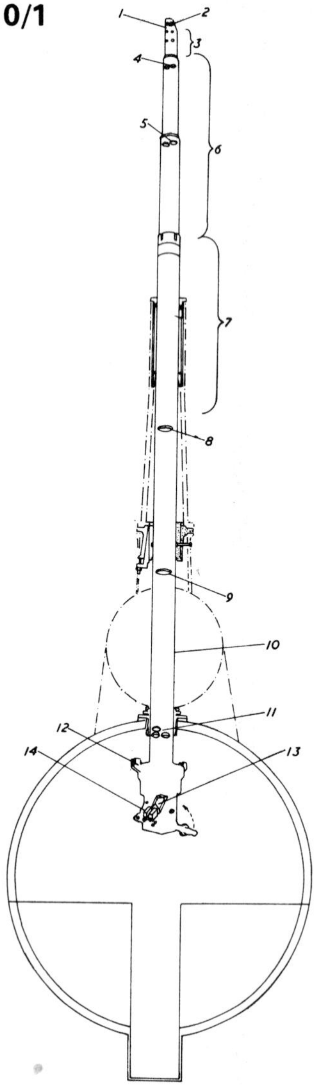

D10/2

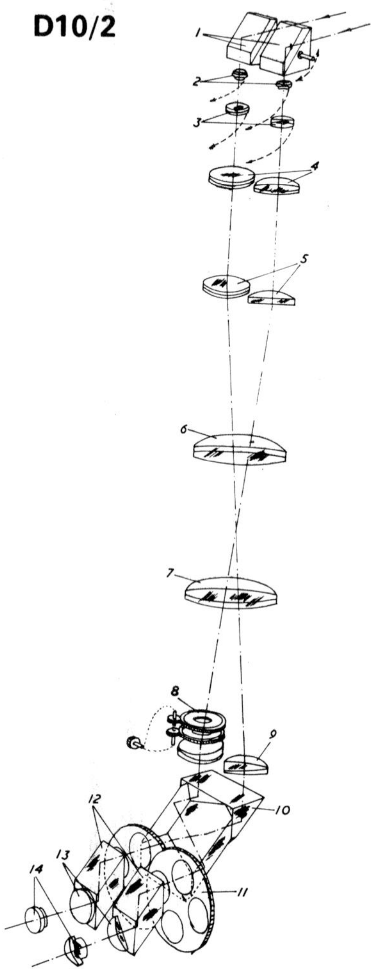

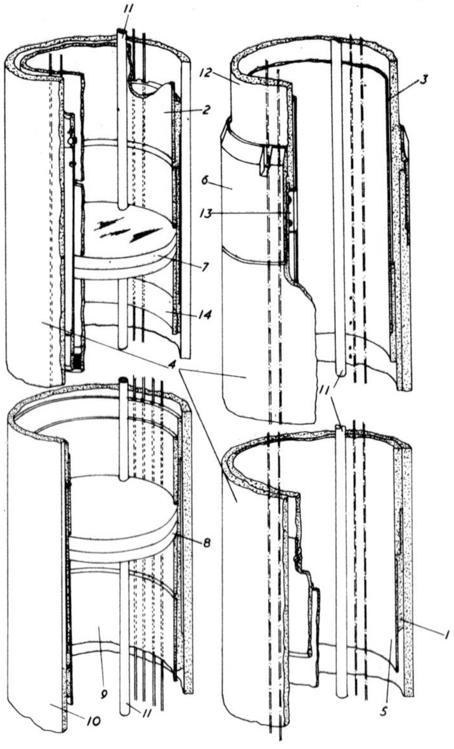

D10/3

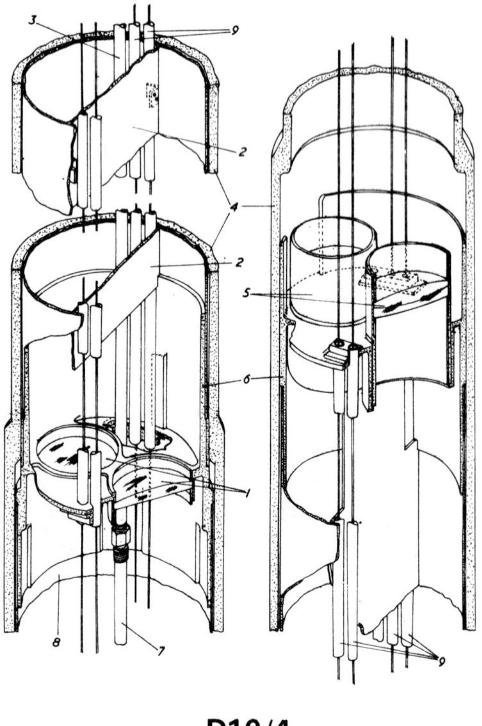

D10/4

D10/5

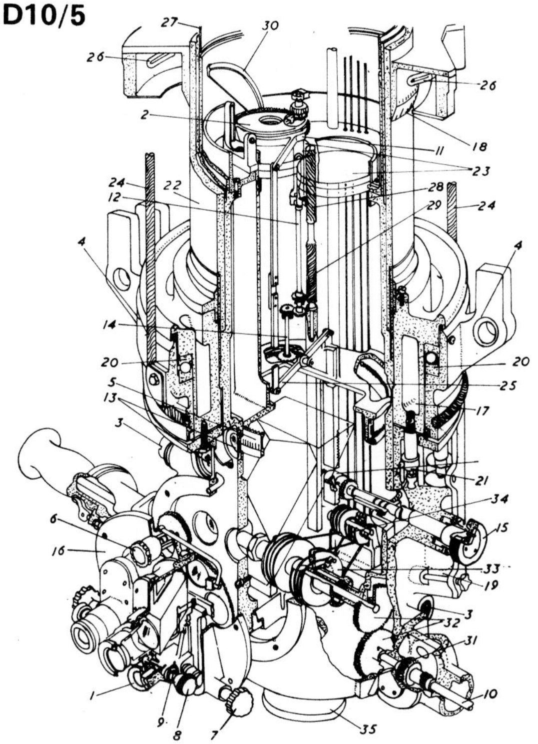

D10/6

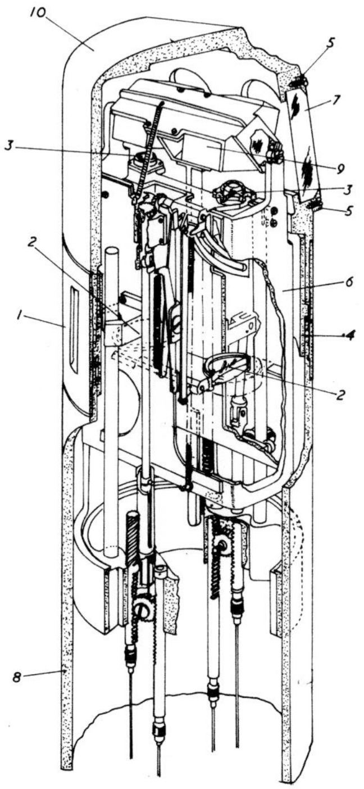

D10/7

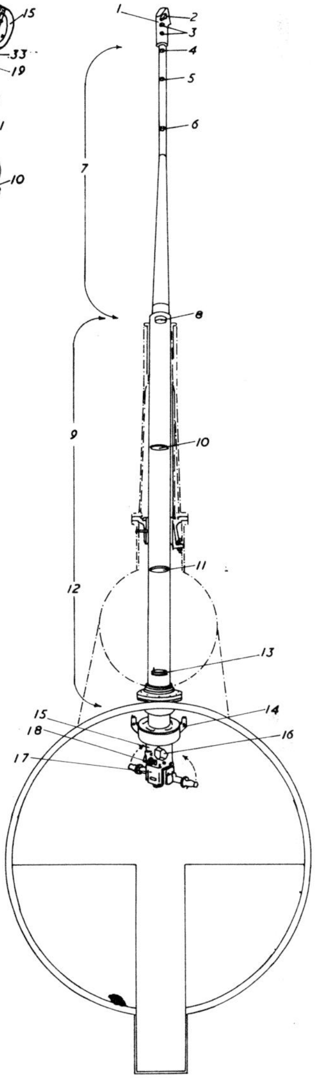

D10/8

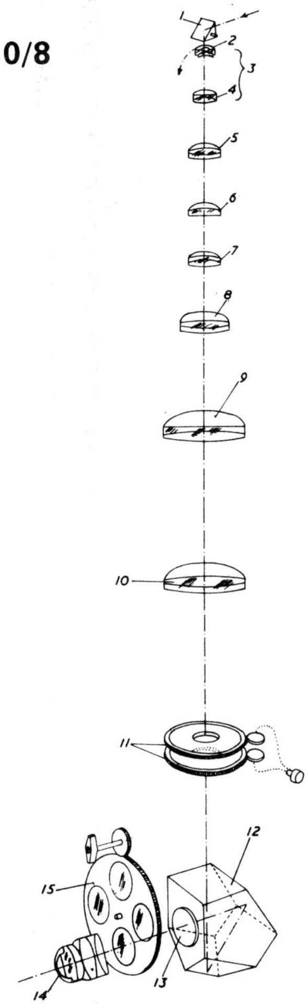

D10/5 Type CK14 bottom casting assembly

1 Interocular distance scale
2 Range estimator prisms
3 Desiccator connection to face plate
4 Outer supporting ring
5 Range estimator scale
6 Light filter operating head
7 Interocular adjusting head
8 Eye piece focussing head
9 Jockey carrying focussing scale
10 Training handle spindle
11 Estimator prism carrier
12 Upper prism driving shaft
13 Windows – inner and outer
14 Estimator scale driving shaft
15 Range estimator operating head
16 Face plate
17 Reservoir
18 Bearing scale
19 Bottom outer casing
20 Ball race
21 Drain cock
22 Main tube
23 Converging lenses
24 Hoisting wire
25 Tilting lever
26 Illuminating lamp
27 Lower frame tube
28 Upper spiral pinion
29 Lower spiral pinion
30 Locking quadrant
31 Handle clutch wheels
32 Spur gears
33 Operating sheaves
34 Guide sheaves
35 Buffer

D10/6 Type CK14 top forging

1 Screwed coupling ring
2 LP positive lenses
3 LP negative lenses
4 Upper frame (fixed)
5 Top window frame
6 Moving top frame
7 Top window
8 Top forging
9 Top prism
10 Head

D10/7 Type CH66 general arrangement

1 Head
2 Top prism
3 Change power telescope
4 First objective
5 Graticule
6 Second objective
7 Top forging
8 Third objective
9 Main tube upper portion
10 Main upper objective
11 Main lower objective
12 Main tube lower portion
13 Range estimator
14 Crosshead
15 Lower casting
16 Bottom prism
17 Face plate
18 Eye lens

D10/8 Type CH66 optical system

1 Top prism
2 Negative change power lens
3 LP telescope
4 Positive change power lens
5 HP first objective
6 Graticule
7 Second objective
8 Third objective
9 Main upper objective
10 Main lower objective
11 Range estimator prisms
12 Bottom prism
13 Collector lens
14 Eye lens
15 Colour filter disc (clear, red, grey and polarised)

D10/9 Type CH66 bottom casting
1 Hoisting wire
2 Bearing scale
3 Lower frame
4 Training handle
5 Ball race
6 Drain cock
7 Bottom prism
8 Lower ring
9 Face plate
10 Reservoir
11 Eye piece cover
12 Focussing rack
13 Eye lens holder
14 Inner support ring
15 Outer support ring
16 Illuminating lamp
17 Buffer knob
18 Operating spindle
19 Scale window
20 Range estimator scale
21 Colour filter disc

D10/10 Type CH66 intermediate sections
1 Bottom end of junction liner
2 Lower main objective holder
3 Range estimator supporting rods
4 Liner casting carrying estimator gear
5 Lower main objective
6 Lens mounting rings
7 Cork packing
8 Desiccator pipe
9 Estimator gear
10 Upper ring
11 Mid ring

D10/11 Type CH66 upper intermediate section
1 Sky search and change power operating wires
2 End piece of upper frame tube
3 Third objective mounting
4 Third objective
5 Screwed coupling ring
6 Upper main objective
7 Slots for desiccator return
8 Upper frame tube
9 Frame casting
10 Desiccator pipe
11 Upper main tube
12 Lower main tube
13 Top forging
14 Air escape
15 Junction liner
16 Slots

D10/12 Type CH66 head and upper frame
1 Head
2 Top window
3 Top prism
4 Ball race
5 LP negative lens
6 Window frame
7 Registering springs
8 LP positive lens
9 Screwed coupling rings
10 Upper frame
11 Registering key
12 Desiccator return
13 HP first objective
14 Graticule
15 Desiccator holes

D10/9

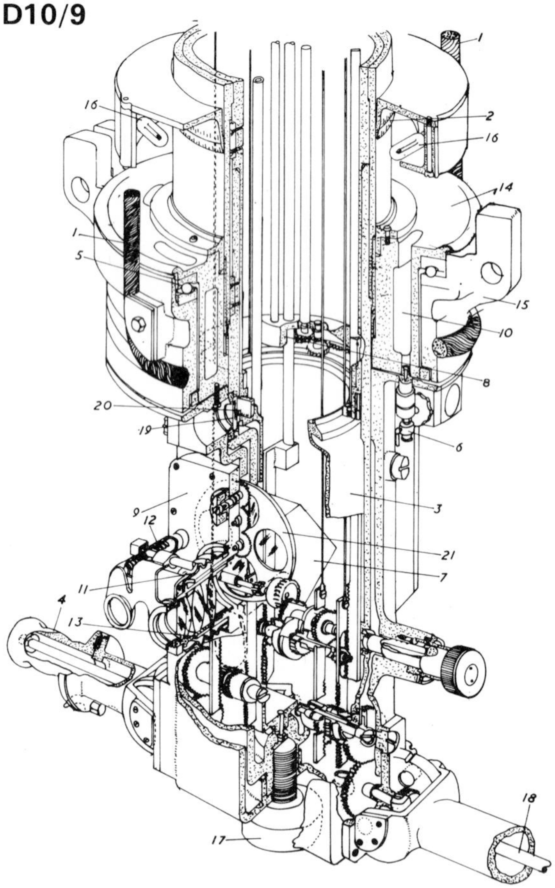

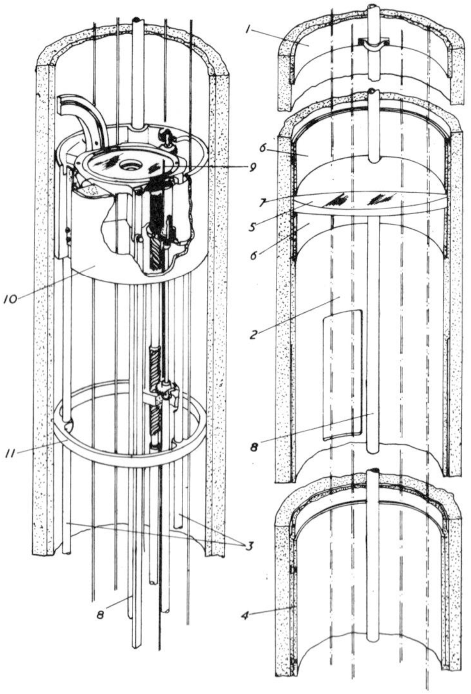

D10/10

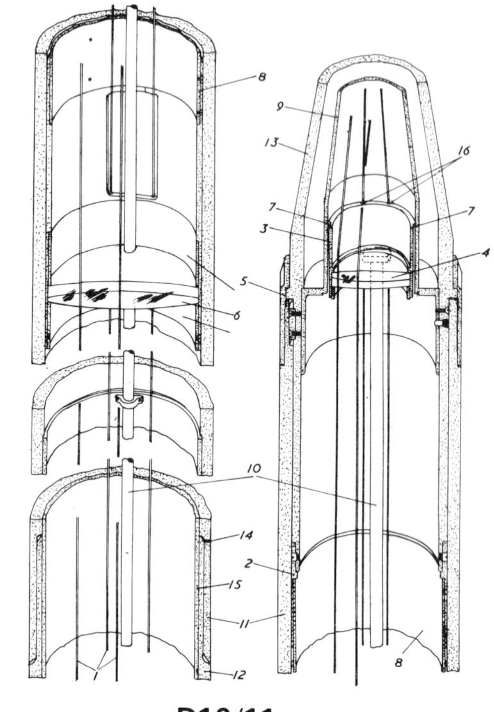

D10/12

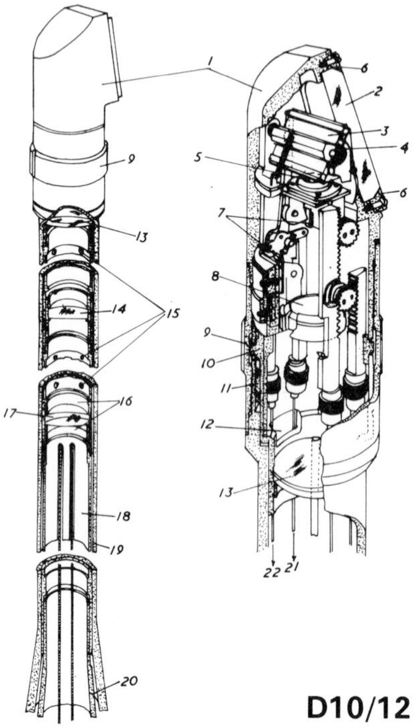

D10/11

16 Mountain ring
17 Second objective
18 Upper lens carrier tube
19 Top forging
20 Top of frame casting
21 To elevate
22 To depress

D10/13 Type CK14 periscope hoist gear

1 Stuffing box assembly
2 Sheave bracket
3 Guide sheaves
4 Sheave
5 Suspending link
6 Hoisting wires
7 Supporting crosshead outer ring
8 Pressure to raise
9 Adjusting eyebolts
10 8in rope sheave
11 10in rope sheave
12 Raising cylinder
13 Moving ram
14 Pin for 10in diam sheaves
15 Lowering tube
16 Side rod supporting bracket
17 Pressure to lower
18 Gland
19 Crosshead
20 Side rod
21 Periscope well
22 Control room

D11 PROJECTOR BINNACLE (ACO Mk II; no scale)

The submarine projector compass assembly provided a projected image of the compass card and lubber's point in the control room for steering, the Pattern 33P magnetic compass being housed in a pressure-tight binnacle external to the hull at the forward end of the bridge. Light was reflected from the lamp box through a prism and lens system, then was projected onto a ground glass screen in front of the helmsman

D11/1 Projector general arrangement

1 First prism
2 Second prism
3 Lamp box
4 Hull pad
5 Compass card
6 Sluice valve
7 Lamp
8 Split flange
9 Elbow prism
10 Top cover
11 Viewing mirror
12 Condenser lenses
13 Pressure-tight binnacle
14 Compass
15 Double prism
16 Lubber's point
17 Projector lens
18 Erector lens
19 Lower field lens
20 Correcting spheres
21 Elbow prism box
22 First rhomboid prism
23 Second rhomboid prism
24 On/off dimmer switch
25 Telescopic screen tube

D11/2 Projector binnacle upper tube

1 Topmost cover
2 Magnet bucket
3 Corrector magnet racks
4 Top double prism
5 Upper field lens
6 Upper pressure-tight cover
7 Lubber's point
8 Soft iron correcting sphere
9 Pattern 33P magnetic compass
10 Compass card
11 Compass housing
12 Angle bracket
13 Gimbals
14 First rhomboid prism
15 Second rhomboid prism
16 5in diameter tube
17 Centering springs
18 Projector lens
19 Supporting bracket
20 Desiccator pipe

D10/13

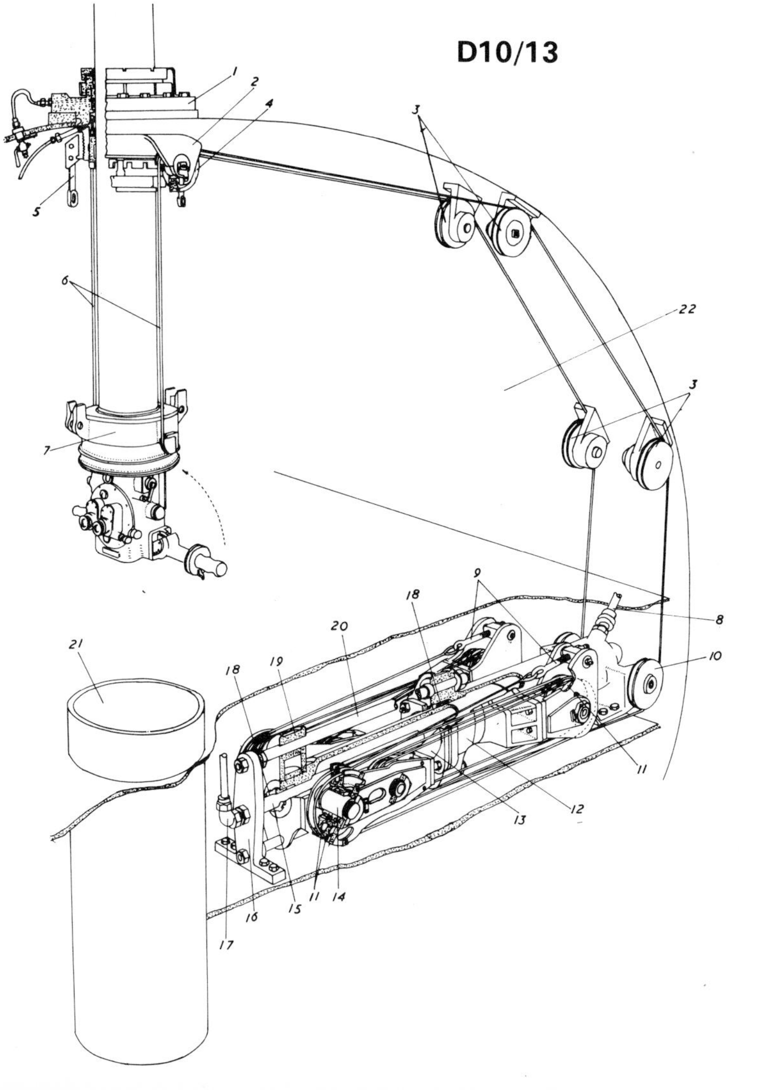

D11/1

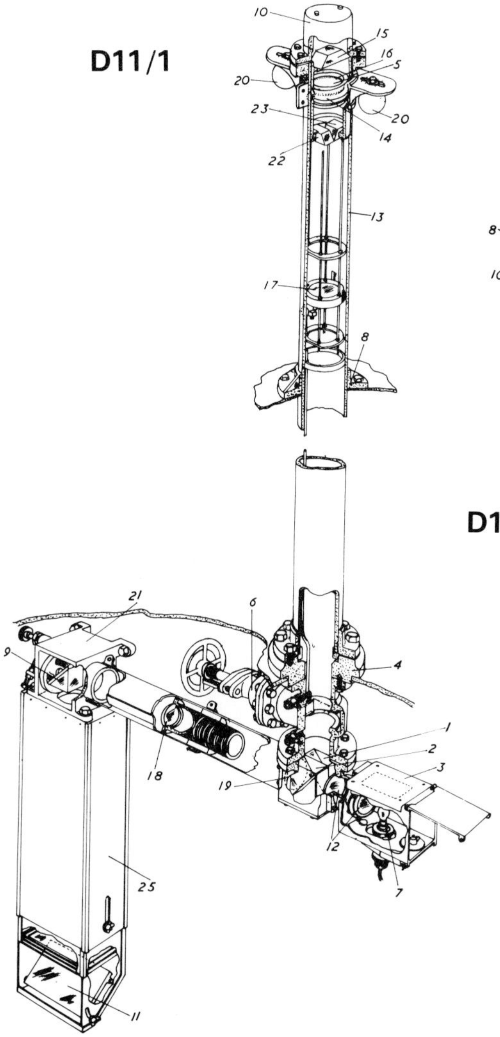

D11/2

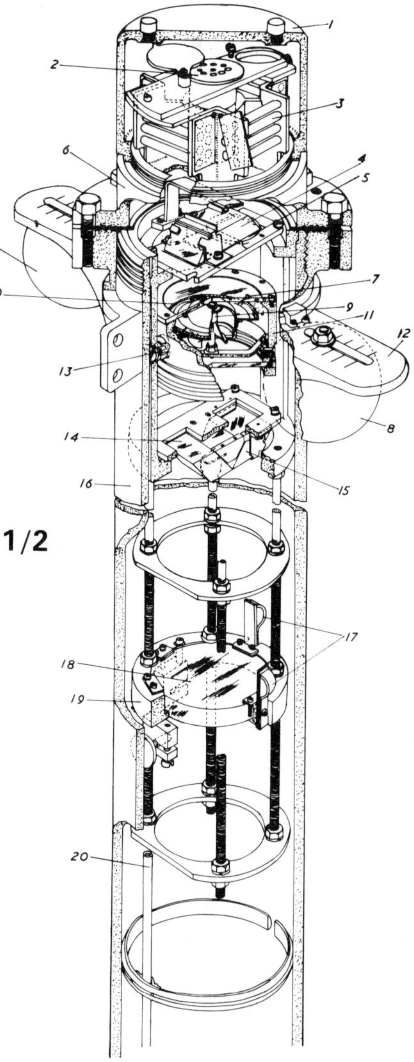

E Machinery

E1 **GENERAL ARRANGEMENT OF ENGINE ROOM (1/96 scale)**

E1/1

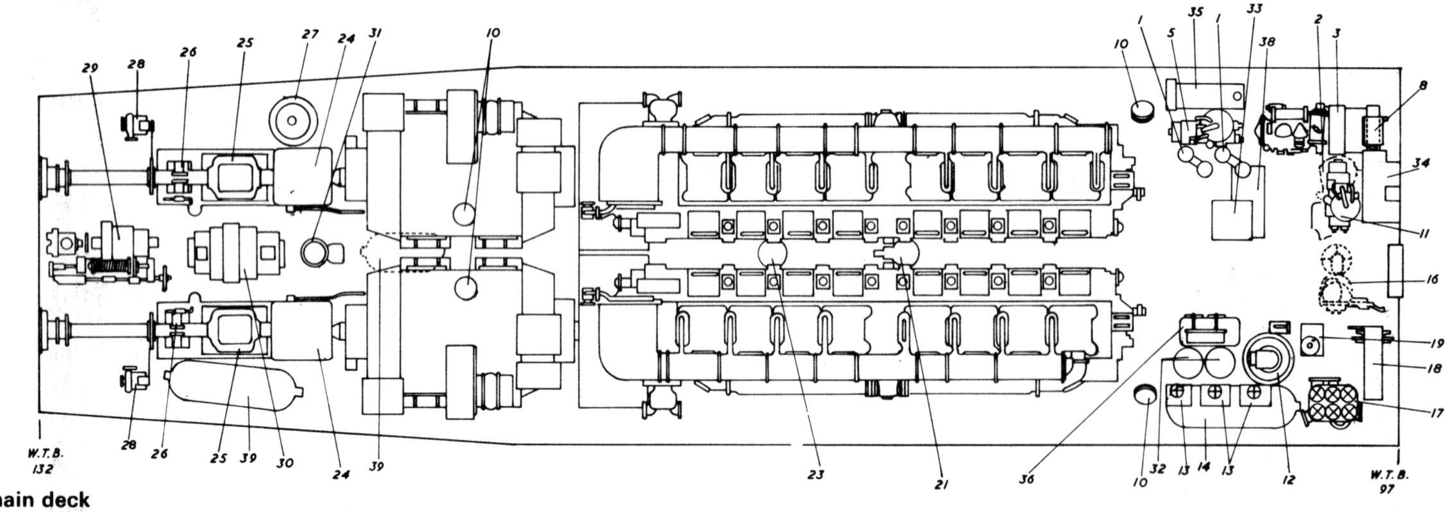

E1/1 **Plan view of main deck**

E1/2 **Plan below engine room platform**

1 Signal ejectors
2 Engine induction valve
3 HP air compressor
4 Circulating water pump
5 Lubricating oil separator
6 Sub pressure pump
7 Oil coolers
8 Lubricating oil pump starter
9 Fuel oil separator starter (not shown)
10 Engine telegraph receivers
11 Fuel oil separator
12 Ballast pump
13 Circulating pump starters
14 Starting air bottle
15 Storage air bottle
16 Battery ventilation valve
17 Six-valve chest
18 Lathe
19 Ballast pump starter
20 Inboard exhaust valve (not shown)
21 Engine turning gear
22 Exhaust tank (not shown)
23 OMD lubricating oil priming pump
24 Aft clutch
25 Thrust block
26 Brake
27 Air-loaded accumulator
28 Emergency circulating water pump
29 Steering gear power unit
30 Reducer
31 Oily bilge pump
32 Lubricating oil strainers
33 Engine room desk
34 Oil fuel gravity tank
35 Lubricating oil heater
36 Vice bench
37 Flowmeter (water service)
38 Lubricating oil separator starter
39 Air bottle for telemotor accumulator

E2/1

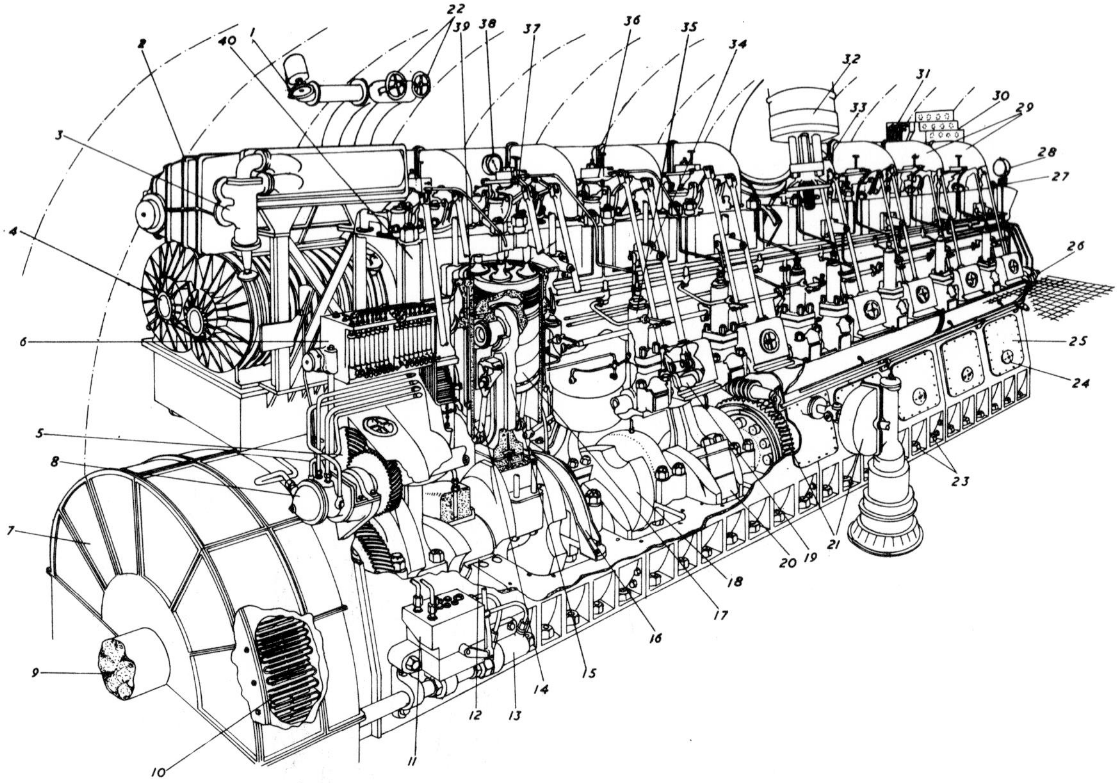

E1/2

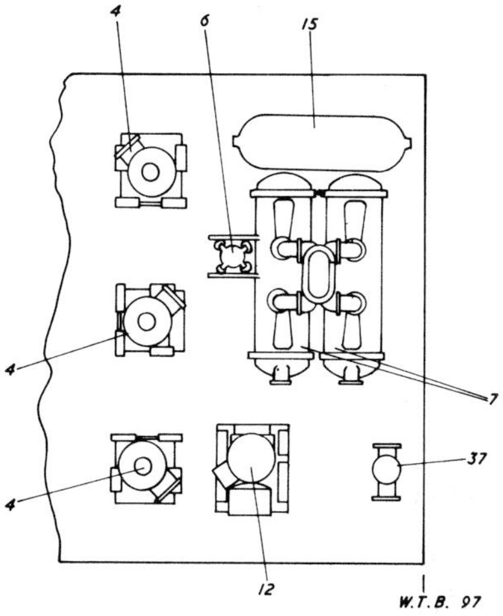

E2/3

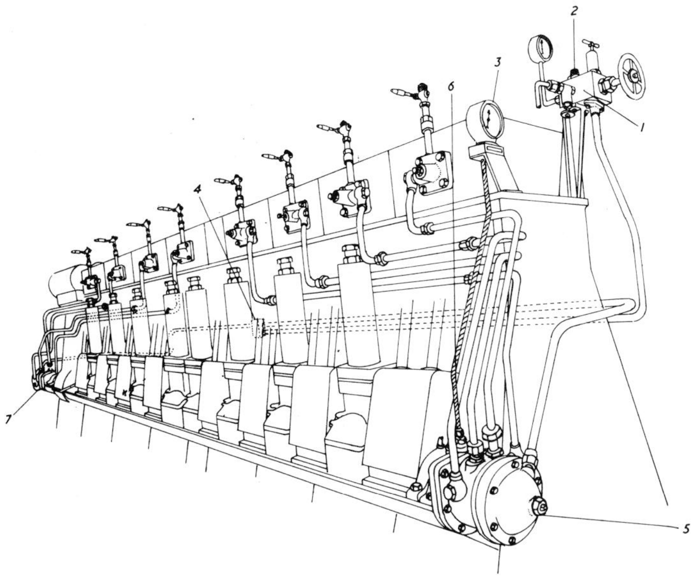

E2/2

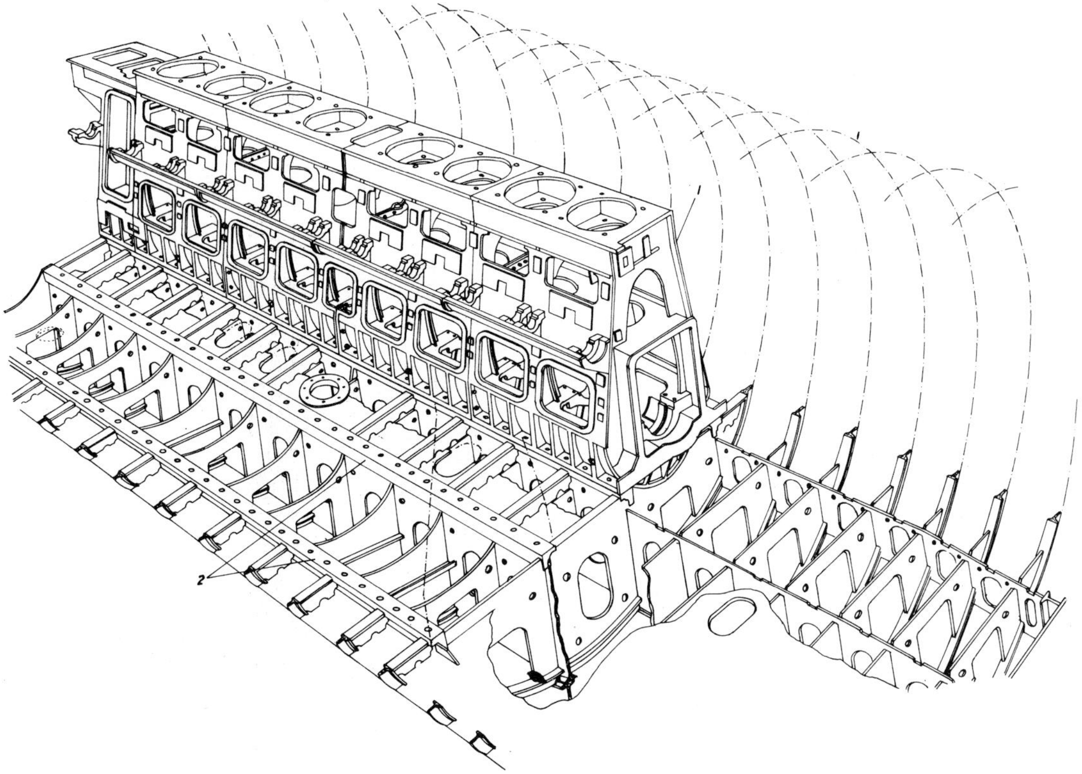

E2 ADMIRALTY MAIN ENGINES (no scale)

E2/1 General arrangement
1 Circulating water system overboard discharge
2 Supercharger air cooler
3 Cooling circulating water control and by-pass
4 Supercharger
5 Gear drive train
6 Cylinder liner mechanical lubricator
7 Main engine clutch
8 After air start distributor
9 Intermediate shafting
10 Bibby coupling springs
11 Clutch control box
12 Main bearing
13 Clutch operating cylinder
14 Piston cooling gear
15 Connecting rod and gudgeon pin
16 Splash guard
17 Piston
18 Crankshaft
19 Camshaft
20 Large end bearing
21 Turning gear
22 Engine circulating water temperature control valves
23 Holding down bolts
24 Handhole door
25 Inspection cover
26 Forward air start distributor
27 Fuel and clutch control levers
28 Revolution tachometer
29 Air induction manifold
30 Gauge board
31 Piston cooling oil tundish
32 Group exhaust valve
33 Indicator cock
34 Air start valve
35 Fuel pump
36 Fuel injector
37 Valve gear
38 Exhaust gas pyrometer
39 Liner and jacket
40 Cylinder head

E2/2 Engine frame and bearers
1 Port engine frame
2 Starboard engine bearers

E2/3 Air start system
1 Air start valve
2 Supply from air bottle
3 Engine tachometer
4 Turning gear interlock valve
5 Forward air start distributor driven off forward end of camshaft
6 Engine tachometer drive off forward air start distributor
7 After air start distributor driven off after end of camshaft

E Machinery

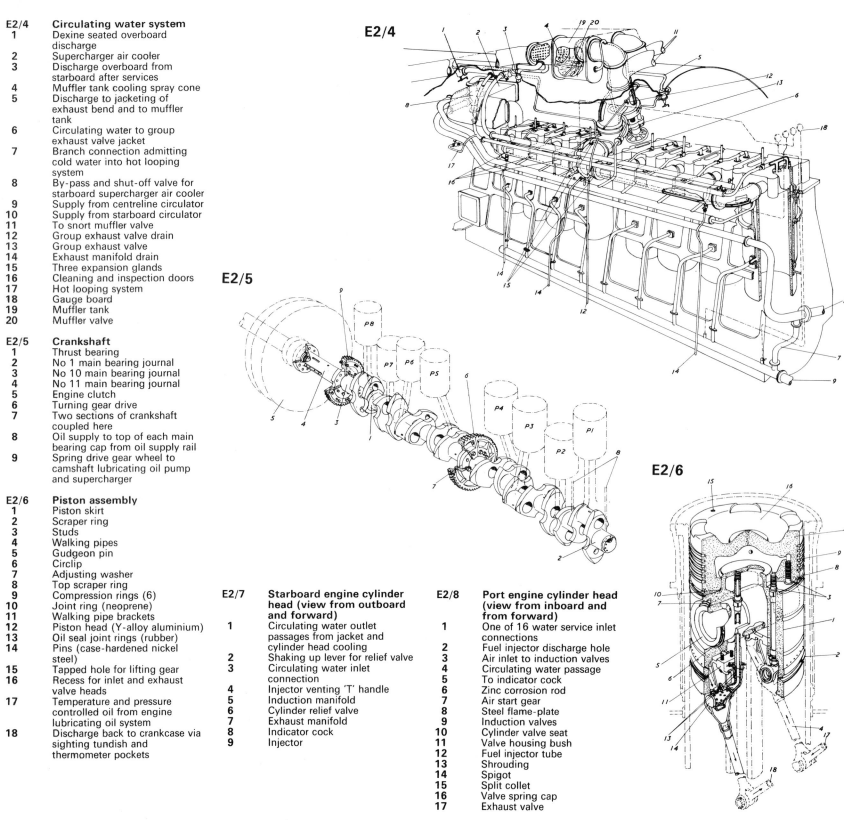

E2/4 Circulating water system

1 Dexine seated overboard discharge
2 Supercharger air cooler
3 Discharge overboard from starboard after services
4 Muffler tank cooling spray cone
5 Discharge to jacketing of exhaust bend and to muffler tank
6 Circulating water to group exhaust valve jacket
7 Branch connection admitting cold water into hot looping system
8 By-pass and shut-off valve for starboard supercharger air cooler
9 Supply from centreline circulator
10 Supply from starboard circulator
11 To snort muffler valve
12 Group exhaust valve drain
13 Group exhaust valve
14 Exhaust manifold drain
15 Three expansion glands
16 Cleaning and inspection doors
17 Hot looping system
18 Gauge board
19 Muffler tank
20 Muffler valve

E2/5 Crankshaft

1 Thrust bearing
2 No 1 main bearing journal
3 No 10 main bearing journal
4 No 11 main bearing journal
5 Engine clutch
6 Turning gear drive
7 Two sections of crankshaft coupled here
8 Oil supply to top of each main bearing cap from oil supply rail
9 Spring drive gear wheel to camshaft lubricating oil pump and supercharger

E2/6 Piston assembly

1 Piston skirt
2 Scraper ring
3 Studs
4 Walking pipes
5 Gudgeon pin
6 Circlip
7 Adjusting washer
8 Top scraper ring
9 Compression rings (6)
10 Joint ring (neoprene)
11 Walking pipe brackets
12 Piston head (Y-alloy aluminium)
13 Oil seal joint rings (rubber)
14 Pins (case-hardened nickel steel)
15 Tapped hole for lifting gear
16 Recess for inlet and exhaust valve heads
17 Temperature and pressure controlled oil from engine lubricating oil system
18 Discharge back to crankcase via sighting tundish and thermometer pockets

E2/4

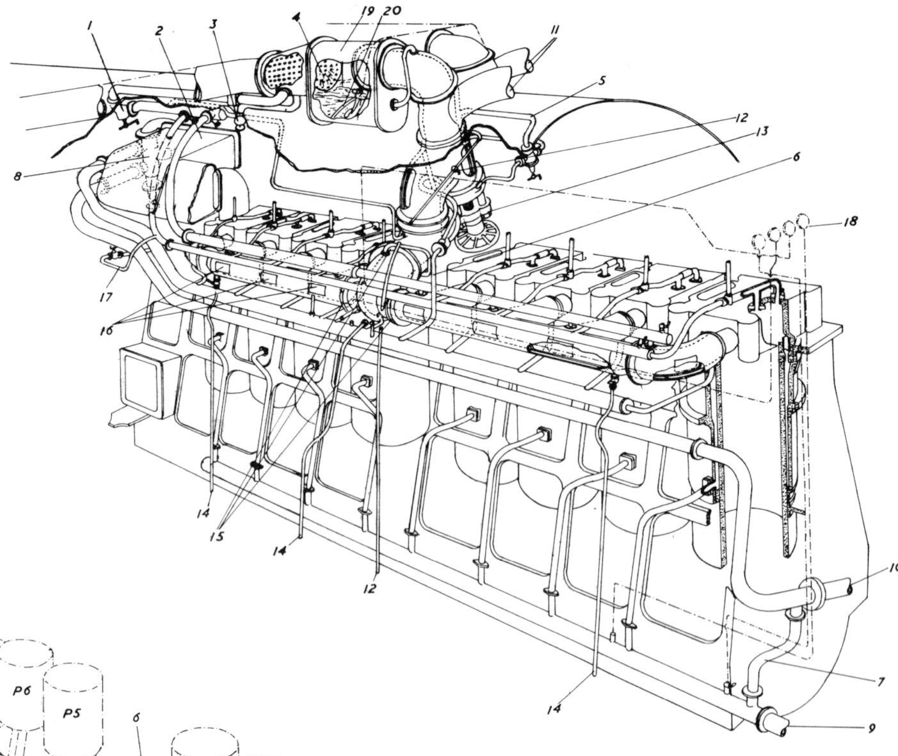

E2/5

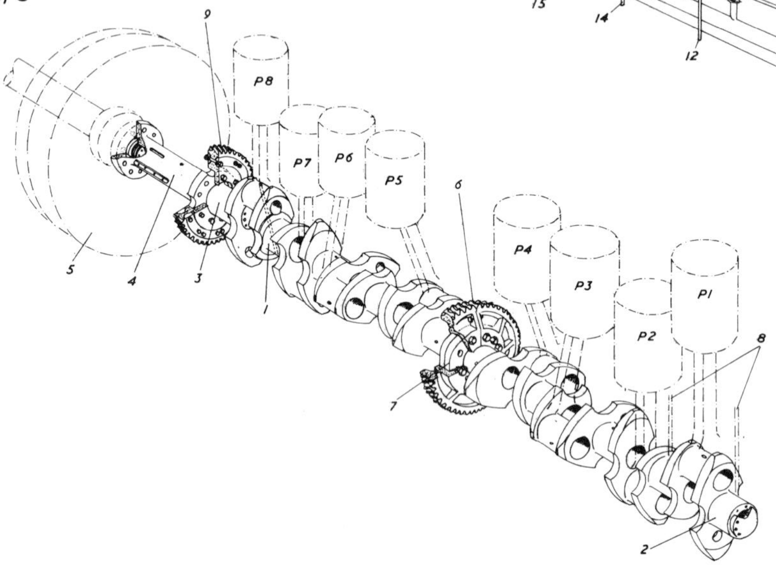

E2/6

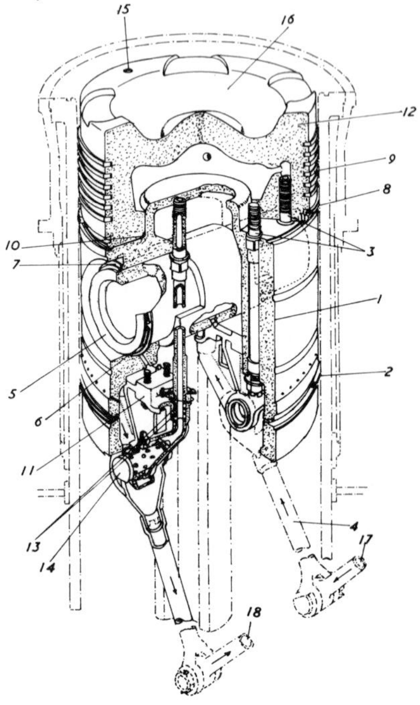

E2/7 Starboard engine cylinder head (view from outboard and forward)

1 Circulating water outlet passages from jacket and cylinder head cooling
2 Shaking up lever for relief valve
3 Circulating water inlet connection
4 Injector venting 'T' handle
5 Induction manifold
6 Cylinder relief valve
7 Exhaust manifold
8 Indicator cock
9 Injector

E2/8 Port engine cylinder head (view from inboard and from forward)

1 One of 16 water service inlet connections
2 Fuel injector discharge hole
3 Air inlet to induction valves
4 Circulating water passage
5 To indicator cock
6 Zinc corrosion rod
7 Air start gear
8 Steel flame-plate
9 Induction valves
10 Cylinder valve seat
11 Valve housing bush
12 Fuel injector tube
13 Shrouding
14 Spigot
15 Split collet
16 Valve spring cap
17 Exhaust valve

E2/7

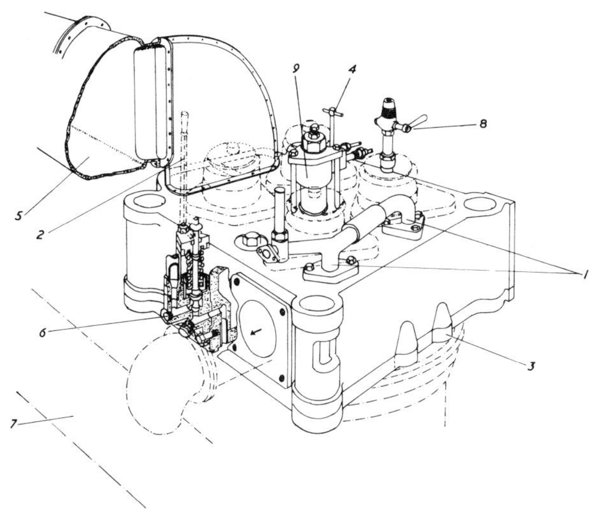

E2/8

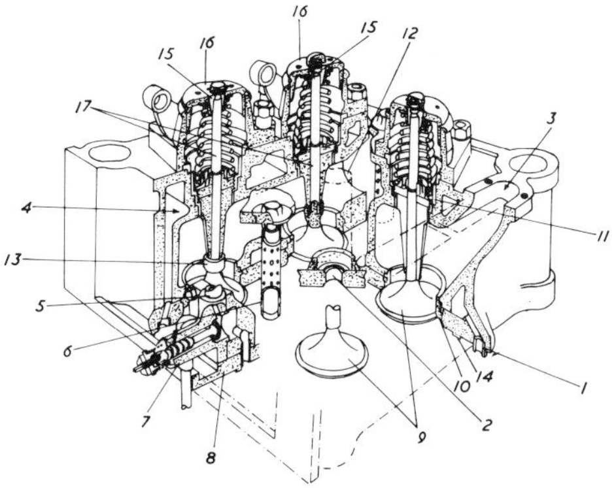

E2/10

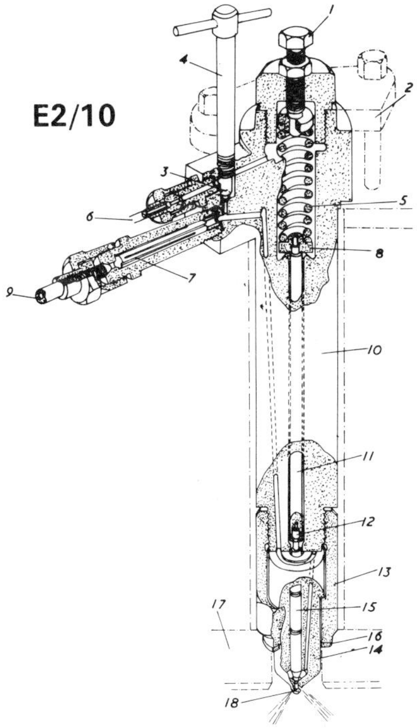

E2/9

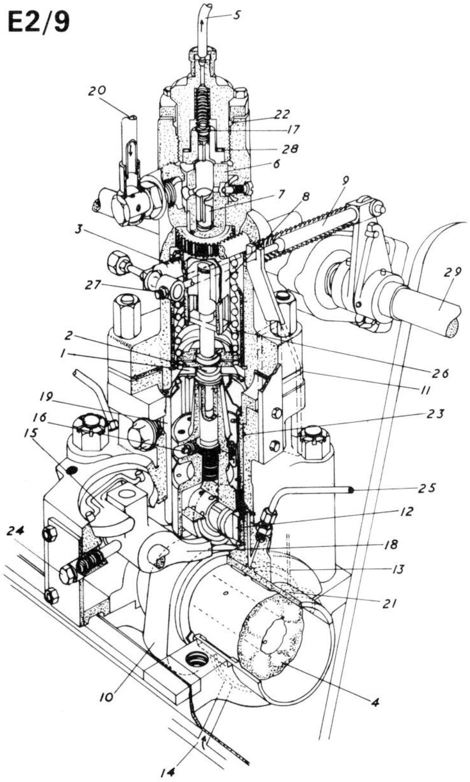

E2/11

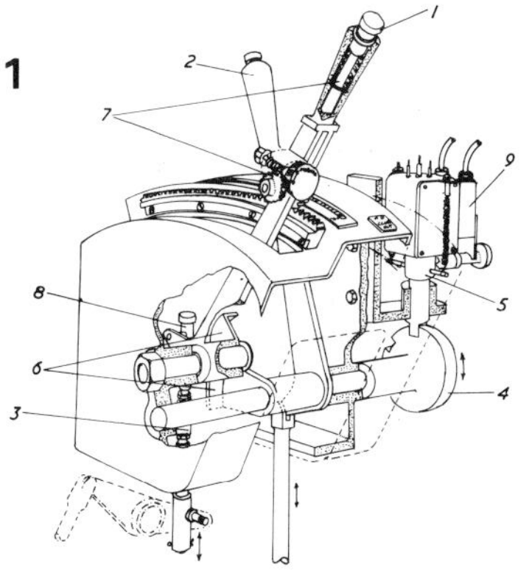

E2/9	**Fuel pump**
1	Oil shield
2	Tappet
3	MM scale
4	Camshaft
5	To injector
6	Pump barrel
7	Pump plunger
8	Control sleeve
9	Actuating rod
10	Fuel pump cam
11	Adjusting liner
12	Tappet roller pin
13	Cam box casing
14	Oil supply camrail
15	Removable horseshoe
16	Adjustment (individual timing)
17	Delivery valve
18	Fuel pump cut-out lever
19	Tappet cylinder liner
20	Fuel supply lead
21	Oil seal ring (felt)
22	Gaco joint ring
23	Joint ring (neoprene)
24	Cut-out lever travel stop
25	Oil supply to valve gear
26	Fuel plunger return ring
27	Adjustment (individual pump output)
28	Hemispherical joint ring (steel)
29	Main operating shaft for all fuel pumps
E2/10	**Fuel injector**
1	Adjusting screw for setting injection pressure at 3200lb per sq in
2	Injector holding down bridge plate
3	Vent valve
4	Venting 'T' Handle
5	Spring
6	Vent pipe led back to drain tank
7	Filter
8	Spring holder
9	Fuel supply pipe from fuel pump
10	Injector body
11	Centre spindle
12	Roller bearing
13	Nozzle holder cap nut
14	Nozzle
15	Needle valve lift
16	Copper asbestos joint ring
17	Bottom of cylinder head flame plate
18	Seven equally spaced holes (135°)
E2/11	**Main engine controls**
1	Fuel lever
2	Clutch lever
3	Adjusting turnbuckle
4	Interlock plate
5	Solenoid operated plunger
6	Clutch to fuel lever interlock
7	Rack and pinion fine adjustment gear disengaged by pulling upwards against spring
8	Spring-loaded drive to fuel pump control shaft
9	Clutch to main motor switchboard interlock gear

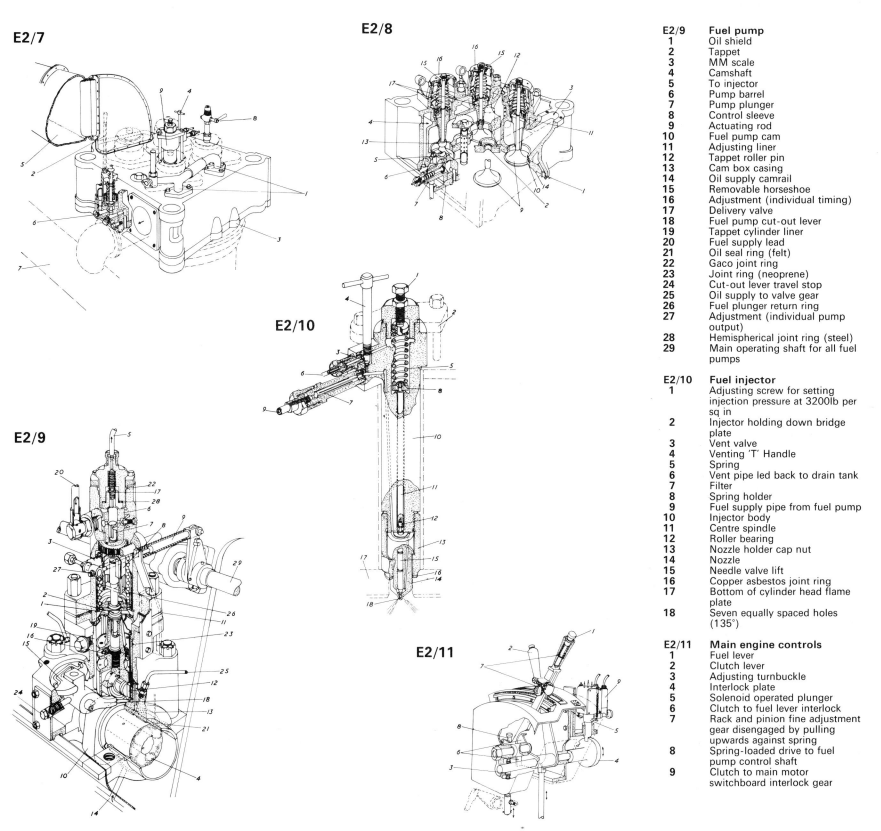

E Machinery

E2/12 Engine frames – port engine

E2/13 Starboard engine

E2/14 Port engine (viewed from aft and outboard)

1 Supercharger seating bracket
2 Geardrive bay
3 Engine frame top plate
4 Bolt plate
5 Vertical sling frame
6 Diaphragm plate
7 No 1 main bearing lower housing
8 Camshaft bearing housing and cam trough (welded integrally with framing)
9 Engine driven lubricating oil pump seating
10 No 11 main bearing lower housing
11 Sections are bolted together; nuts are secured by welding – no keys are fitted between sections

E2/15 Circulating water system in engine room

1 Discharge overboard to muffler tank cooling sprays (port and starboard)
2 By-pass and shut-off valve for starboard supercharger air cooler
3 Connections to emergency circulator
4 After services supply pipe
5 Jacket and cylinder head looping system (port and starboard)
6 Supercharger air cooler and exhaust manifold cooling system
7 Sub pressure pump priming connection
8 Circulating water to main motor bearings and air coolers and to thrust block and stern glands (port and starboard)
9 Main inlet (port and starboard)
10 Weed trap
11 Relief valve
12 Starboard engine
13 Port engine
14 60psi relief
15 Duplex oil cooler
16 Vent and blow connection
17 Running down valve
18 Main circulator (port and starboard)
19 Centreline main circulator
20 Differential pressure gauge
21 Flexible pipe connections
22 To group exhaust valve jacket
23 Exhaust manifold discharge valve
24 Discharge from starboard after services
25 HP air compressor inboard discharge
26 Compensating water master valve
27 Branch connection admitting cold water into hot looping system
28 Cross connection by-pass and shut-off valves
29 Oil fuel compensating water three-valve chest
30 Circulating water discharging forward to air conditioning and refrigerating machinery
31 Control valve for regulating temperature of jacket and cylinder head looping system

E2/16 Aft circulating water system

1 Relief
2 Stern gland
3 Stern gland cock
4 Weed trap
5 Shaft brake
6 Shaft coupling
7 Supply line

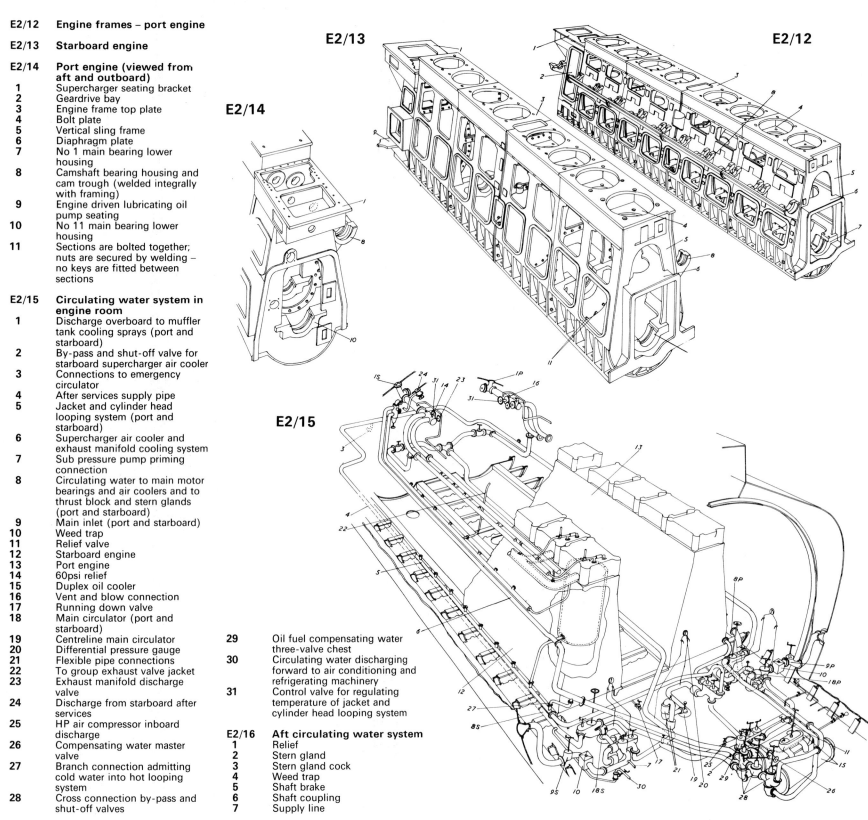

E2/13

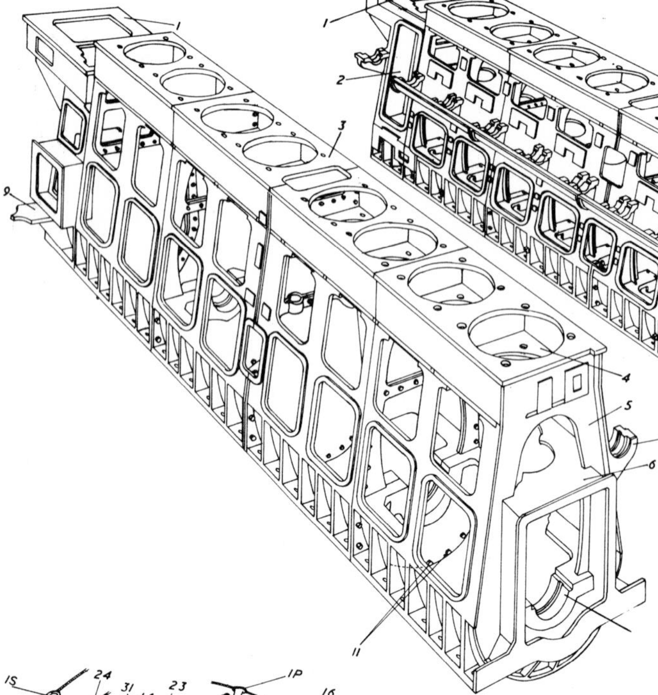

E2/12

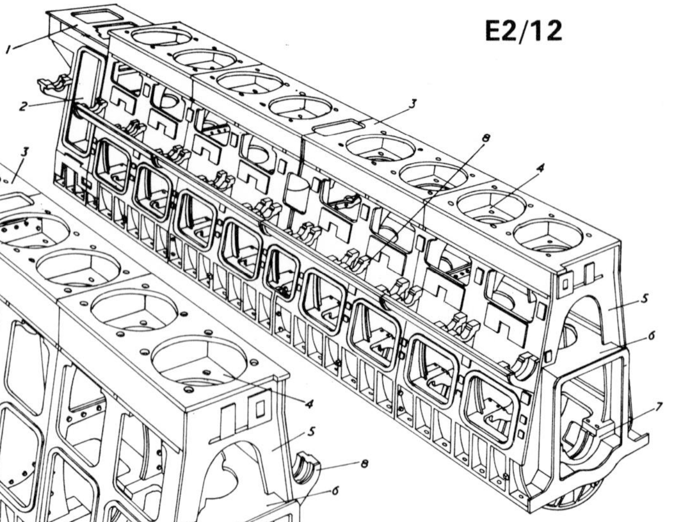

E2/14

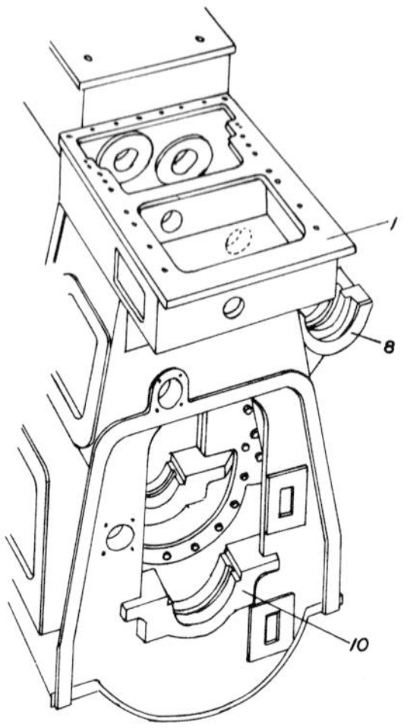

E2/15

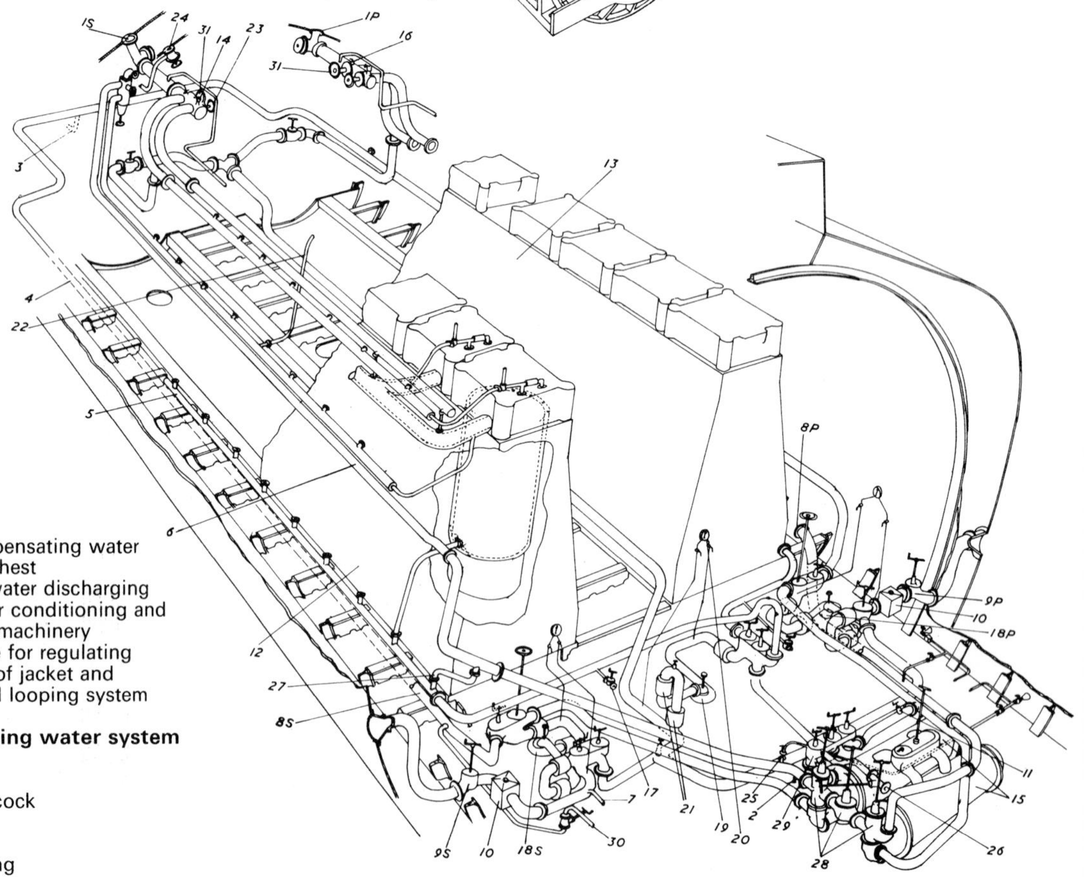

E2/16

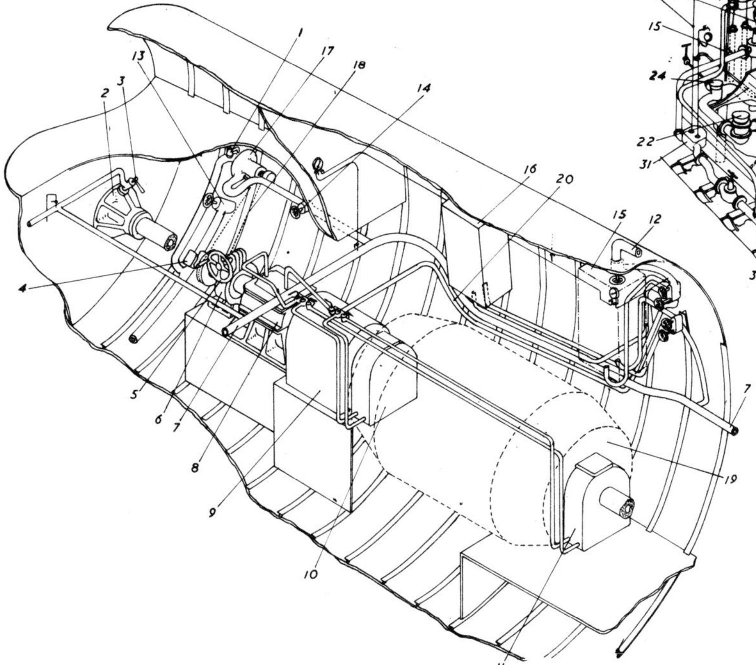

E2/18

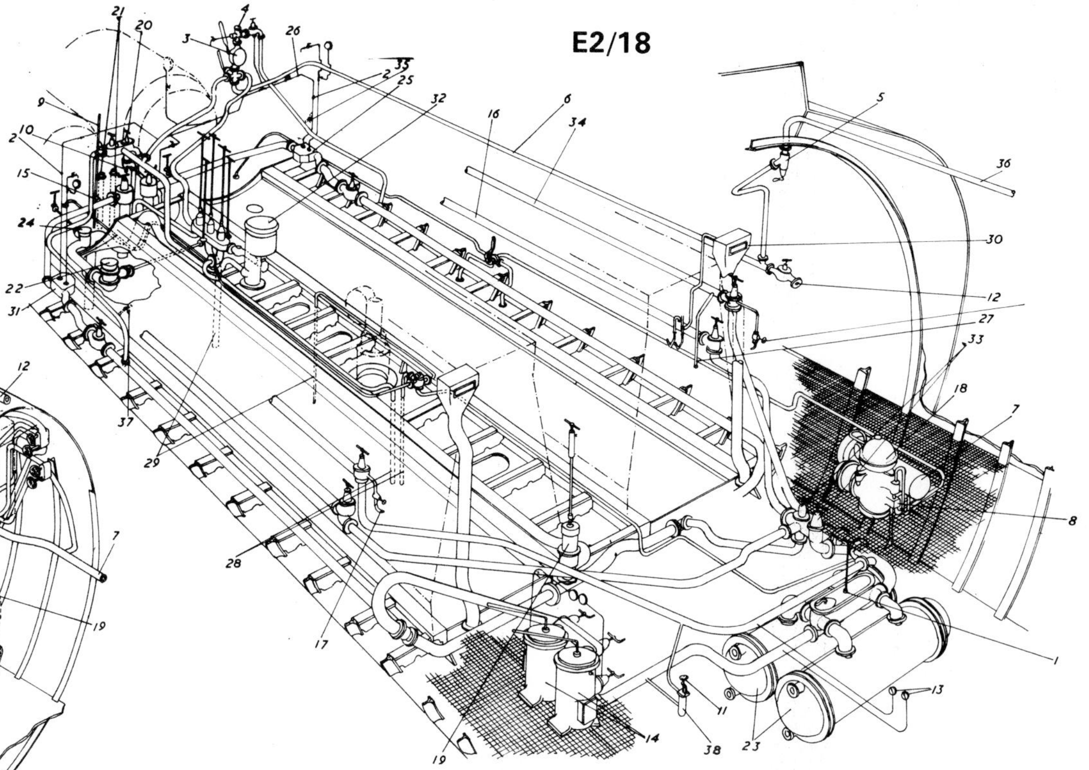

E2/17

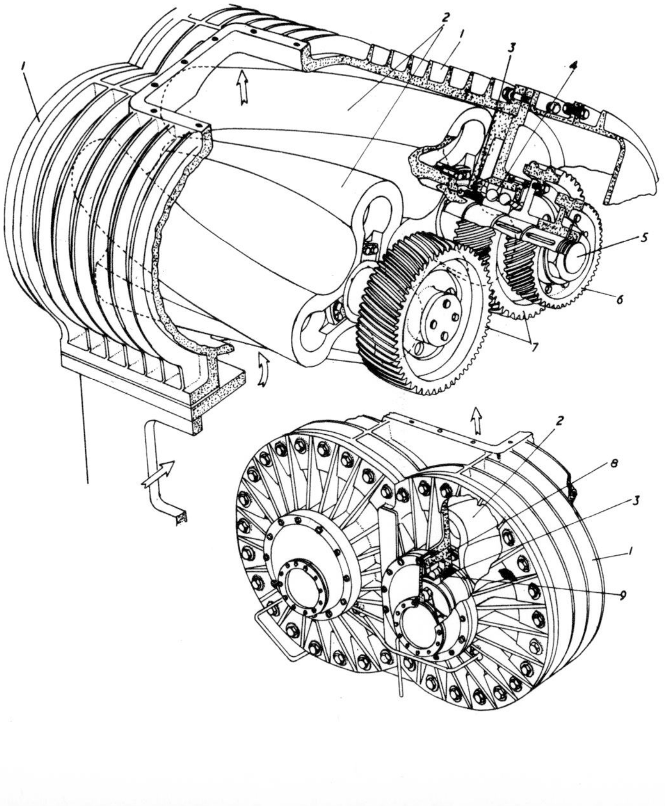

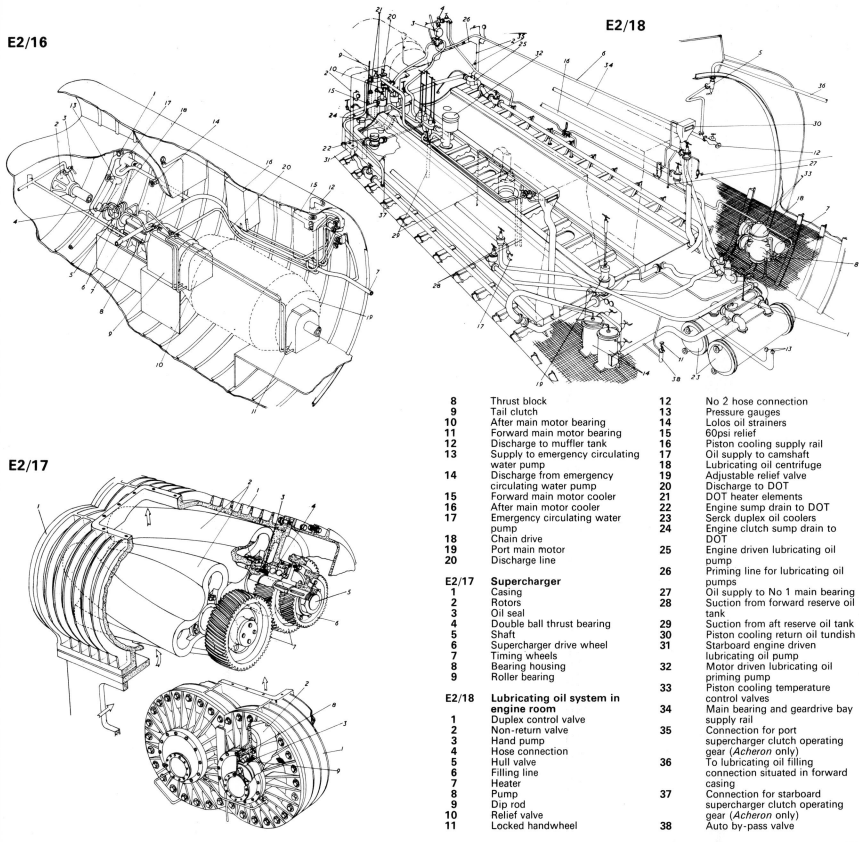

8 Thrust block
9 Tail clutch
10 After main motor bearing
11 Forward main motor bearing
12 Discharge to muffler tank
13 Supply to emergency circulating water pump
14 Discharge from emergency circulating water pump
15 Forward main motor cooler
16 After main motor cooler
17 Emergency circulating water pump
18 Chain drive
19 Port main motor
20 Discharge line

E2/17 Supercharger

1 Casing
2 Rotors
3 Oil seal
4 Double ball thrust bearing
5 Shaft
6 Supercharger drive wheel
7 Timing wheels
8 Bearing housing
9 Roller bearing

E2/18 Lubricating oil system in engine room

1 Duplex control valve
2 Non-return valve
3 Hand pump
4 Hose connection
5 Hull valve
6 Filling line
7 Heater
8 Pump
9 Dip rod
10 Relief valve
11 Locked handwheel
12 No 2 hose connection
13 Pressure gauges
14 Lolos oil strainers
15 60psi relief
16 Piston cooling supply rail
17 Oil supply to camshaft
18 Lubricating oil centrifuge
19 Adjustable relief valve
20 Discharge to DOT
21 DOT heater elements
22 Engine sump drain to DOT
23 Serck duplex oil coolers
24 Engine clutch sump drain to DOT
25 Engine driven lubricating oil pump
26 Priming line for lubricating oil pumps
27 Oil supply to No 1 main bearing
28 Suction from forward reserve oil tank
29 Suction from aft reserve oil tank
30 Piston cooling return oil tundish
31 Starboard engine driven lubricating oil pump
32 Motor driven lubricating oil priming pump
33 Piston cooling temperature control valves
34 Main bearing and geardrive bay supply rail
35 Connection for port supercharger clutch operating gear (*Acheron* only)
36 To lubricating oil filling connection situated in forward casing
37 Connection for starboard supercharger clutch operating gear (*Acheron* only)
38 Auto by-pass valve

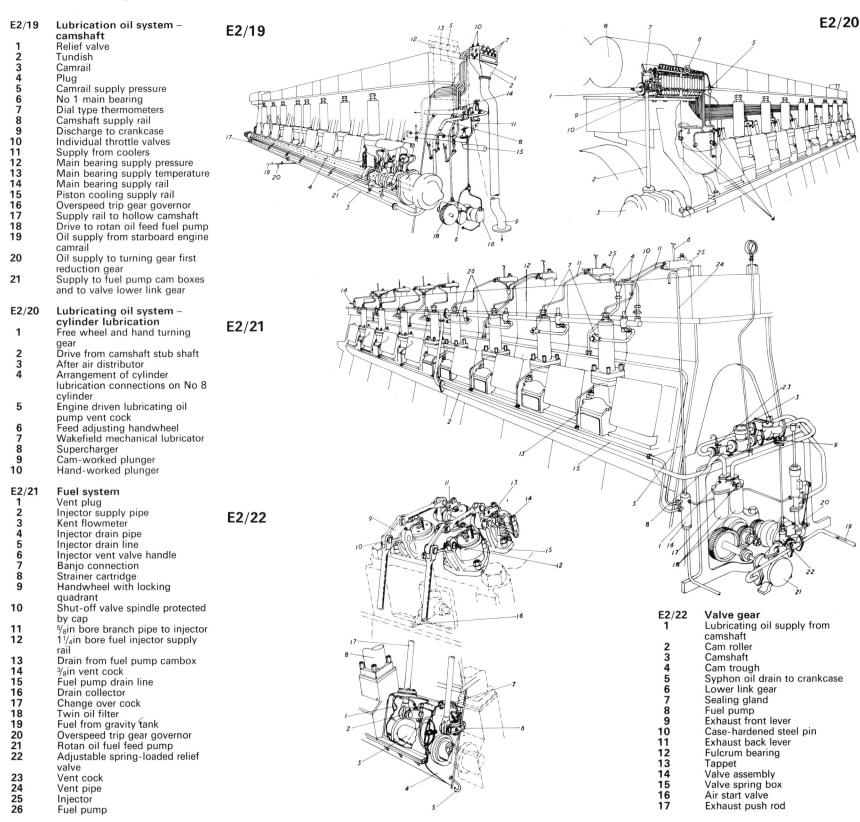

E2/19 Lubrication oil system – camshaft
1 Relief valve
2 Tundish
3 Camrail
4 Plug
5 Camrail supply pressure
6 No 1 main bearing
7 Dial type thermometers
8 Camshaft supply rail
9 Discharge to crankcase
10 Individual throttle valves
11 Supply from coolers
12 Main bearing supply pressure
13 Main bearing supply temperature
14 Main bearing supply rail
15 Piston cooling supply rail
16 Overspeed trip gear governor
17 Supply rail to hollow camshaft
18 Drive to rotan oil feed fuel pump
19 Oil supply from starboard engine camrail
20 Oil supply to turning gear first reduction gear
21 Supply to fuel pump cam boxes and to valve lower link gear

E2/20 Lubricating oil system – cylinder lubrication
1 Free wheel and hand turning gear
2 Drive from camshaft stub shaft
3 After air distributor
4 Arrangement of cylinder lubrication connections on No 8 cylinder
5 Engine driven lubricating oil pump vent cock
6 Feed adjusting handwheel
7 Wakefield mechanical lubricator
8 Supercharger
9 Cam-worked plunger
10 Hand-worked plunger

E2/21 Fuel system
1 Vent plug
2 Injector supply pipe
3 Kent flowmeter
4 Injector drain pipe
5 Injector drain line
6 Injector vent valve handle
7 Banjo connection
8 Strainer cartridge
9 Handwheel with locking quadrant
10 Shut-off valve spindle protected by cap
11 $^5/_8$in bore branch pipe to injector
12 $1^1/_4$in bore fuel injector supply rail
13 Drain from fuel pump cambox
14 $^3/_8$in vent cock
15 Fuel pump drain line
16 Drain collector
17 Change over cock
18 Twin oil filter
19 Fuel from gravity tank
20 Overspeed trip gear governor
21 Rotan oil fuel feed pump
22 Adjustable spring-loaded relief valve
23 Vent cock
24 Vent pipe
25 Injector
26 Fuel pump

E2/19

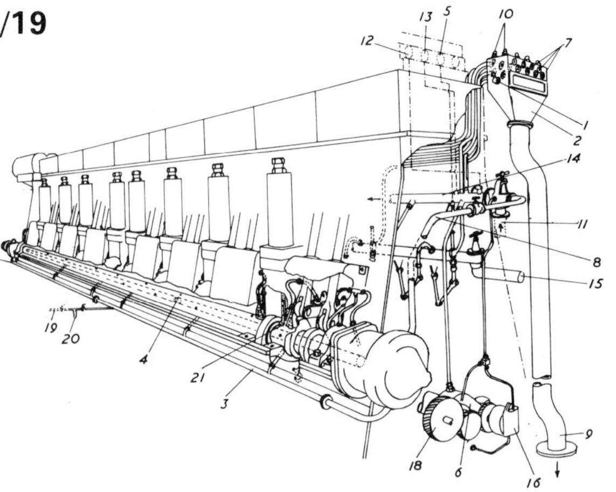

E2/20

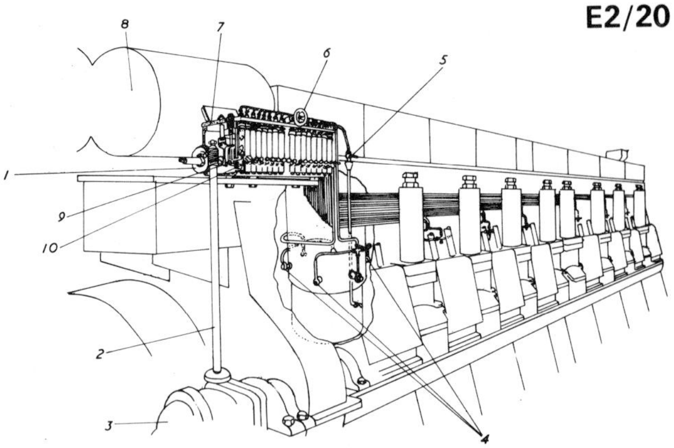

E2/21

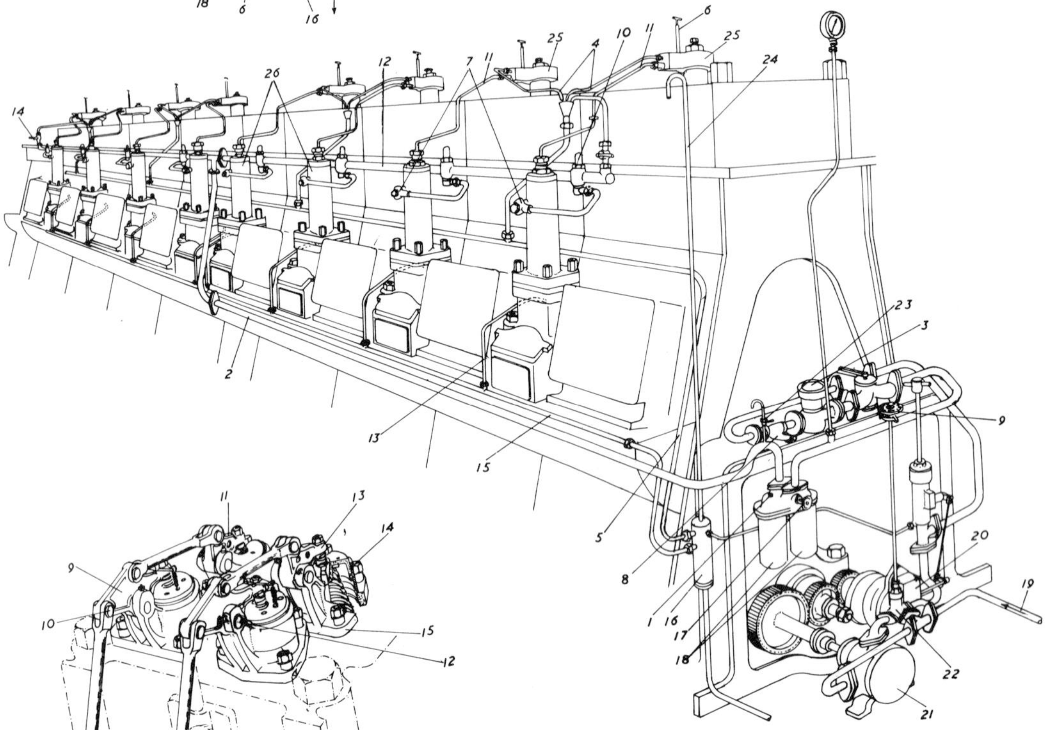

E2/22

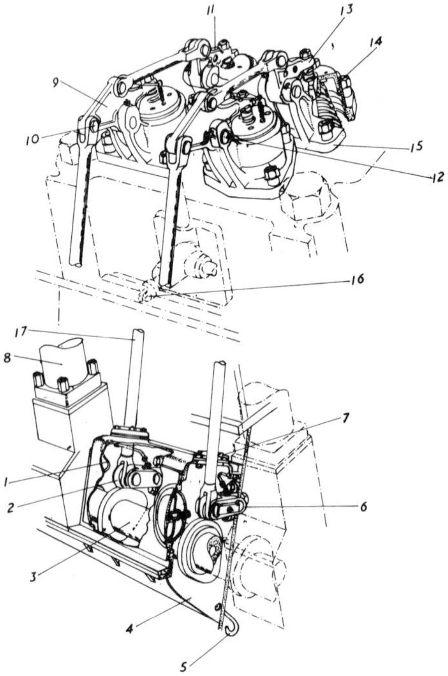

E2/22 Valve gear
1 Lubricating oil supply from camshaft
2 Cam roller
3 Camshaft
4 Cam trough
5 Syphon oil drain to crankcase
6 Lower link gear
7 Sealing gland
8 Fuel pump
9 Exhaust front lever
10 Case-hardened steel pin
11 Exhaust back lever
12 Fulcrum bearing
13 Tappet
14 Valve assembly
15 Valve spring box
16 Air start valve
17 Exhaust push rod

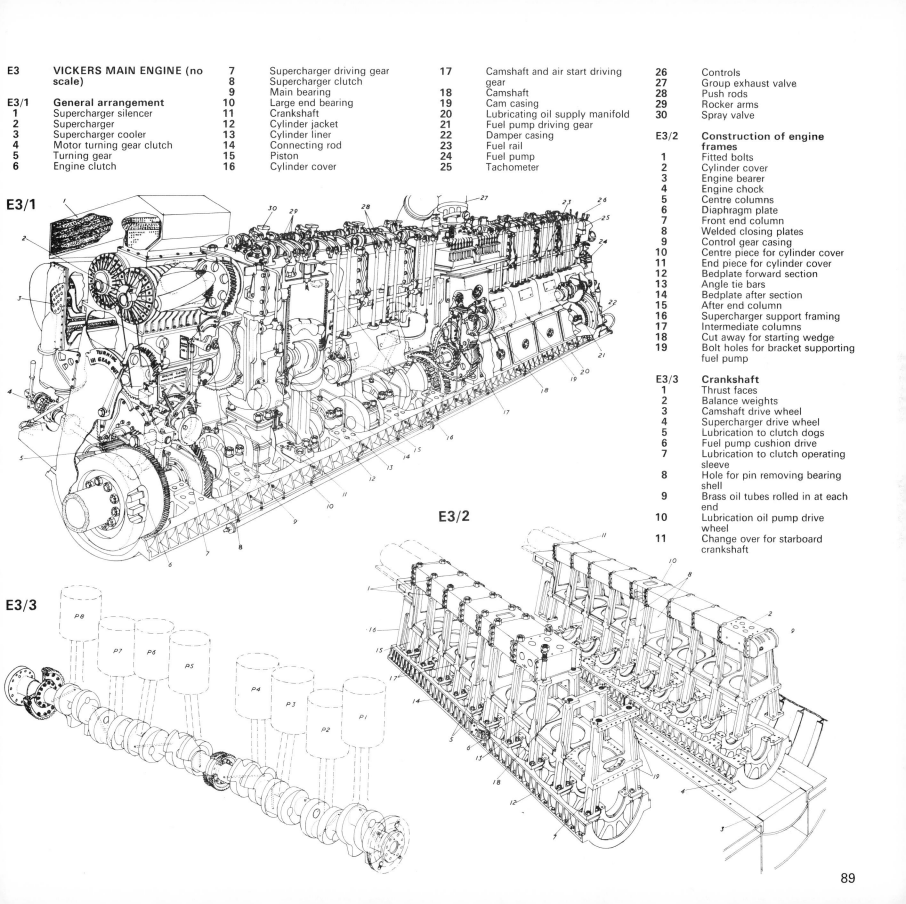

E3 VICKERS MAIN ENGINE (no scale)

E3/1 General arrangement

1 Supercharger silencer
2 Supercharger
3 Supercharger cooler
4 Motor turning gear clutch
5 Turning gear
6 Engine clutch
7 Supercharger driving gear
8 Supercharger clutch
9 Main bearing
10 Large end bearing
11 Crankshaft
12 Cylinder jacket
13 Cylinder liner
14 Connecting rod
15 Piston
16 Cylinder cover
17 Camshaft and air start driving gear
18 Camshaft
19 Cam casing
20 Lubricating oil supply manifold
21 Fuel pump driving gear
22 Damper casing
23 Fuel rail
24 Fuel pump
25 Tachometer
26 Controls
27 Group exhaust valve
28 Push rods
29 Rocker arms
30 Spray valve

E3/2 Construction of engine frames

1 Fitted bolts
2 Cylinder cover
3 Engine bearer
4 Engine chock
5 Centre columns
6 Diaphragm plate
7 Front end column
8 Welded closing plates
9 Control gear casing
10 Centre piece for cylinder cover
11 End piece for cylinder cover
12 Bedplate forward section
13 Angle tie bars
14 Bedplate after section
15 After end column
16 Supercharger support framing
17 Intermediate columns
18 Cut away for starting wedge
19 Bolt holes for bracket supporting fuel pump

E3/3 Crankshaft

1 Thrust faces
2 Balance weights
3 Camshaft drive wheel
4 Supercharger drive wheel
5 Lubrication to clutch dogs
6 Fuel pump cushion drive
7 Lubrication to clutch operating sleeve
8 Hole for pin removing bearing shell
9 Brass oil tubes rolled in at each end
10 Lubrication oil pump drive wheel
11 Change over for starboard crankshaft

E3/1

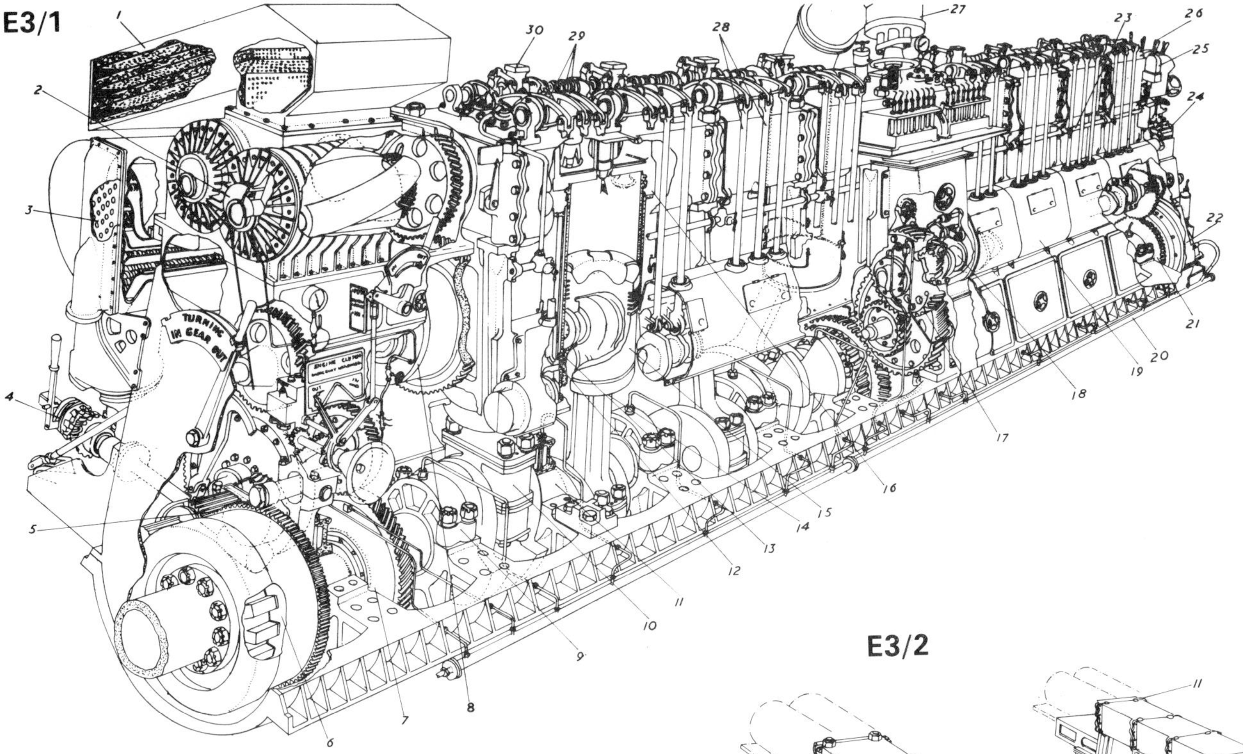

E3/2

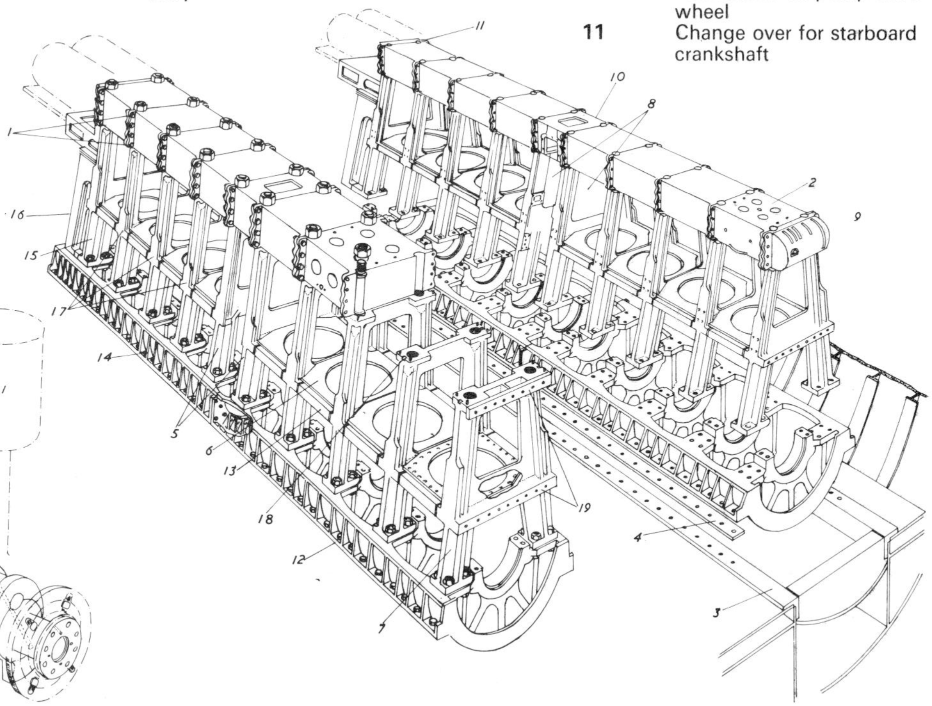

E3/3

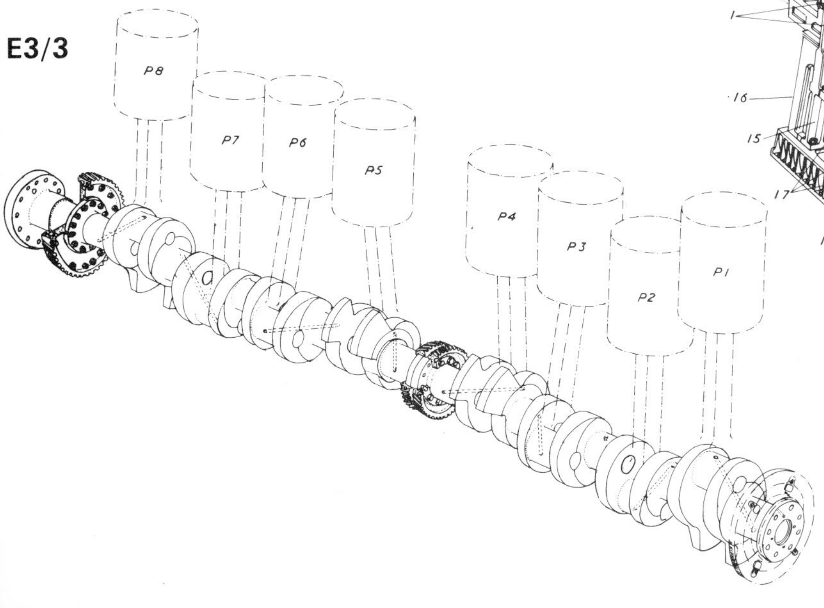

E3/4 Circulating water system

1 Discharge to muffler tank
2 Supercharger cooler
3 To after services
4 From after services
5 Supply from pump
6 Cylinder liner
7 Jacket
8 Cylinder flange
9 Cylinder cover
10 Exhaust valve boxes
11 Group exhaust valve

E3/5 Oil fuel system in engine room

1 Flowmeter
2 Strainer
3 By-pass cocks
4 To engine fuel pump
5 Amal pump
6 Air vessel
7 Booster pump
8 Drain tank
9 Measuring vessel
10 Supply to centrifuge
11 Snap tank gauge glass
12 Valve chest
13 Centrifuge
14 Hand pump
15 Snap tank
16 Vent pipe
17 Cock chest
18 Drain
19 To bucket
20 Main drain tank
21 Water discharge from centrifuge
22 Booster by-pass and shut-off cock
23 Hand priming pump suction
24 Oil fuel gravity tank
25 Float-operated valve
26 Tank inlet cock
27 From oil fuel groups
28 Water sighting gauge glass
29 Fuel discharge from centrifuge
30 Leak off drains from engines
31 Lolos strainer

E3/6 Fuel spray valve

1 Fuel inlet
2 Nozzle
3 Nozzle nut
4 Ground joint
5 Strainer
6 Gland sleeve
7 Valve spindle
8 Tappet lever
9 Tappet roller
10 Tappet lever spring
11 Ram sleeve securing ring
12 Eccentric pin
13 Gland sleeve nut
14 Vent and leak offs
15 Body
16 Indicator spindle
17 Indicator guide
18 Indicator bracket
19 Indicator tappet
20 Indicator plunger
21 Clamp ring
22 Micrometer
23 Locking screw
24 Indicator sleeve
25 Ram sleeve
26 Ram
27 Oil box
28 Ram strainer
29 Top cap
30 Dexine ring
31 HP joint ring
32 Ram gland
33 Spring
34 Guide
35 Tappet
36 Bush

E3/4

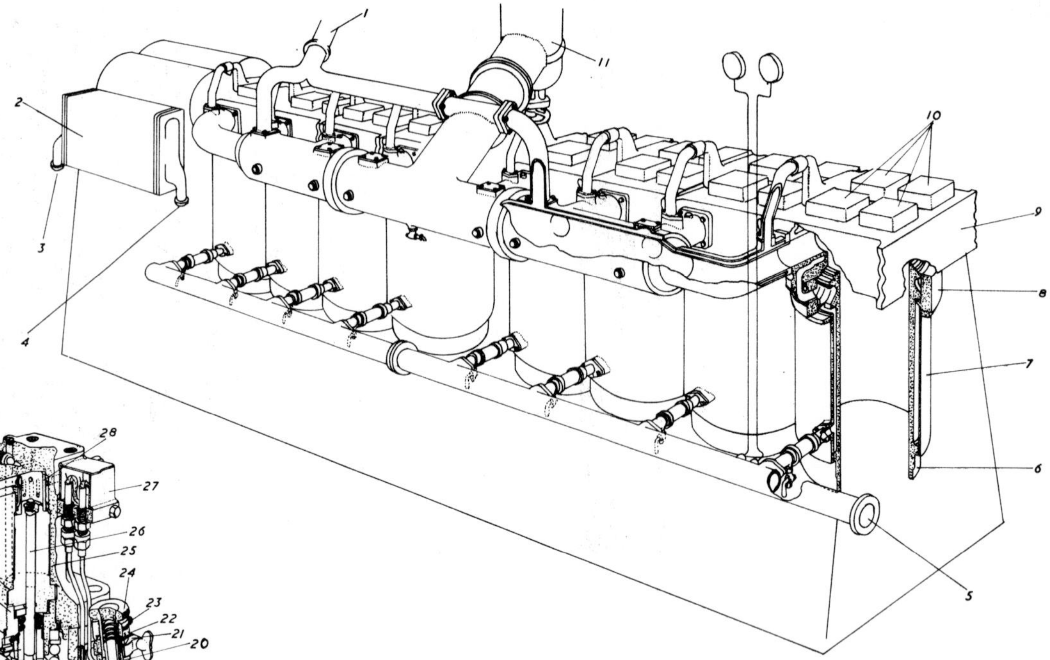

E3/6

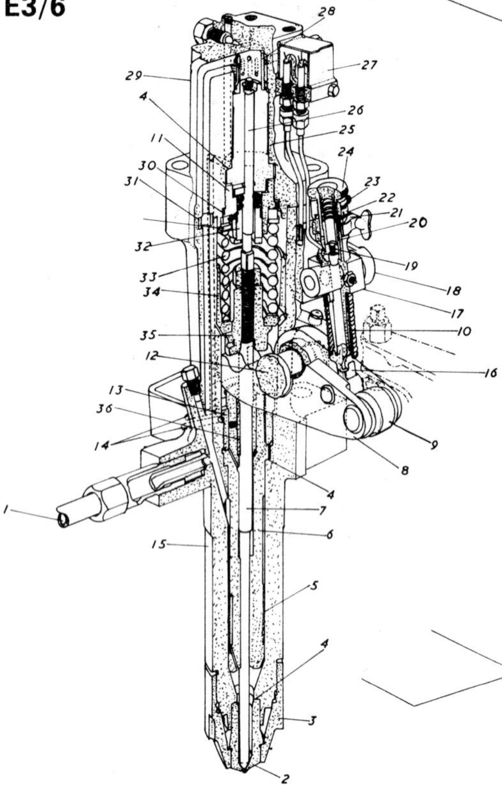

E3/5

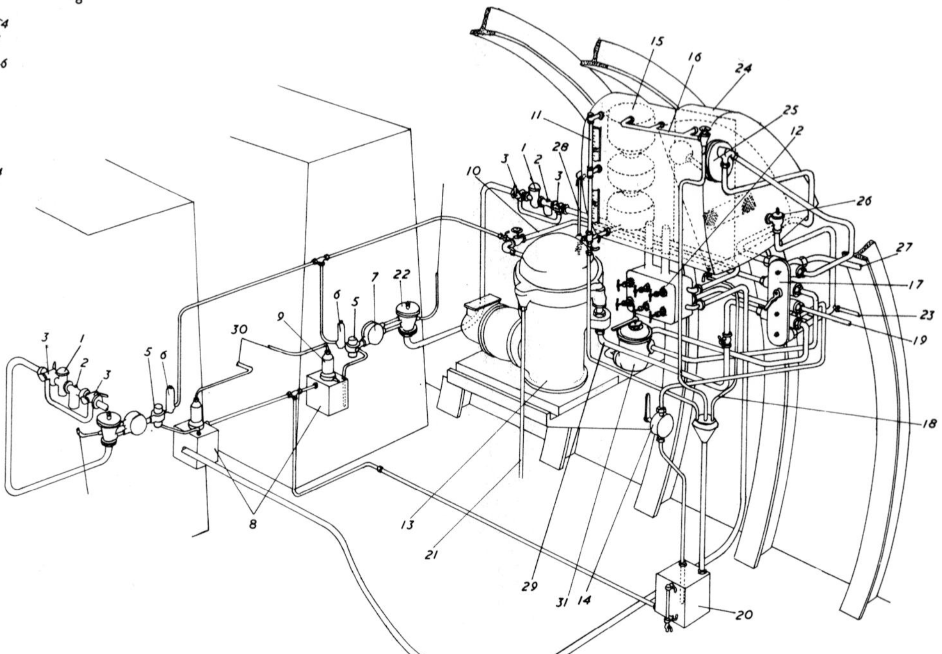

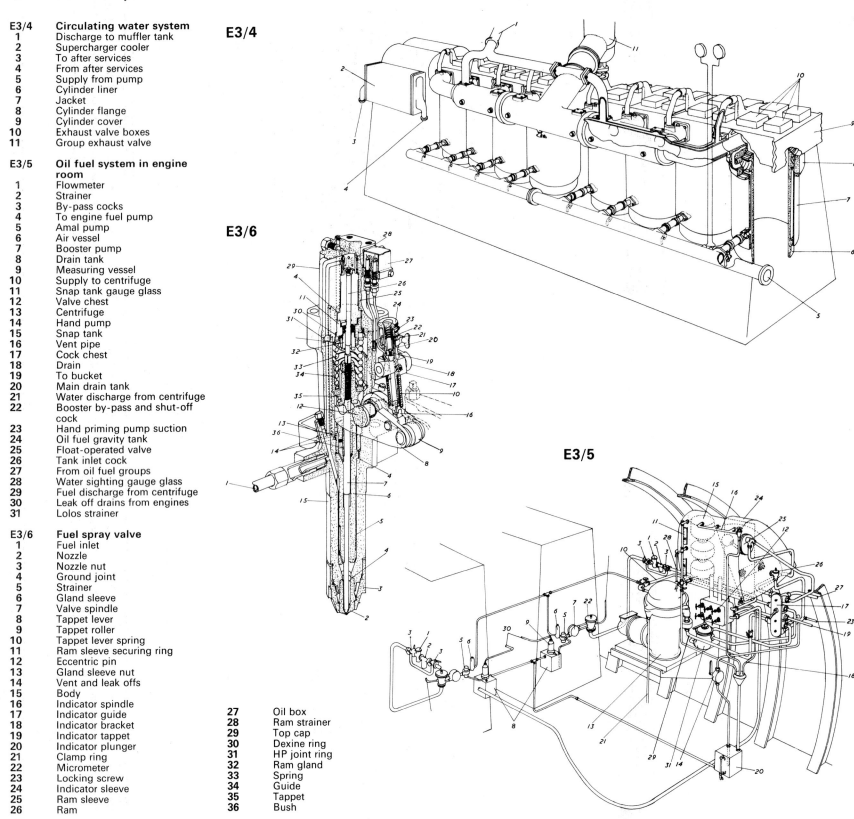

E3/7

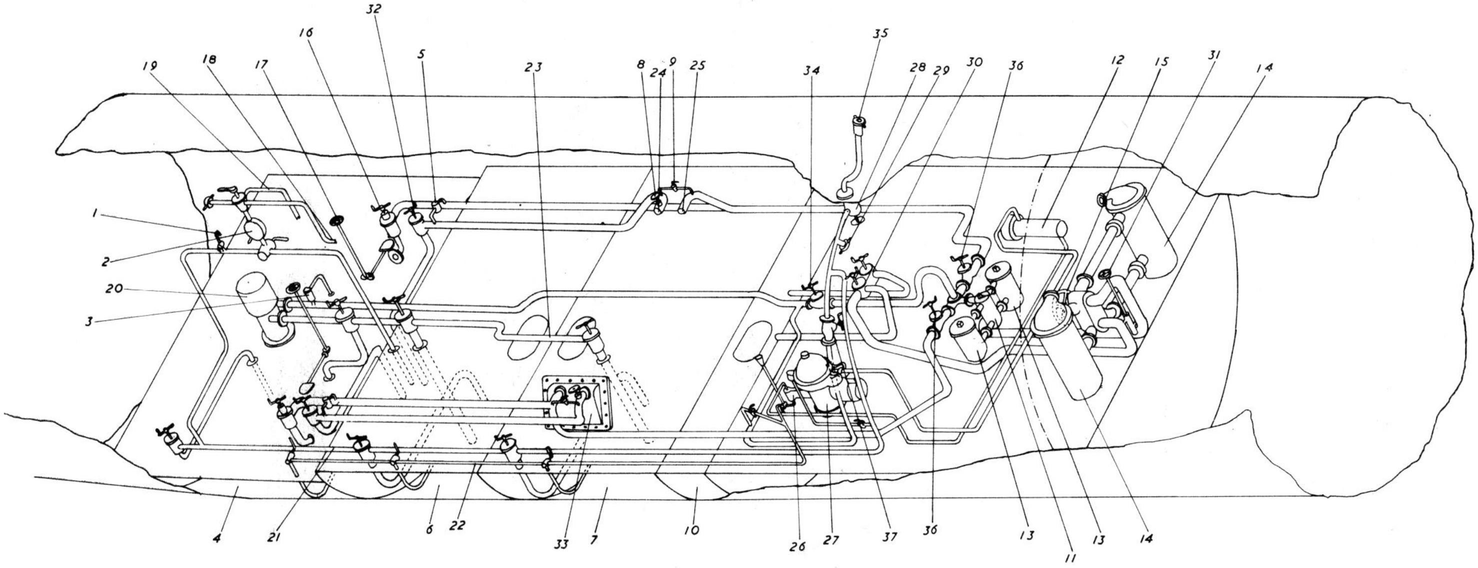

E3/8

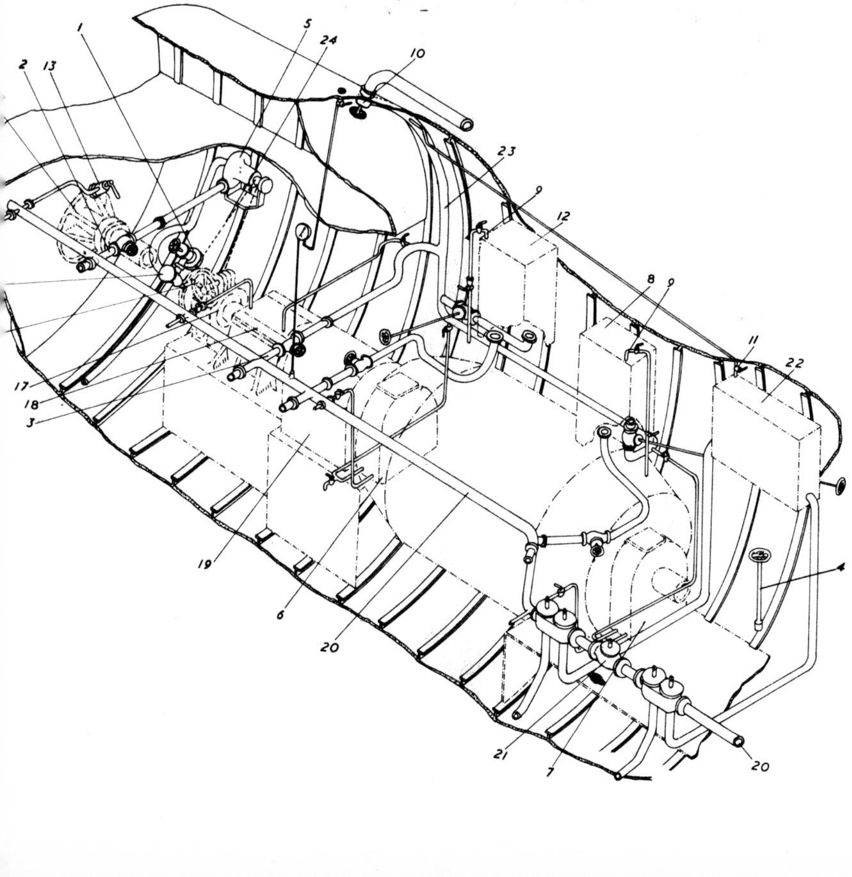

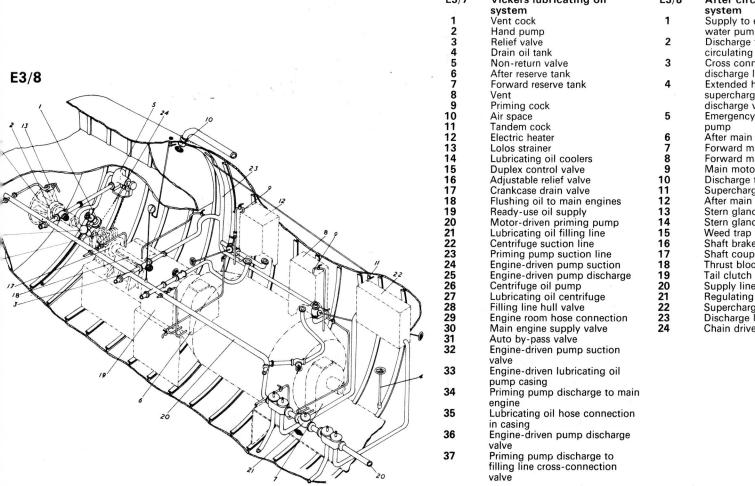

E3/7 Vickers lubricating oil system

1 Vent cock
2 Hand pump
3 Relief valve
4 Drain oil tank
5 Non-return valve
6 After reserve tank
7 Forward reserve tank
8 Vent
9 Priming cock
10 Air space
11 Tandem cock
12 Electric heater
13 Lolos strainer
14 Lubricating oil coolers
15 Duplex control valve
16 Adjustable relief valve
17 Crankcase drain valve
18 Flushing oil to main engines
19 Ready-use oil supply
20 Motor-driven priming pump
21 Lubricating oil filling line
22 Centrifuge suction line
23 Priming pump suction line
24 Engine-driven pump suction
25 Engine-driven pump discharge
26 Centrifuge oil pump
27 Lubricating oil centrifuge
28 Filling line hull valve
29 Engine room hose connection
30 Main engine supply valve
31 Auto by-pass valve
32 Engine-driven pump suction valve
33 Engine-driven lubricating oil pump casing
34 Priming pump discharge to main engine
35 Lubricating oil hose connection in casing
36 Engine-driven pump discharge valve
37 Priming pump discharge to filling line cross-connection valve

E3/8 After circulating water system

1 Supply to emergency circulating water pump
2 Discharge from emergency circulating water pump
3 Cross connection supply to discharge line
4 Extended handwheel for superchargers supply and discharge valves
5 Emergency circulating water pump
6 After main motor bearing
7 Forward main motor bearing
8 Forward main motor cooler
9 Main motor cooler vents
10 Discharge to muffler tank
11 Supercharger cooler vent
12 After main motor cooler
13 Stern gland cock
14 Stern gland
15 Weed trap
16 Shaft brake
17 Shaft coupling
18 Thrust block
19 Tail clutch
20 Supply line
21 Regulating valve
22 Supercharger cooler
23 Discharge line
24 Chain drive

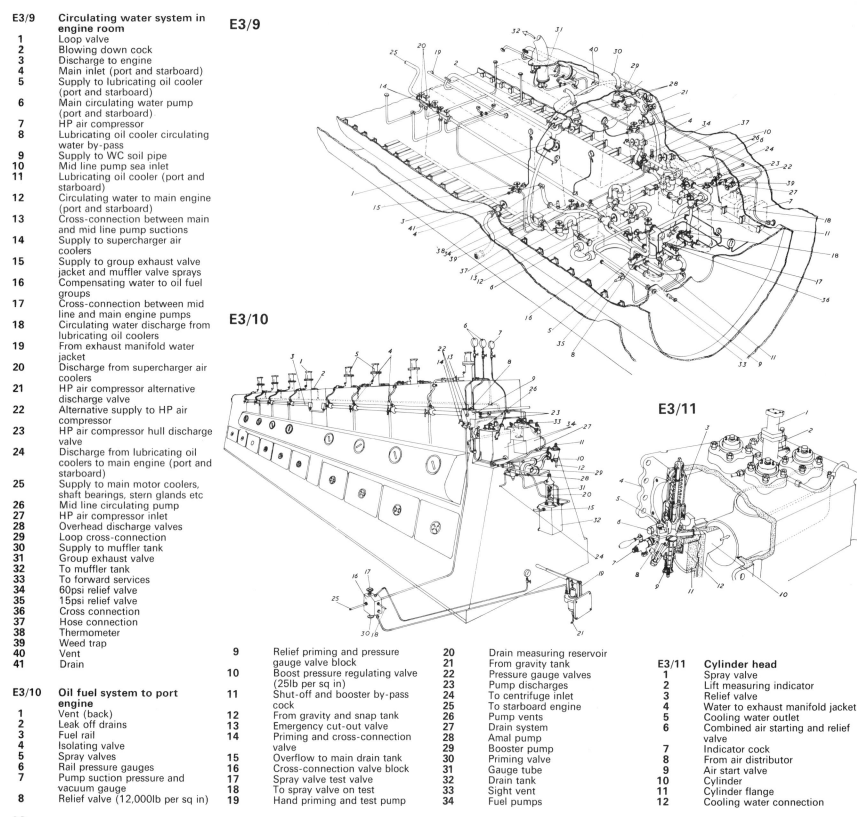

E3/9 Circulating water system in engine room

1 Loop valve
2 Blowing down cock
3 Discharge to engine
4 Main inlet (port and starboard)
5 Supply to lubricating oil cooler (port and starboard)
6 Main circulating water pump (port and starboard)
7 HP air compressor
8 Lubricating oil cooler circulating water by-pass
9 Supply to WC soil pipe
10 Mid line pump sea inlet
11 Lubricating oil cooler (port and starboard)
12 Circulating water to main engine (port and starboard)
13 Cross-connection between main and mid line pump suctions
14 Supply to supercharger air coolers
15 Supply to group exhaust valve jacket and muffler valve sprays
16 Compensating water to oil fuel groups
17 Cross-connection between mid line and main engine pumps
18 Circulating water discharge from lubricating oil coolers
19 From exhaust manifold water jacket
20 Discharge from supercharger air coolers
21 HP air compressor alternative discharge valve
22 Alternative supply to HP air compressor
23 HP air compressor hull discharge valve
24 Discharge from lubricating oil coolers to main engine (port and starboard)
25 Supply to main motor coolers, shaft bearings, stern glands etc
26 Mid line circulating pump
27 HP air compressor inlet
28 Overhead discharge valves
29 Loop cross-connection
30 Supply to muffler tank
31 Group exhaust valve
32 To muffler tank
33 To forward services
34 60psi relief valve
35 15psi relief valve
36 Cross connection
37 Hose connection
38 Thermometer
39 Weed trap
40 Vent
41 Drain

E3/9

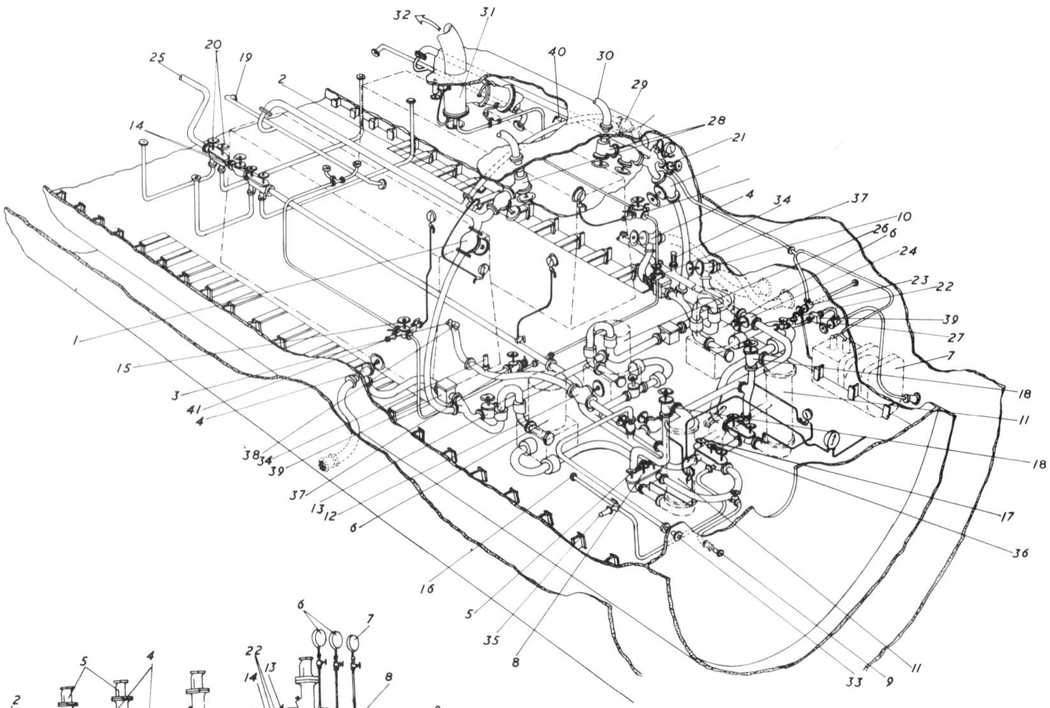

E3/10

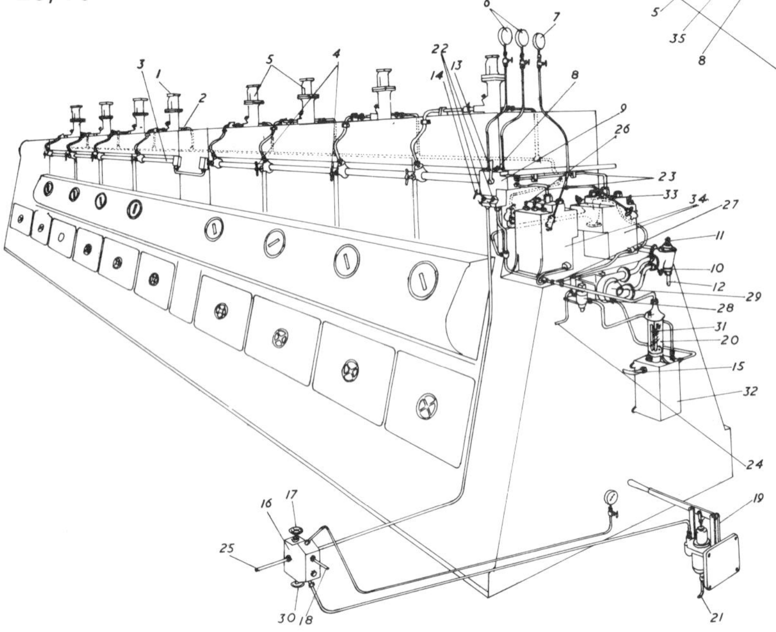

E3/11

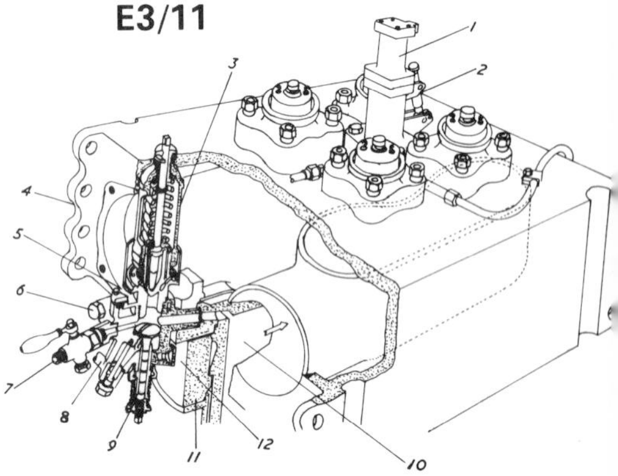

E3/10 Oil fuel system to port engine

1 Vent (back)
2 Leak off drains
3 Fuel rail
4 Isolating valve
5 Spray valves
6 Rail pressure gauges
7 Pump suction pressure and vacuum gauge
8 Relief valve (12,000lb per sq in)
9 Relief priming and pressure gauge valve block
10 Boost pressure regulating valve (25lb per sq in)
11 Shut-off and booster by-pass cock
12 From gravity and snap tank
13 Emergency cut-out valve
14 Priming and cross-connection valve
15 Overflow to main drain tank
16 Cross-connection valve block
17 Spray valve test valve
18 To spray valve on test
19 Hand priming and test pump
20 Drain measuring reservoir
21 From gravity tank
22 Pressure gauge valves
23 Pump discharges
24 To centrifuge inlet
25 To starboard engine
26 Pump vents
27 Drain system
28 Amal pump
29 Booster pump
30 Priming valve
31 Gauge tube
32 Drain tank
33 Sight vent
34 Fuel pumps

E3/11 Cylinder head

1 Spray valve
2 Lift measuring indicator
3 Relief valve
4 Water to exhaust manifold jacket
5 Cooling water outlet
6 Combined air starting and relief valve
7 Indicator cock
8 From air distributor
9 Air start valve
10 Cylinder
11 Cylinder flange
12 Cooling water connection

E3/12

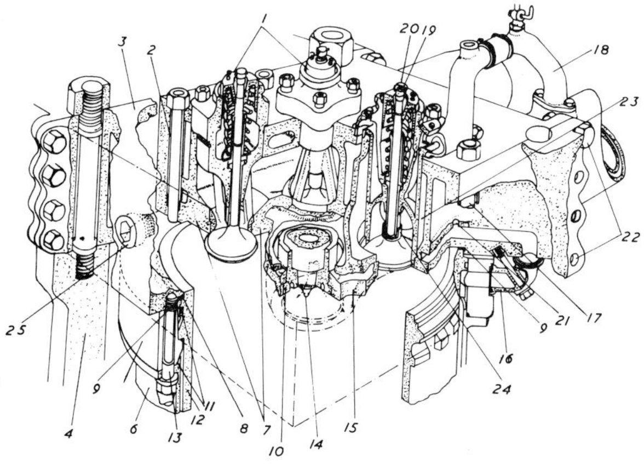

E3/13

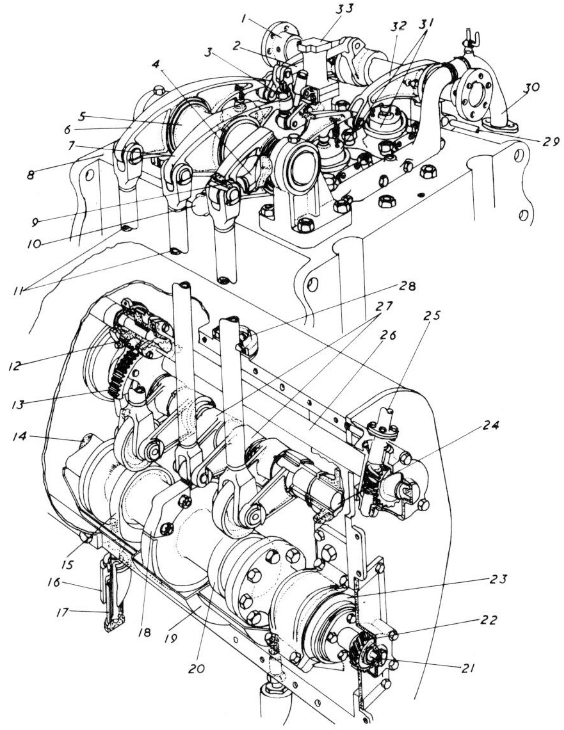

E3/14

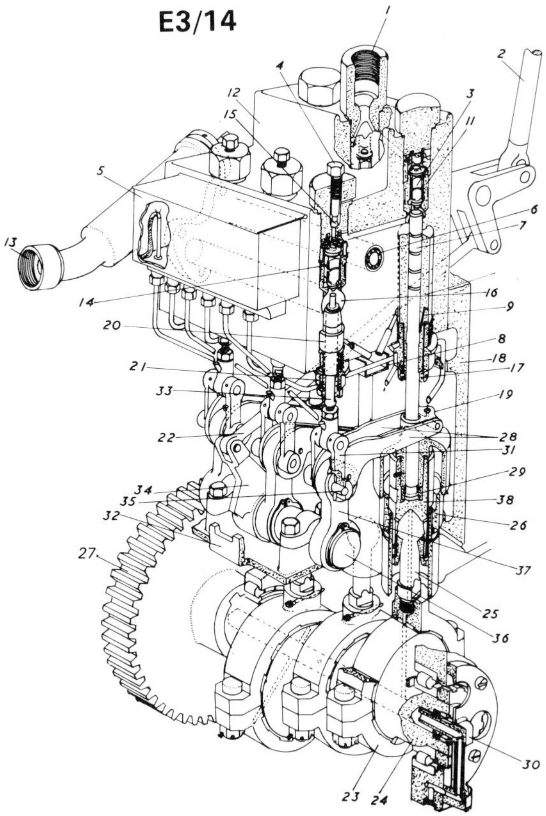

E3/12	**Cylinder head (cutaway)**
1	Induction valves
2	Through bolt tubes
3	Cover casting
4	Engine column
5	Cylinder flange
6	Cylinder jacket
7	Induction port
8	Gas joint ring
9	Welded insert
10	Spray valve tube
11	Cylinder flange joints
12	Cylinder liner
13	Flange supporting stud
14	Spray valve nozzle
15	Combustion plate
16	Elbow connection
17	Flange supporting bolts
18	Water outlet connection
19	Adjusting discs
20	Exhaust valve
21	Vent hole
22	Fitted bolts
23	Exhaust port
24	Shroud
25	Core plug

E3/13	**Valve gear**
1	Spray valve control shaft
2	Spray valve control link
3	Spray valve tappet
4	Spray valve lever toe piece
5	Upper fulcrum shaft
6	Induction valve front lever
7	Spray valve lever
8	Cylinder cover
9	32 needle rollers
10	Spray valve lever buffer
11	Push rods
12	Timing shaft spur wheel
13	Fulcrum shaft quadrant
14	Camshaft
15	Induction cam
16	Support welded onto front of crankcase
17	Camcase drain trap
18	Fuel cam toe piece
19	Oil tray
20	Exhaust cam
21	For portable tachometer
22	Tachometer drive
23	Camshaft bearing
24	Lower fulcrum shaft
25	To timing control
26	Timing shaft
27	Spray valve radius links
28	Push rod gland
29	Supercharger clutch operating rod
30	Circulating water outlet
31	Exhaust valves
32	Exhaust valve back lever
33	Spray valve

E3/14	**Vickers fuel pump**
1	Pump discharge to common rail
2	Control rod
3	Discharge valves
4	Vent screw
5	Oil box
6	Strainer
7	Plunger
8	Drip tray
9	Leak off
10	Valve housing
11	Plunger sleeve
12	Pump body
13	Fuel inlet
14	Suction valves
15	Vent valve
16	Suction passage
17	Plunger gland
18	Pump bracket
19	Plunger crosshead
20	Tappet guide
21	Tappet gland
22	Control link
23	Eccentric strap
24	Eccentric shaft
25	Connecting rod
26	Guide sleeve
27	Drive wheel
28	Crosshead lever
29	Plunger ring
30	Lubricating oil connection
31	Eccentric link
32	Stop for toe piece
33	Suction valve tappet
34	Eccentric control shaft lever
35	Crosshead lever eccentric
36	Eccentric control shaft
37	Control shaft lever
38	Connecting rod guide

E3/15 Vickers engine controls

1 Valve lever fulcrum shaft
2 Main motor solenoid interlock
3 Tappet lever eccentric
4 Lift measuring indicator
5 Timing control locking wheel
6 Timing shaft worm drive
7 Lower fulcrum shaft
8 Lower fulcrum shaft quadrant
9 Induction valve push rod
10 Exhaust valve push rod
11 Timing shaft gear wheel
12 Spray valve lever buffer
13 Handlever fine adjustment
14 Handlever quadrant
15 Fuel pump control shaft
16 Bevel wheel bearing shaft
17 Spray valve push rod
18 Fuel pump control handlever
19 Worm shaft bevel wheel
20 Spray valve lever
21 Timing worm shaft
22 Timing indicator shaft
23 Camshaft
24 Timing shaft
25 Sliding nut
26 Needle rollers
27 Solenoid shaft
28 Spray valve
29 Timing pointer
30 Tappet lever
31 Tappet
32 Spray valve control connecting link
33 Indicator shaft bevel wheel
34 Supercharger air start interlock lever
35 Fuel roller links on eccentrics on fulcrum shaft
36 Air shaft handlever
37 Engine clutch handlever
38 Spray valve control shaft
39 Spray valve control link
40 Supercharger clutch operating link
41 Supercharger clutch operating lever
42 Automatic induction valve operating lever
43 Supercharger clutch control shaft
44 Engine clutch control shaft
45 Supercharger clutch handlever
46 Handlever locking spindle
47 Engine clutch operating rod
48 Spray valve control handlever

E4 MAIN MOTORS (no scale)

E4/1 General arrangement of propulsion equipment

1 Main batteries
2 Main engine
3 Engine clutch
4 Main motor
5 Tail clutch
6 Propeller

E4/2 External view of main motors

1 Main terminals
2 Shunt coil terminal cover
3 Holes in which jacking tools engage
4 Holes for lifting stirrup securing bolts
5 Forward cradle
6 Holes for jacking tool securing bolts
7 Heater connections
8 Forward adjustable pedestal
9 After cradle
10 Cradle bolts
11 Cradle bolt dowel
12 Pedestal shoe
13 After adjustable pedestal
14 Screw wedges

E3/15

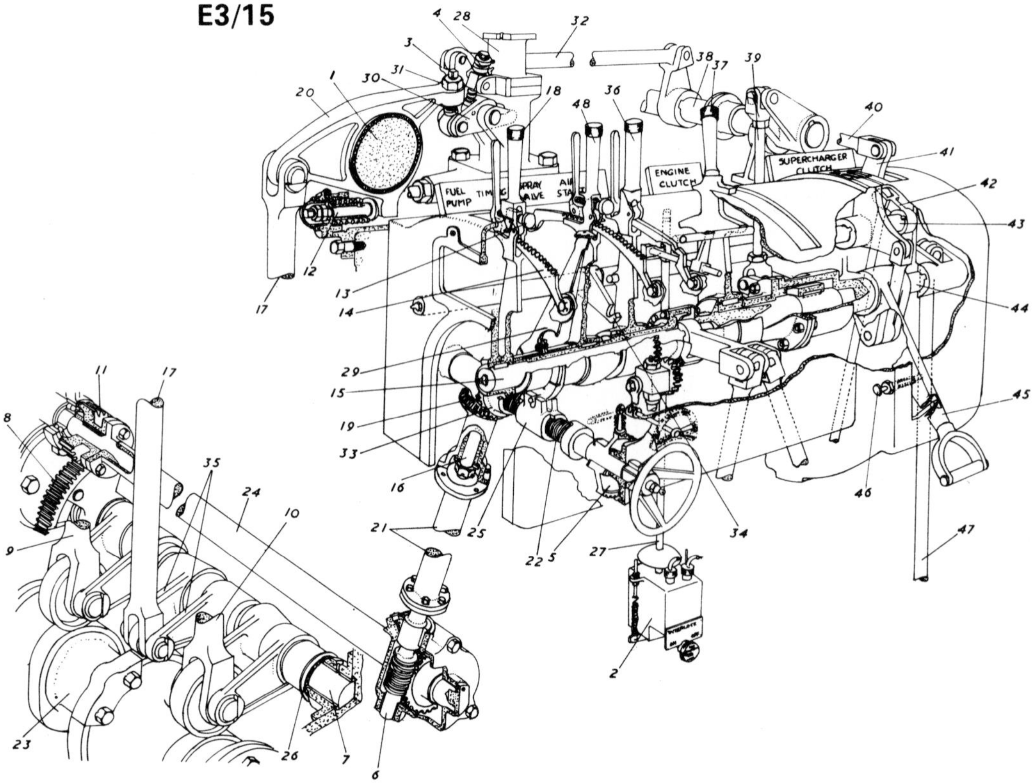

E4/1

E4/2

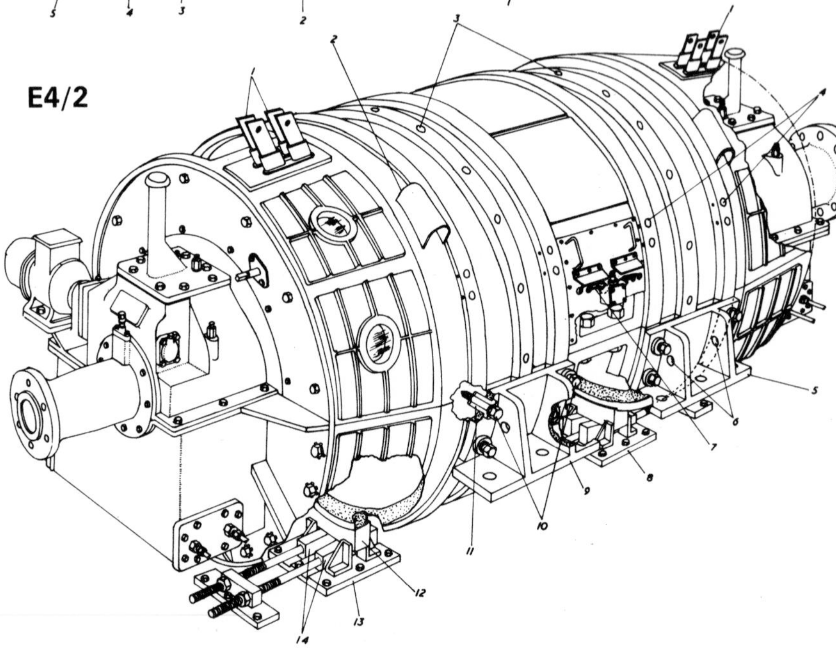

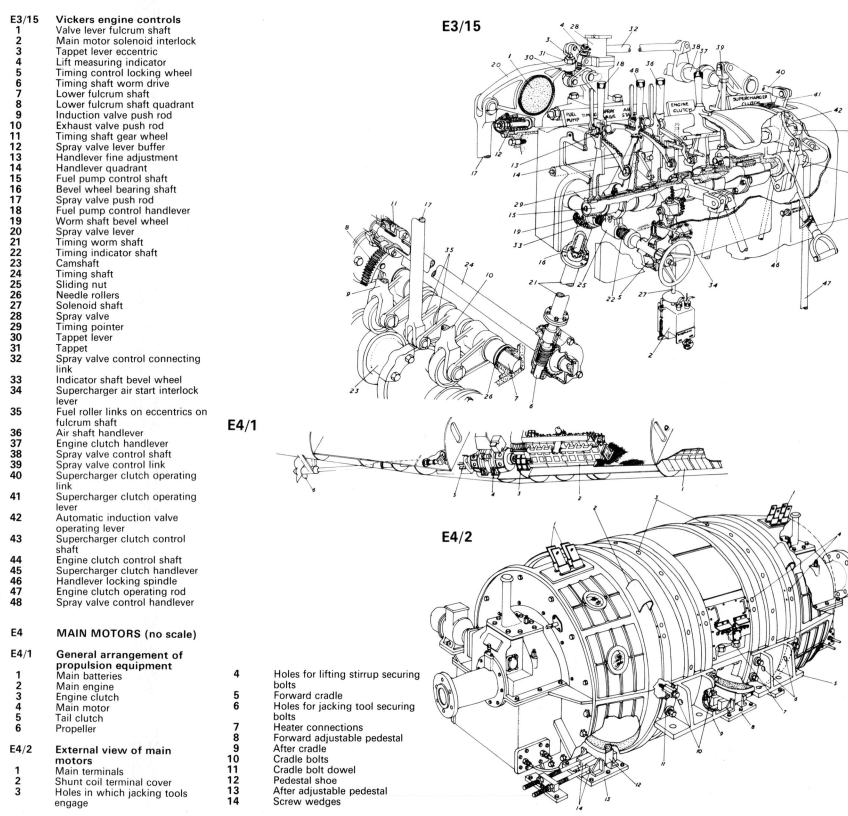

E4/3

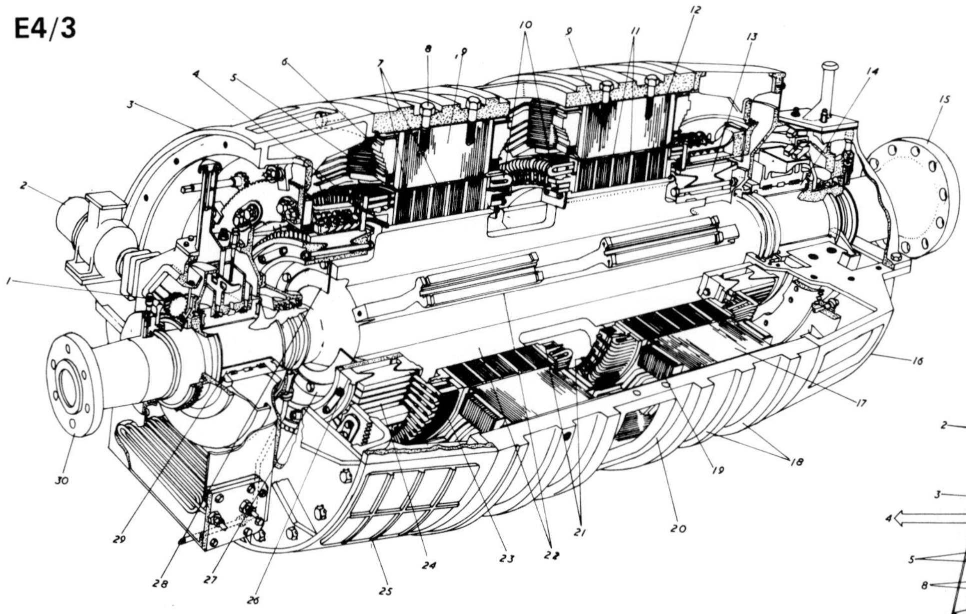

E4/5

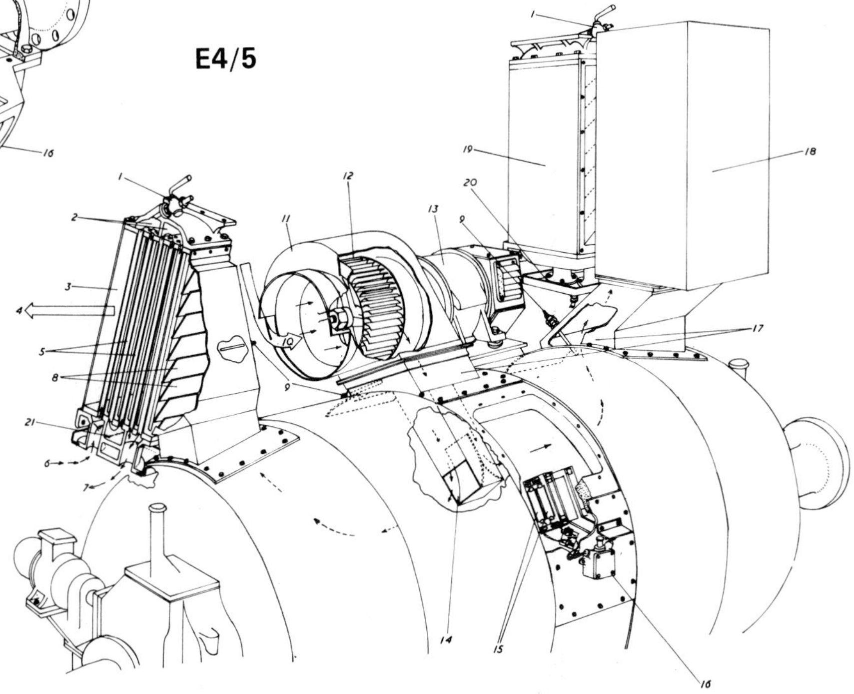

E4/4

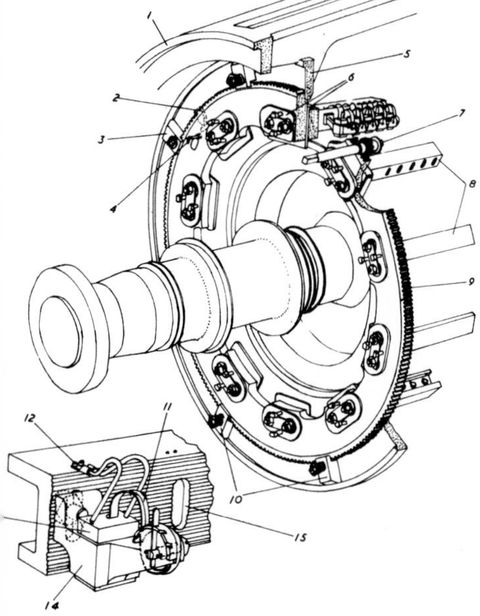

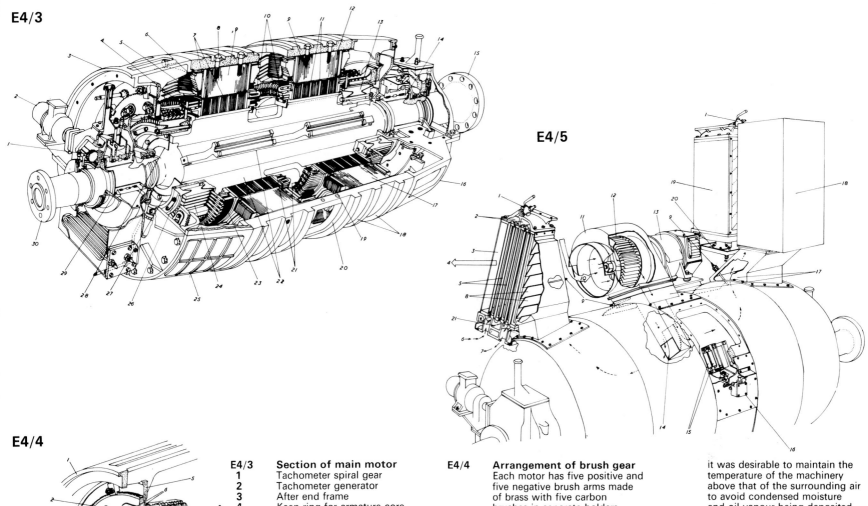

DETAILS OF BRUSH HOLDER

E4/3 Section of main motor

1 Tachometer spiral gear
2 Tachometer generator
3 After end frame
4 Keep ring for armature core
5 Main pole series coil
6 Main pole shunt coil
7 Armature laminations
8 Main pole securing bolt
9 Main pole
10 Armature coils
11 Armature spacers and air passages
12 Main pole liners
13 Forward commutator segments
14 Forward bearings
15 Forward flanged coupling
16 Forward end frame
17 Inter pole
18 Magnet yoke ribs
19 Inter pole coil
20 Magnet yoke
21 Equalising rings
22 Spider
23 After commutator risers
24 After commutator segments
25 Cover plate
26 After quill
27 Quill keep ring
28 Air baffle
29 After bearing
30 After flanged coupling

E4/4 Arrangement of brush gear

Each motor has five positive and five negative brush arms made of brass with five carbon brushes in separate holders bolted to each arm

1 End frame
2 Brush position indicator
3 Solid clamp
4 Fall ended pin
5 Steel end frame ring
6 Paxolin bushes
7 Pinion with square head to fit ratchet spanner
8 Brush arms
9 Rocker ring
10 Spring-loaded clamps
11 Adjustable spring
12 Brush terminal
13 Carbon brush
14 Brush holder
15 Elongated hole for adjusting brush holder

E4/5 Main motor cooling and heating

If the temperature of the main motor were allowed to rise with use, a point would soon be reached where the insulation would be seriously damaged or cause a fire. On the other hand it was desirable to maintain the temperature of the machinery above that of the surrounding air to avoid condensed moisture and oil vapour being deposited on the insulation. To prevent a rise in temperature, main motor coolers are fitted; conversely heaters were provided to keep the equipment from becoming too cold

1 Venting and test cock
2 Upper water box
3 After air cooler
4 Air outlet
5 Cupro-nickel tubes
6 Cooling water inlet
7 Cooling water outlet
8 Air louvres
9 Thermometer bulbs
10 Air inlet
11 Fan casing
12 Fan impeller
13 Fan motor
14 Air chute
15 Motor heaters
16 Heater plug and socket
17 Air duct
18 Shunt regulator resistance
19 Forward air cooler
20 Drip tray
21 Lower water box

E Machinery

E4/6

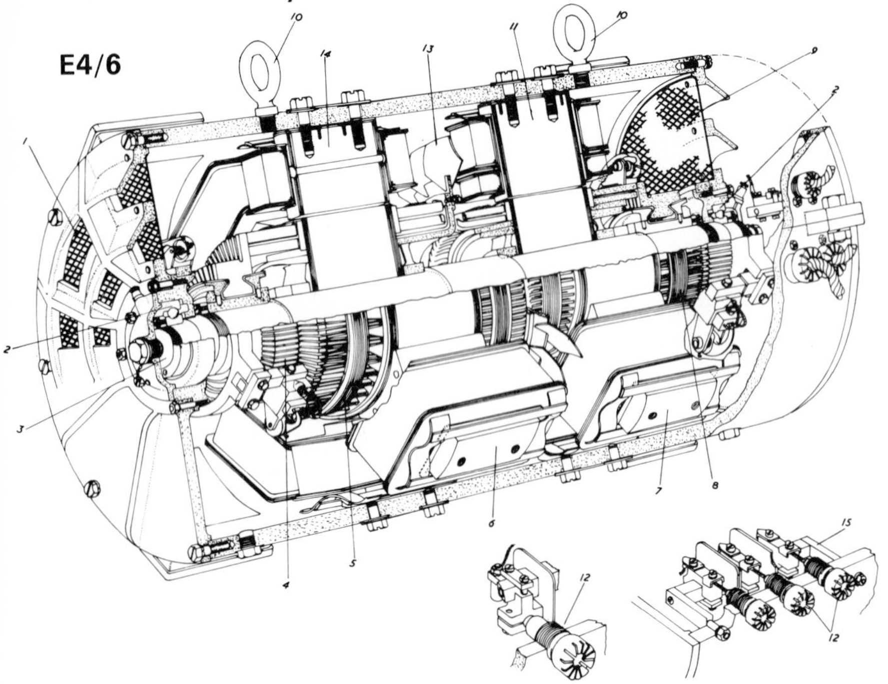

E4/7

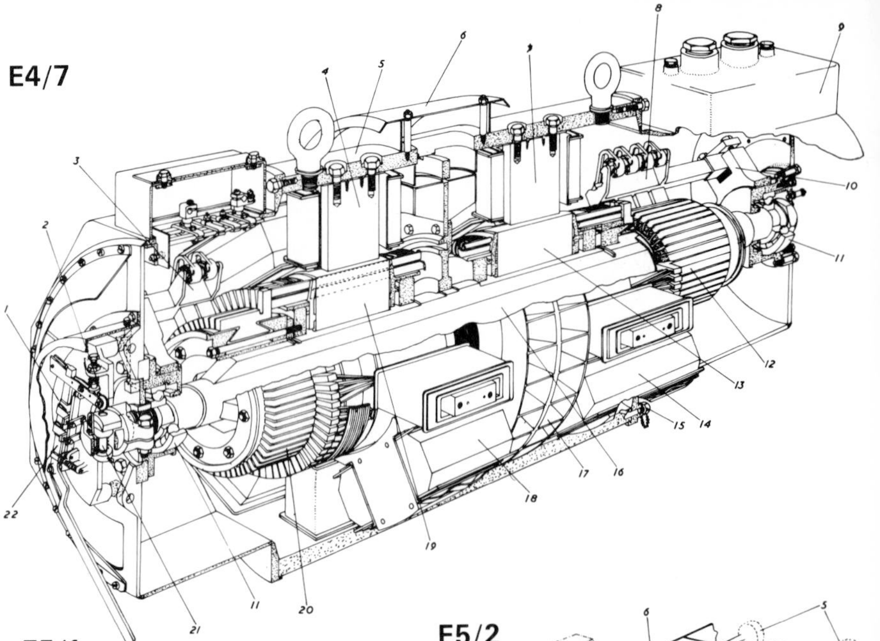

E5/1

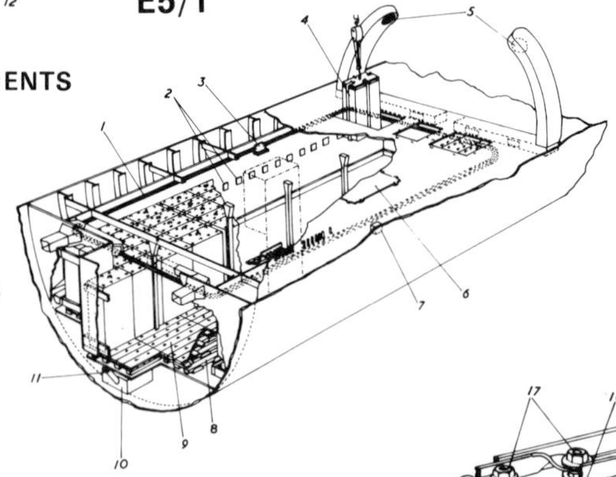

E5/2

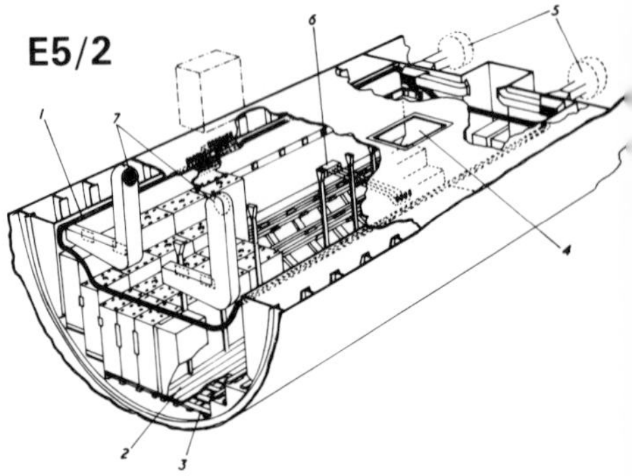

E5/3

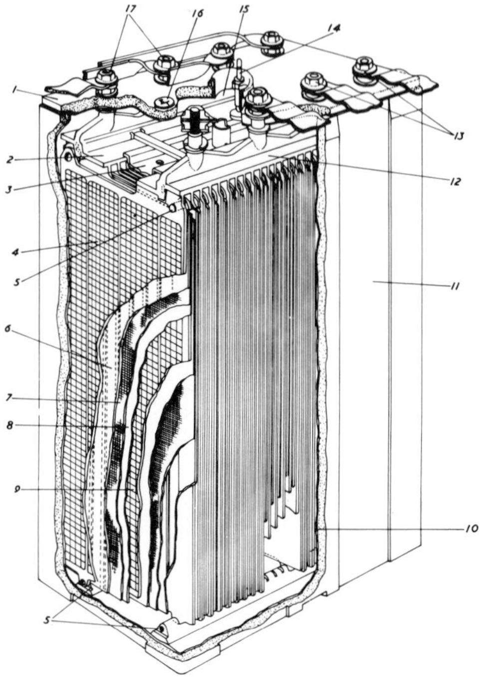

E4/6 Low power (2kW) motor generator and starter

1 Air inlet
2 Roller bearing
3 Shaft
4 Commutator
5 Motor armature
6 Motor main pole
7 Generator main pole
8 Generator armature
9 Air outlet
10 Lifting bolt
11 Generator interpole
12 Gland
13 Fan blades
14 Motor interpole
15 Terminal blocks

E4/7 Reducer

1 Overspeed trip contacts
2 Spring-operated catch
3 'D' machine brush gear
4 'D' machine interpole
5 Field frame
6 Ventilation cowling
7 'M' machine interpole
8 'M' machine brush gear
9 End shield
10 Split ring
11 Bearing
12 'M' machine commutator
13 'M' machine armature
14 'M' shunt field
15 Drain plug
16 Shaft
17 Fan impeller
18 'D' shunt field
19 'D' machine armature
20 'D' machine commutator
21 Spring constrained trip
22 Tripping lever

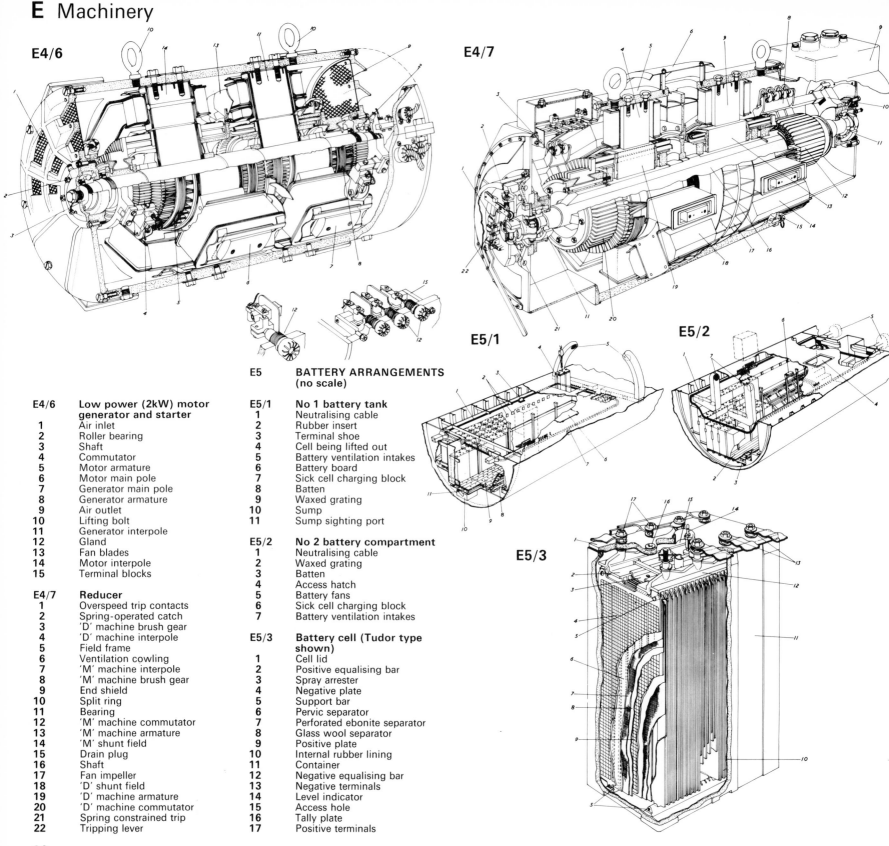

E5 BATTERY ARRANGEMENTS (no scale)

E5/1 No 1 battery tank

1 Neutralising cable
2 Rubber insert
3 Terminal shoe
4 Cell being lifted out
5 Battery ventilation intakes
6 Battery board
7 Sick cell charging block
8 Batten
9 Waxed grating
10 Sump
11 Sump sighting port

E5/2 No 2 battery compartment

1 Neutralising cable
2 Waxed grating
3 Batten
4 Access hatch
5 Battery fans
6 Sick cell charging block
7 Battery ventilation intakes

E5/3 Battery cell (Tudor type shown)

1 Cell lid
2 Positive equalising bar
3 Spray arrester
4 Negative plate
5 Support bar
6 Pervic separator
7 Perforated ebonite separator
8 Glass wool separator
9 Positive plate
10 Internal rubber lining
11 Container
12 Negative equalising bar
13 Negative terminals
14 Level indicator
15 Access hole
16 Tally plate
17 Positive terminals

E5/4

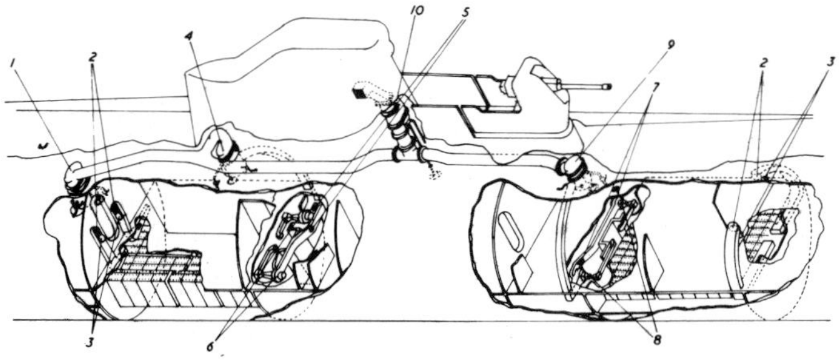

E5/5

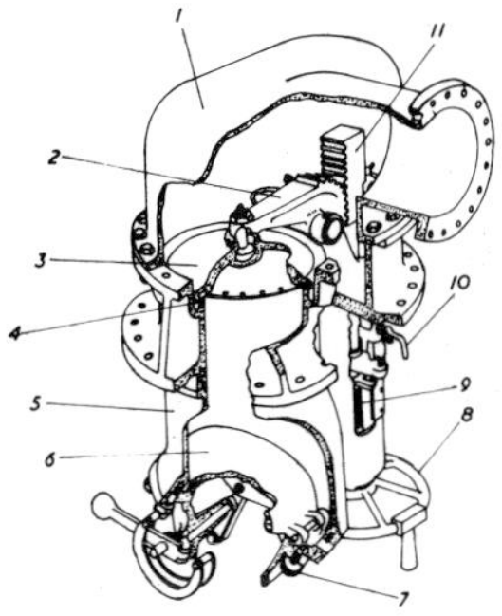

E5/6

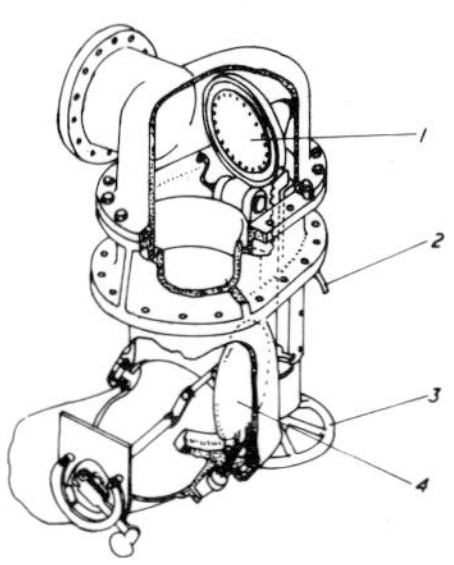

E5/7

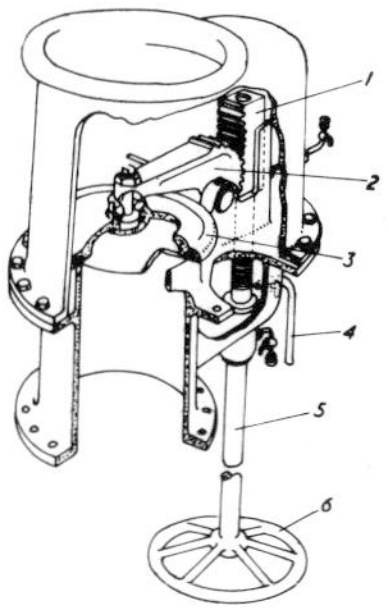

E6/1

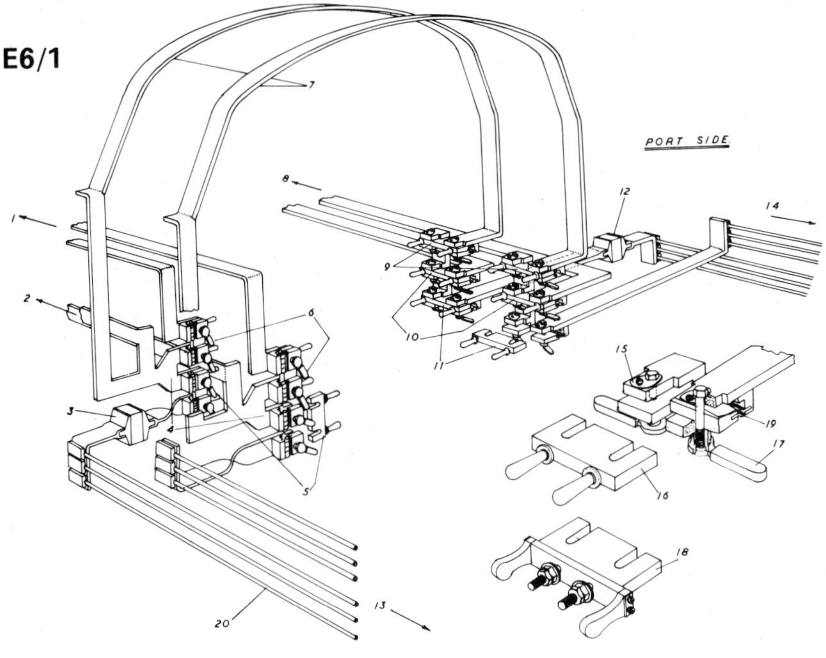

E5/4 General layout of battery ventilation system

The battery ventilation system has two functions: (1) to remove the battery gas generated during charging and to ensure that no local concentration of battery gas forms in the battery tank or compartment; (2) to cool the battery during charge or discharge. Both are achieved by causing a large volume of air to flow through the two battery tanks or compartments and discharging the resultant mixture of air and battery gas either to atmosphere when in harbour or into the engine room when at sea

1 Inboard ventilation hull valve
2 Natural intakes
3 Rubber seated flap valves
4 No 2 section hull valve
5 Flap valves
6 No 2 section exhaust fans
7 No 1 section exhaust fans
8 Sluice valves
9 No 1 section hull valve
10 Master outboard ventilation valve

E5/5 Inboard ventilation hull valve

1 Dome
2 Pinion lever
3 Valve
4 Valve seat
5 Valve casing
6 Quick-acting flap valve
7 Inboard drain
8 Operating handwheel
9 Valve spindle
10 Outboard drain fitted with shut-off cock
11 Rack

E5/6 Section hull valve

1 Valve
2 Outboard drain fitted with shut-off cock
3 Operating handwheel
4 Quick-acting flap valve

E5/7 Master outboard ventilation valve

1 Rack
2 Pinion lever
3 Valve
4 Open ended drain
5 Valve spindle
6 Operating handwheel

E6 ELECTRICAL DISTRIBUTION SYSTEMS (no scale)

Supply from the battery panels reaches the motor room through armoured cables as shown. Three cables per pole and six cables from No 1 battery panel run down the starboard side of the submarine to the starboard switchboard, and those from No 2 battery down the port side to the port switchboard. The cables terminated in spills clamped to copper straps; in the negative straps were ammeter shunts to show battery charge and discharge currents. Connection was made to the main busbars by means of isolating links allowing the battery to be disconnected from the busbar if required. The links were solid copper and bridged the gaps between two jaws

E6/1 Battery connections

1 To starboard main motor
2 To auxiliary services panel
3 No 1 battery ammeter shunt
4 Main busbars
5 No 1 battery links
6 Starboard main motor links
7 Cross-connecting straps
8 To port main motor
9 Cross-connecting links
10 Port main motor links
11 No 2 battery links
12 No 2 battery ammeter shunt
13 To No 1 battery
14 To No 2 battery
15 Locking washer
16 Isolating link
17 Locking arm
18 Replacement link for external supply
19 Hinge
20 Paper insulated lead covered and armoured cables

E6/2

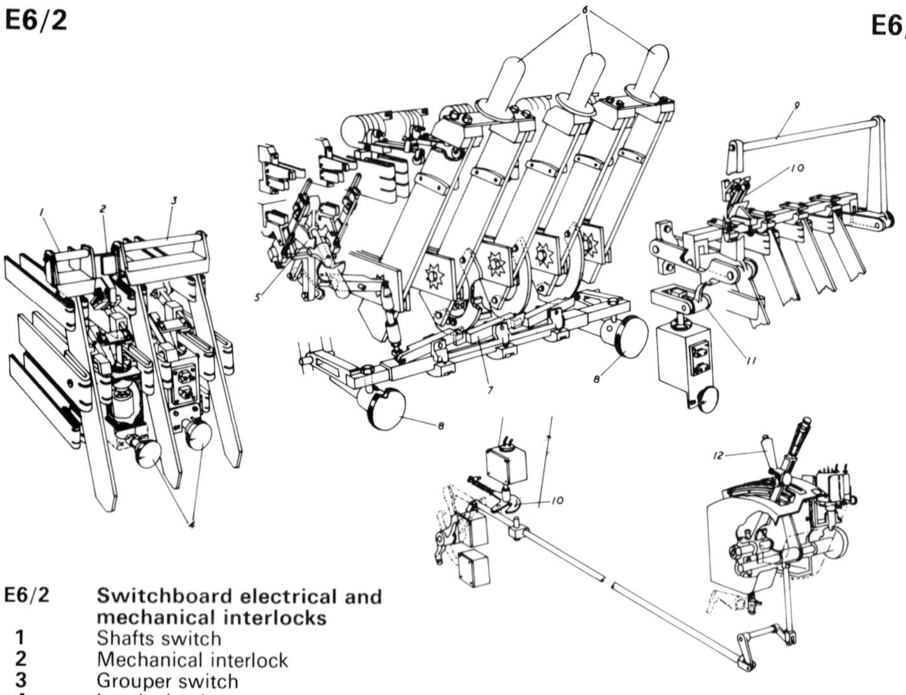

E6/3

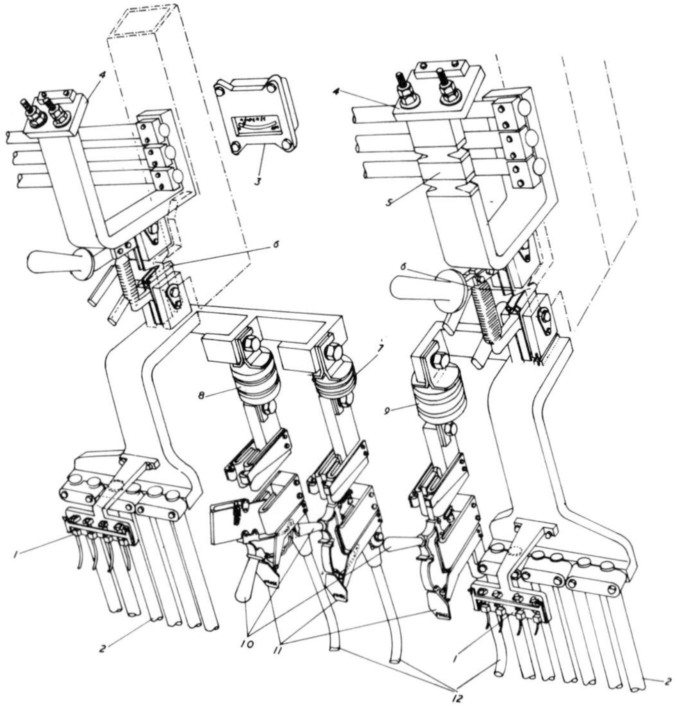

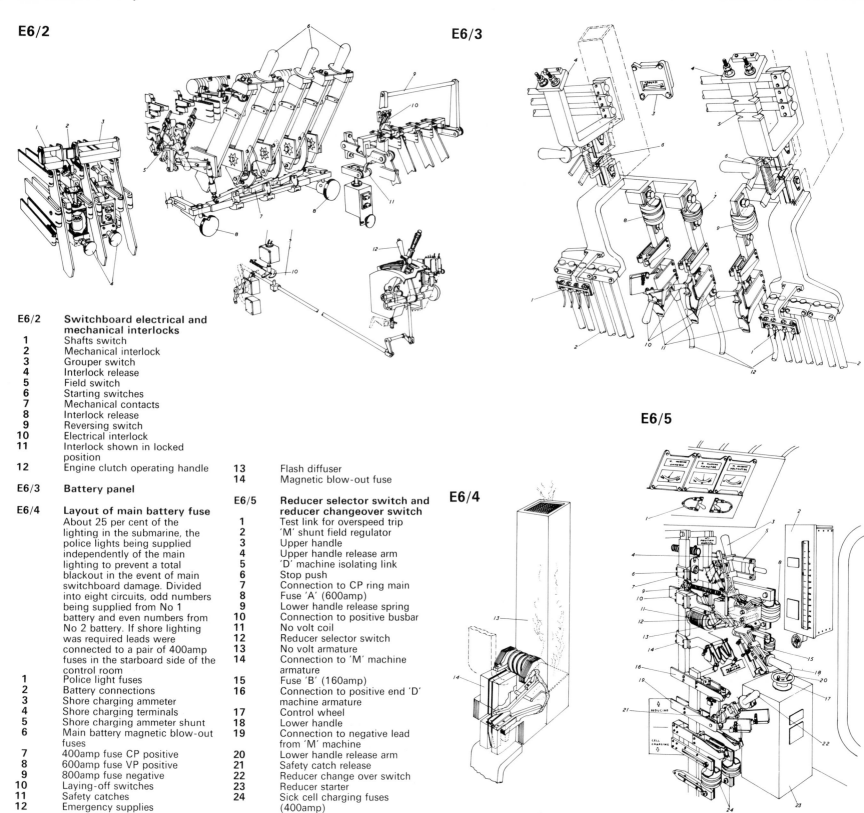

E6/2 **Switchboard electrical and mechanical interlocks**

1 Shafts switch
2 Mechanical interlock
3 Grouper switch
4 Interlock release
5 Field switch
6 Starting switches
7 Mechanical contacts
8 Interlock release
9 Reversing switch
10 Electrical interlock
11 Interlock shown in locked position
12 Engine clutch operating handle

E6/3 **Battery panel**

E6/4 **Layout of main battery fuse**

About 25 per cent of the lighting in the submarine, the police lights being supplied independently of the main lighting to prevent a total blackout in the event of main switchboard damage. Divided into eight circuits, odd numbers being supplied from No 1 battery and even numbers from No 2 battery. If shore lighting was required leads were connected to a pair of 400amp fuses in the starboard side of the control room

1 Police light fuses
2 Battery connections
3 Shore charging ammeter
4 Shore charging terminals
5 Shore charging ammeter shunt
6 Main battery magnetic blow-out fuses
7 400amp fuse CP positive
8 600amp fuse VP positive
9 800amp fuse negative
10 Laying-off switches
11 Safety catches
12 Emergency supplies
13 Flash diffuser
14 Magnetic blow-out fuse

E6/5 **Reducer selector switch and reducer changeover switch**

1 Test link for overspeed trip
2 'M' shunt field regulator
3 Upper handle
4 Upper handle release arm
5 'D' machine isolating link
6 Stop push
7 Connection to CP ring main
8 Fuse 'A' (600amp)
9 Lower handle release spring
10 Connection to positive busbar
11 No volt coil
12 Reducer selector switch
13 No volt armature
14 Connection to 'M' machine armature
15 Fuse 'B' (160amp)
16 Connection to positive end 'D' machine armature
17 Control wheel
18 Lower handle
19 Connection to negative lead from 'M' machine
20 Lower handle release arm
21 Safety catch release
22 Reducer change over switch
23 Reducer starter
24 Sick cell charging fuses (400amp)

E6/4

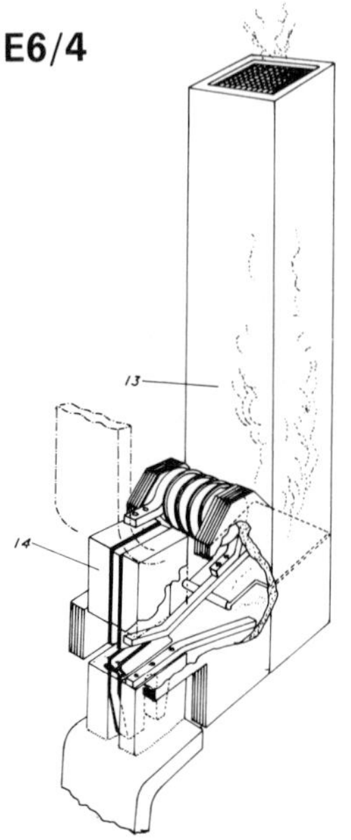

E6/5

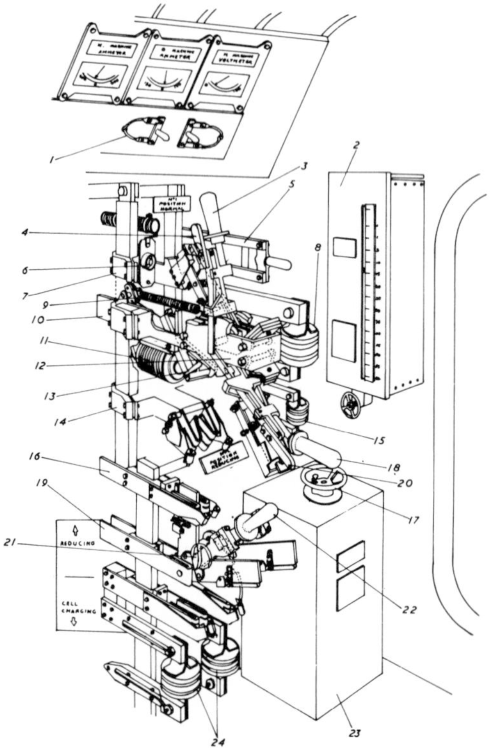

E7/1

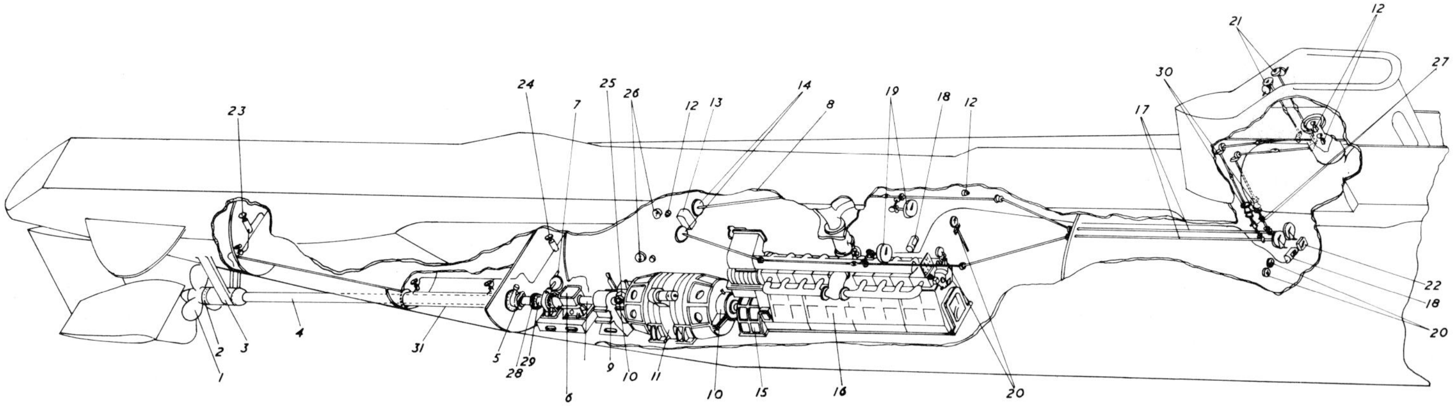

E7/2

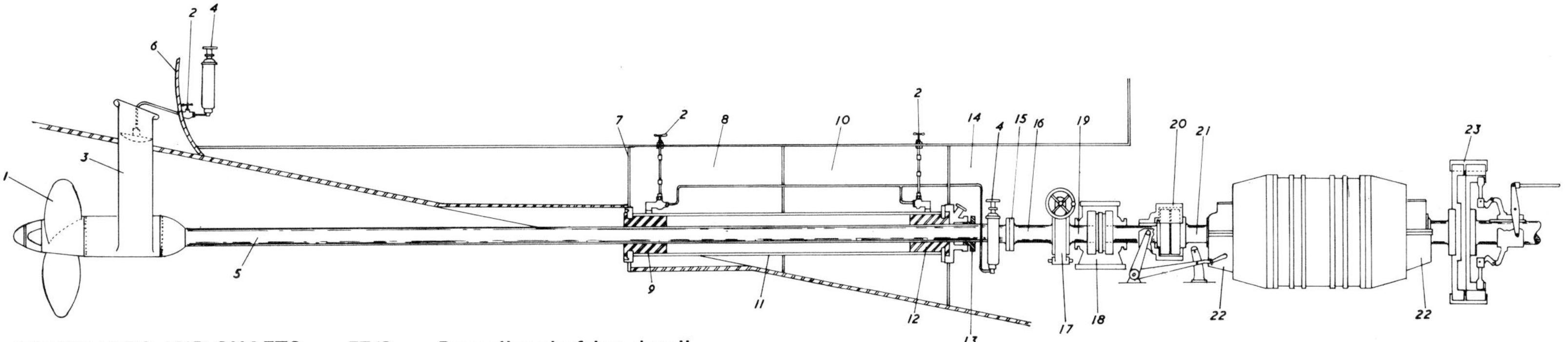

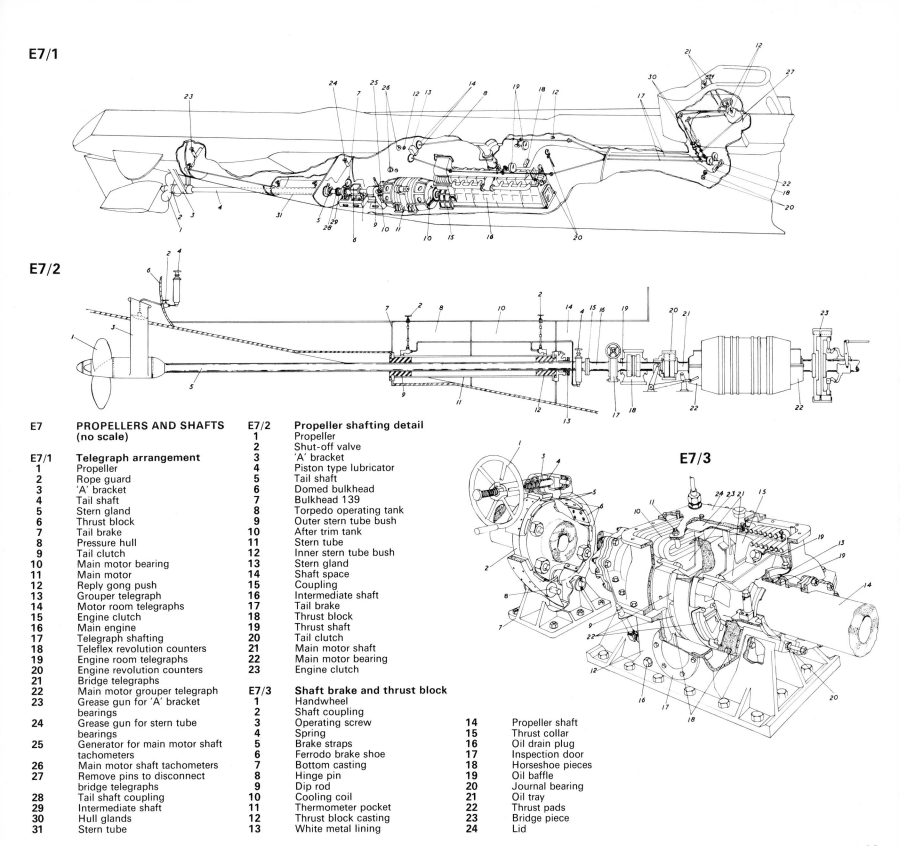

E7 PROPELLERS AND SHAFTS (no scale)

E7/1 Telegraph arrangement
1 Propeller
2 Rope guard
3 'A' bracket
4 Tail shaft
5 Stern gland
6 Thrust block
7 Tail brake
8 Pressure hull
9 Tail clutch
10 Main motor bearing
11 Main motor
12 Reply gong push
13 Grouper telegraph
14 Motor room telegraphs
15 Engine clutch
16 Main engine
17 Telegraph shafting
18 Teleflex revolution counters
19 Engine room telegraphs
20 Engine revolution counters
21 Bridge telegraphs
22 Main motor grouper telegraph
23 Grease gun for 'A' bracket bearings
24 Grease gun for stern tube bearings
25 Generator for main motor shaft tachometers
26 Main motor shaft tachometers
27 Remove pins to disconnect bridge telegraphs
28 Tail shaft coupling
29 Intermediate shaft
30 Hull glands
31 Stern tube

E7/2 Propeller shafting detail
1 Propeller
2 Shut-off valve
3 'A' bracket
4 Piston type lubricator
5 Tail shaft
6 Domed bulkhead
7 Bulkhead 139
8 Torpedo operating tank
9 Outer stern tube bush
10 After trim tank
11 Stern tube
12 Inner stern tube bush
13 Stern gland
14 Shaft space
15 Coupling
16 Intermediate shaft
17 Tail brake
18 Thrust block
19 Thrust shaft
20 Tail clutch
21 Main motor shaft
22 Main motor bearing
23 Engine clutch

E7/3

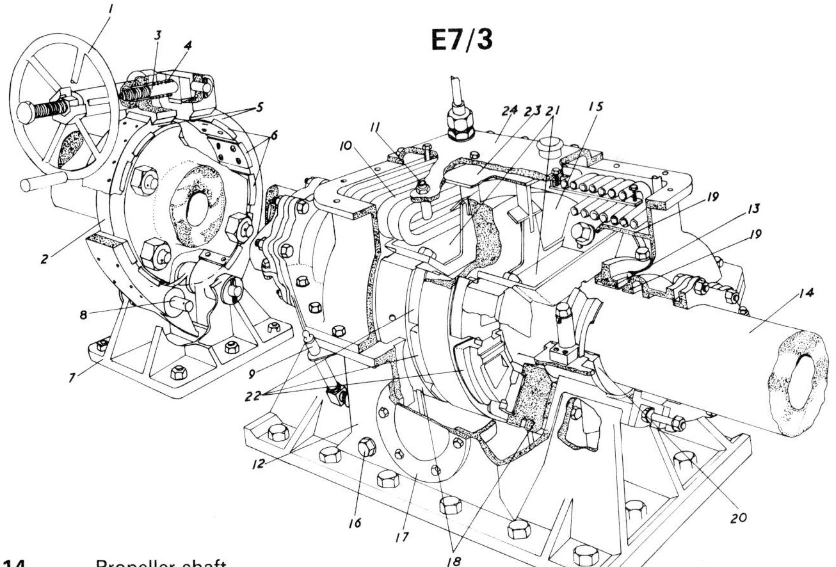

E7/3 Shaft brake and thrust block
1 Handwheel
2 Shaft coupling
3 Operating screw
4 Spring
5 Brake straps
6 Ferrodo brake shoe
7 Bottom casting
8 Hinge pin
9 Dip rod
10 Cooling coil
11 Thermometer pocket
12 Thrust block casting
13 White metal lining
14 Propeller shaft
15 Thrust collar
16 Oil drain plug
17 Inspection door
18 Horseshoe pieces
19 Oil baffle
20 Journal bearing
21 Oil tray
22 Thrust pads
23 Bridge piece
24 Lid

E7/4 Propeller lifting arrangements

1 Propeller ring spanner
2 End cap
3 Propeller nut
4 Stop plate
5 Lifting groove
6 Locking stop plate
7 Strongback
8 Withdrawing bolts
9 Propeller boss
10 Lifting shackle
11 Chain purchases
12 Eyeplate
13 25lb strengthening girder
14 Securing rivets
15 No 5 main ballast tank plating
16 Domed bulkhead
17 25lb plate collar
18 Forged steel arms
19 Forged steel shell
20 Detachable end plate
21 Tail shaft
22 Fairing plate
23 Inbossing plate
24 Outbossing plate
25 Shut-off valve
26 Outer stern tube bush end flange
27 Piston type lubricator
28 Grease hole
29 Rope guard
30 To port 'A' bracket bush
31 Lifting eyebolt

E8 AUXILIARY MACHINERY

E8/1 The Imo Telemotor pump

The working pressure of 1250–1515lb per sq in in the telemotor system was maintained by two motor-driven 'Imo' pumps. These took their suction from the replenishing tank and discharged to two air-loaded accumulators in which the oil was stored under pressure to work the telemotor-operated equipment. The control of the pumps was normally automatic, the pumps starting when the pressure fell to 1250lb per sq in and stopping when the pressure reached 1515lb per sq in

1 Screwed plug
2 Relief valve discharge
3 Relief valve
4 Discharge coupling
5 Locating peg
6 Leather insert spring-loaded oil seal
7 Oil seal sleeve
8 Spigot
9 Lubricator
10 Oil seal
11 Retaining nut
12 Vents
13 Rotor
14 Sleeve
15 Dowel
16 Idlers
17 End cover
18 Coupling flages
19 From replenishing tank
20 Ball thrust bearing
21 Lolos strainer
22 Vent pipe
23 Suction pipe
24 Pump body
25 Delivery end bearing housing
26 Bearing bush oilway
27 Leak off pipe
28 Thrust bearing
29 Stud coupling
30 Idler spill
31 Ball thrust retaining ring
32 Oil seal retaining ring
33 Pressure balancing tube
34 Pressure balancing cover
35 Suction end cover
36 Non-return discharge valve
37 Oilways
38 Grub screw
39 Screwed plug
40 Shut-off cock
41 Priming funnel
42 Rotor spill
43 Locating screw
44 Sleeve carrier

E8/2 Distilling plant general arrangement

1 Feed tank
2 Duplex feed strainer
3 Brine pump
4 Brine discharge
5 Chemical injection pump
6 Distilled water pump
7 Chemical injection tank
8 Salinometer
9 Distilled water outlet
10 Evaporator
11 Salinometer instrument box
12 Salinometer warning lamp
13 Motor starter
14 Control panel

E8/3 Evaporator (section)

1 Brine pump discharge
2 Vapour by-pass valve
3 Distilled water pump discharge
4 Vapour compressor
5 6hp motor
6 Brine sediment trap
7 Distilled water priming funnel and switch cock
8 Distilled water valve
9 Distilled water pump suction
10 Distilled water control vessel
11 Brining valve
12 Brine pump suction
13 Blow-down valve
14 Distilled water and brine cooler feed heater
15 Condenser
16 Division plate
17 Lower shell
18 Immersion heater
19 Water gauge
20 Feed inlet
21 Automatic feed regulator
22 Light fitting
23 Float box balance pipe
24 Light switch
25 Shell relief valve
26 Upper shell
27 Lifting lug
28 Vapour separator

E7/4

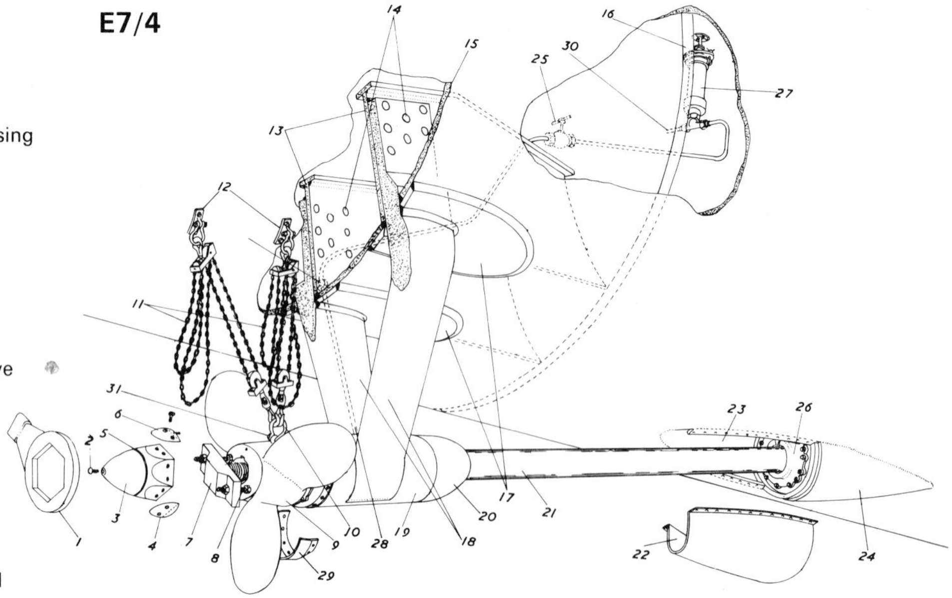

E8/1

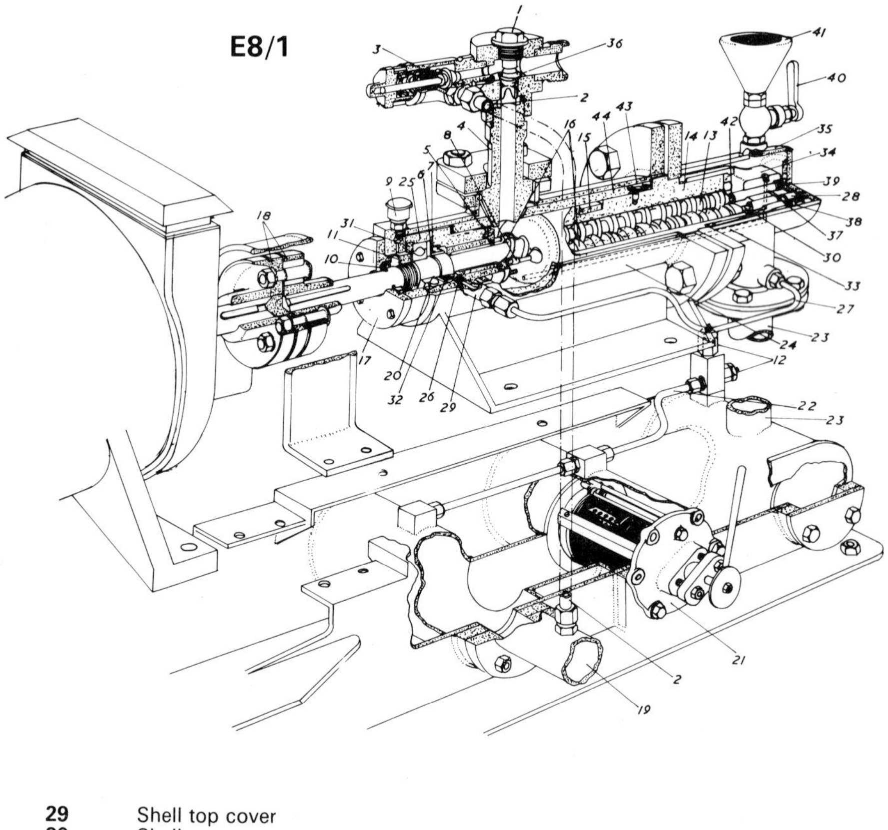

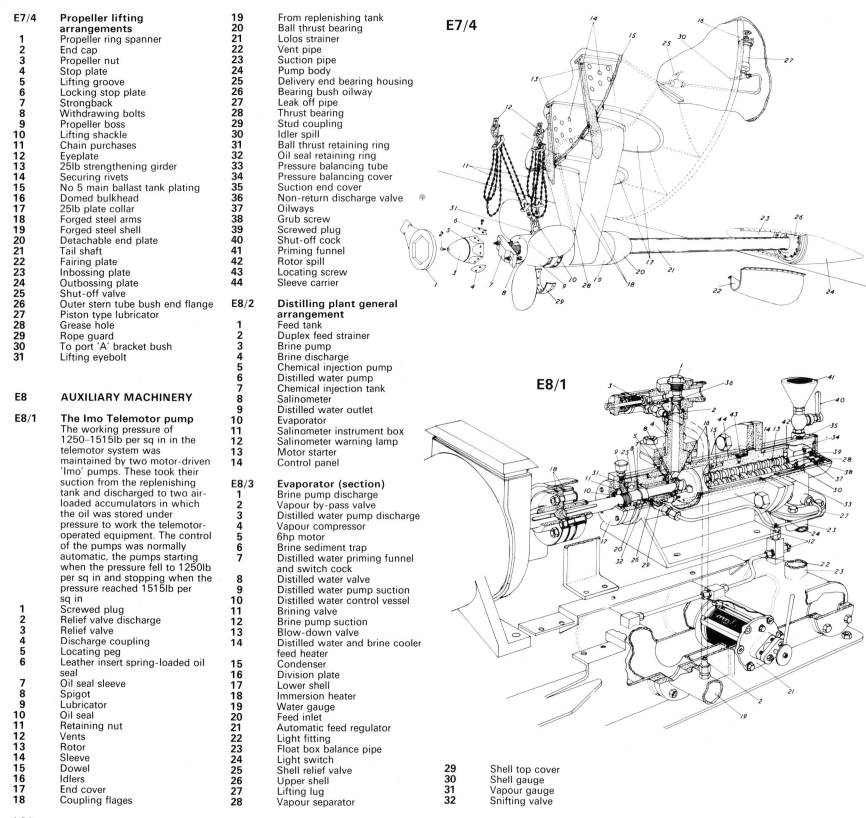

29 Shell top cover
30 Shell gauge
31 Vapour gauge
32 Snifting valve

E8/2

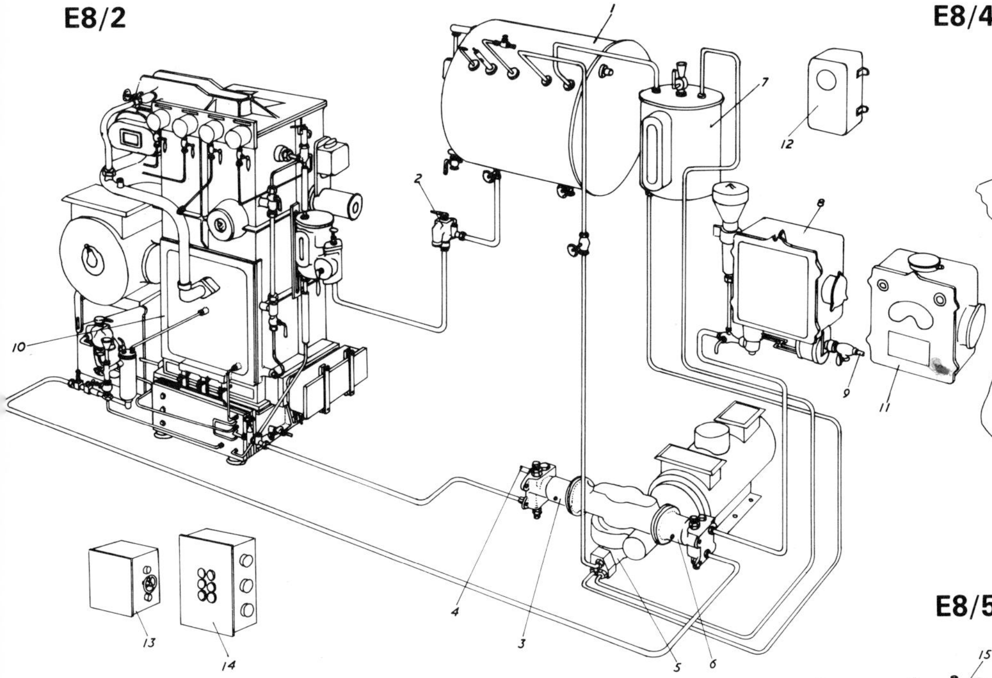

E8/4

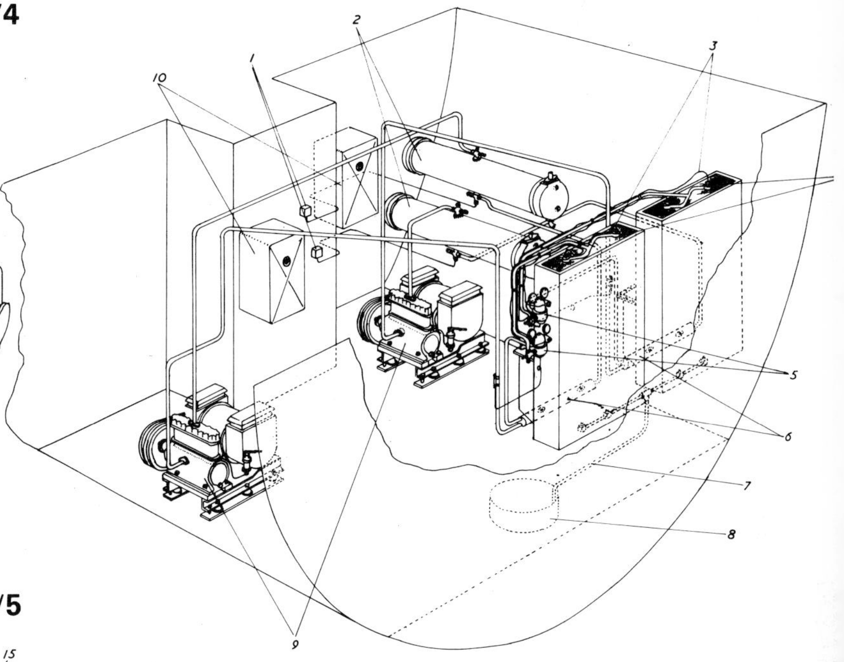

E8/3

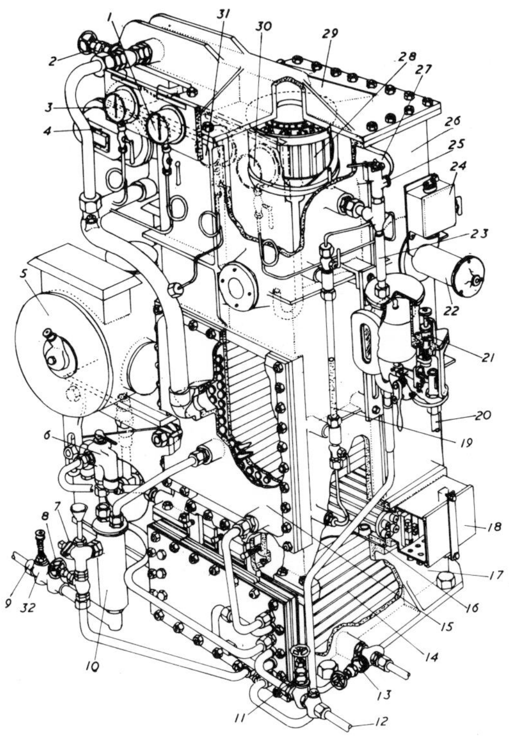

E8/5

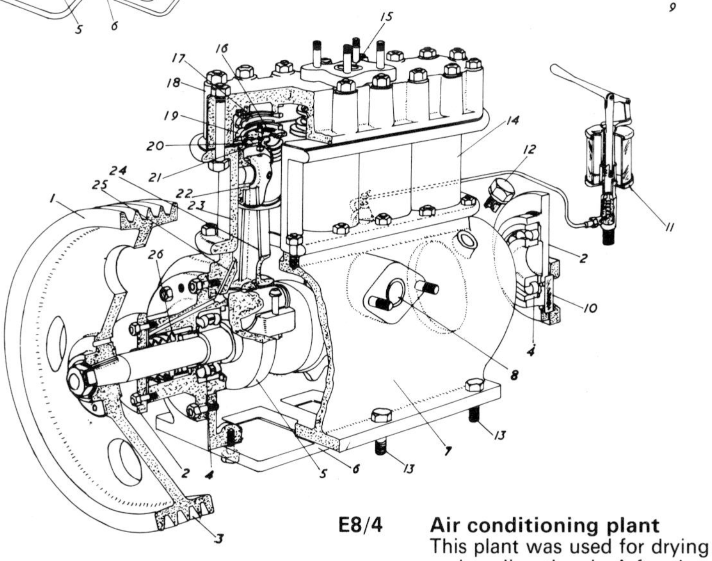

E8/4 Air conditioning plant

This plant was used for drying and cooling the air. A fan drew air through an air cooler and passed it to the ship's ventilation system. Moisture from the air precipitated and was drained off to the radar mast well bilge. Two plants were fitted in a compartment below the control room, and the two units could be used singly or together. Each was designed to absorb 55,000 BTUs per hour from 36,000cu ft of air per hour

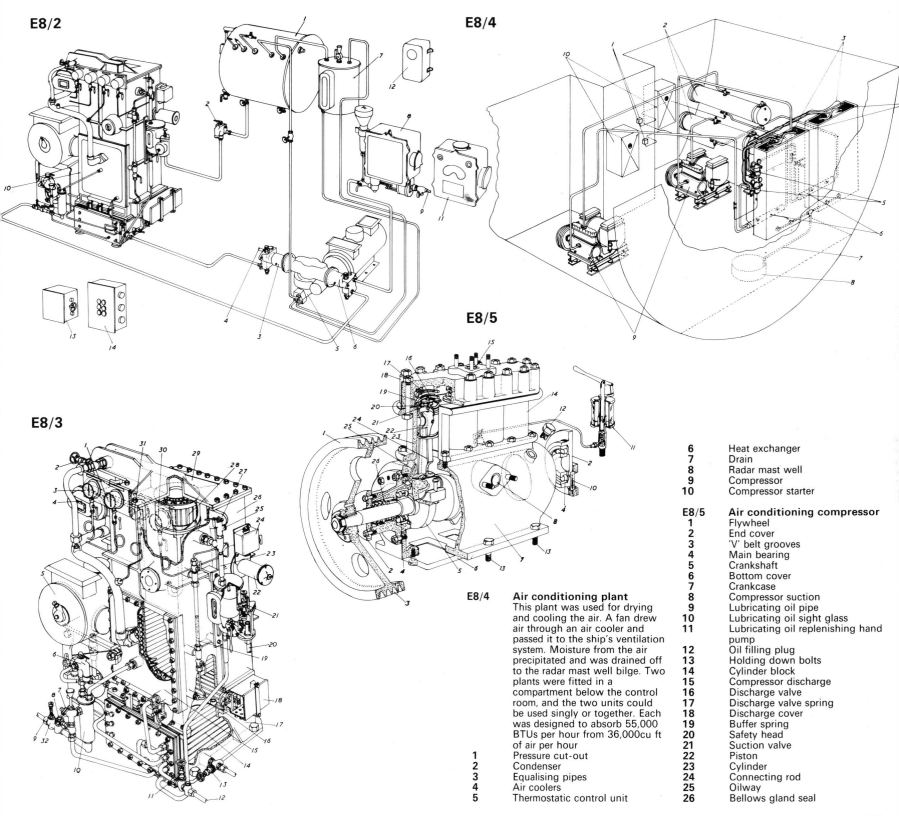

1 Pressure cut-out
2 Condenser
3 Equalising pipes
4 Air coolers
5 Thermostatic control unit
6 Heat exchanger
7 Drain
8 Radar mast well
9 Compressor
10 Compressor starter

E8/5 Air conditioning compressor

1 Flywheel
2 End cover
3 'V' belt grooves
4 Main bearing
5 Crankshaft
6 Bottom cover
7 Crankcase
8 Compressor suction
9 Lubricating oil pipe
10 Lubricating oil sight glass
11 Lubricating oil replenishing hand pump
12 Oil filling plug
13 Holding down bolts
14 Cylinder block
15 Compressor discharge
16 Discharge valve
17 Discharge valve spring
18 Discharge cover
19 Buffer spring
20 Safety head
21 Suction valve
22 Piston
23 Cylinder
24 Connecting rod
25 Oilway
26 Bellows gland seal

E8/6

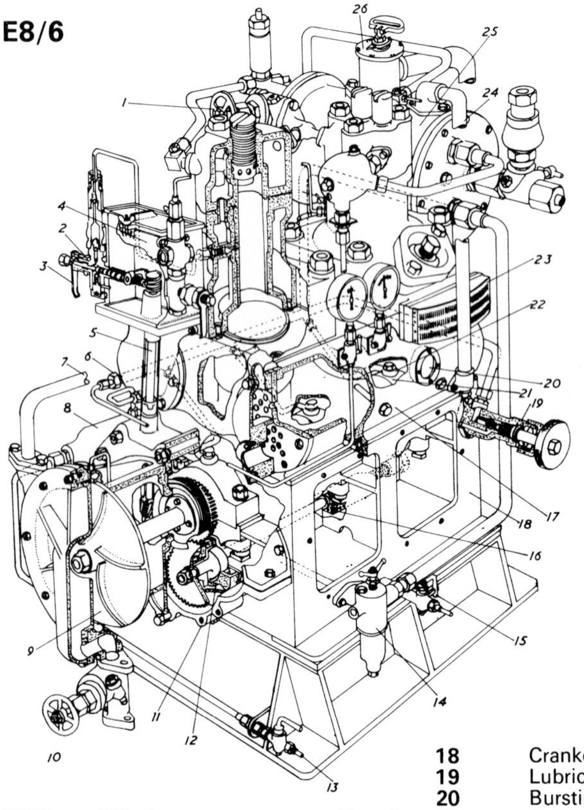

E8/7

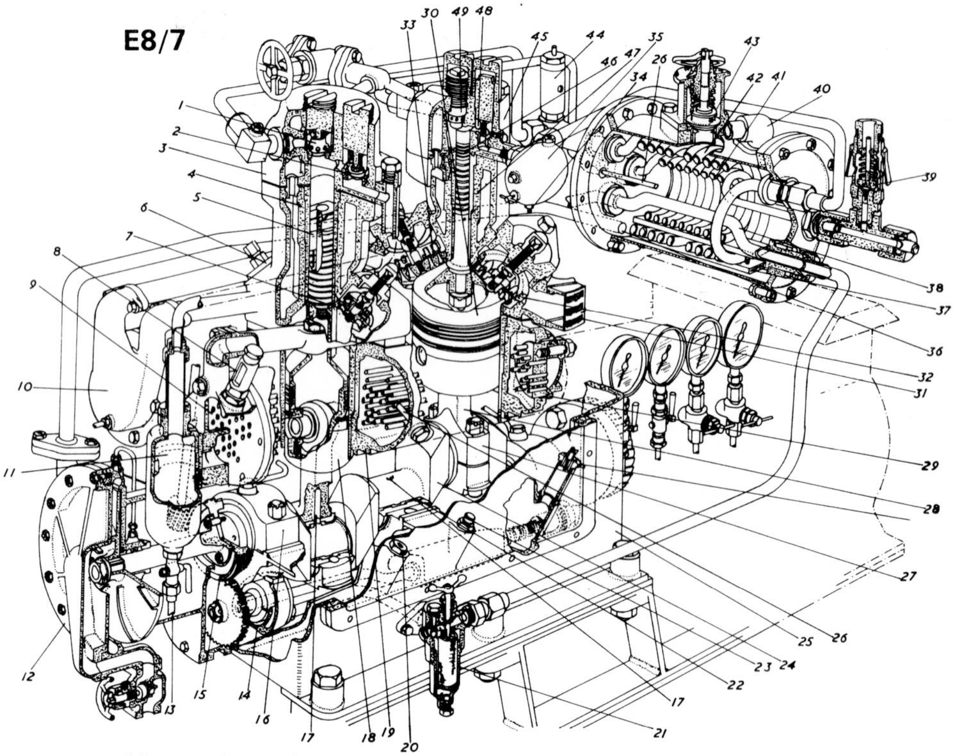

E8/6 HP air compressors – oil and water systems

Two motor-driven Reavell high pressure air compressors, Type TC4, were fitted in 'A' class submarines to replenish the HP air system. They took a suction from atmosphere and discharged at 4000lb per sq in to a ring main and into four groups of air bottles (total capacity 136.5cu ft) fitted inside the hull. Each compressor was capable of filling a reservoir of 15cu ft capacity with air at 4000lb per sq in pressure in 80 minutes, when running at 800rpm

1 Circulating water discharge valve
2 Adjustable sleeve
3 Hand trigger
4 Mechanical cylinder lubricator
5 Lubricator driving shaft
6 Lubricating oil manifold
7 Circulating water discharge
8 First stage separator bottle
9 Circulating water pump impeller
10 Circulating water suction connection
11 Extension piece
12 Forced lubrication pump
13 First stage drain
14 Auto-clean strainer
15 Sump drain cock
16 Lubrication suction strainer
17 First and second stage cylinder block
18 Crankcase
19 Lubricating oil relief valve
20 Bursting disc
21 Bearing cap
22 Oil supply to main bearing
23 Air inlet silencer
24 Circulating water outlet
25 Third and fourth stage cooler
26 Circulating water relief valve

E8/7 HP air compressor general arrangement

1 Third stage delivery valve
2 Third stage suction valve
3 Third stage cylinder head
4 Third stage cylinder
5 Third stage plunger
6 Second stage suction valve
7 Second stage delivery valve
8 Second stage relief valve
9 Second stage cooler
10 First stage cooler
11 Second stage separator bottle
12 Circulating water pump
13 Second stage drain
14 Forced lubrication pump
15 Oil thrower
16 Bearing cap
17 Oil hole
18 Second stage piston
19 First and second stage cylinder block
20 Thermometer pocket
21 Auto-clean strainer
22 Main bearing
23 Dip rod
24 Crankshaft
25 Crankcase
26 Corrosion rod
27 Large end bearing
28 Connecting rod
29 Gland
30 First stage piston
31 Air inlet silencer
32 First stage suction valve
33 First stage delivery valve
34 Third stage drain
35 Third stage separator bottle
36 Circulating water inlet
37 Teak clip
38 Lubricating oil cooler
39 Fourth stage relief valve
40 Third and fourth stage cooler
41 Fourth stage cooling coil
42 Third stage cooling coil
43 Circulating water relief valve
44 Third stage relief valve
45 Fourth stage cylinder head
46 Fourth stage plunger
47 Fourth stage cylinder
48 Fourth stage suction valve
49 Fourth stage delivery valve

E8/8 De Laval centrifuge

1 Dial thermometer
2 Liquid inlet
3 Frame hood
4 Rubber joints
5 Water discharge sight glass
6 Centrifuge casing
7 Counter shaft
8 Friction clutch
9 Wormwheel shaft
10 Oil-bath sight glass
11 Tapered pin
12 Wormwheel
13 Duplex bearing
14 Bearing bush
15 Bearing sleeve
16 Counter shaft pinion
17 Pump shaft pinion
18 Pump gear wheel
19 Pump shaft
20 Grease cap
21 Gear wheel pump
22 Relief valve
23 Pump casting
24 Bowl spindle
25 Phosphor-bronze bush
26 Conveyor blade
27 Conveyor plug
28 Brake
29 Motor
30 Cam lever
31 Spring
32 Drip cap
33 Bowl body
34 Filling plug
35 Regulating tube
36 Sight glass
37 Distributor tube
38 Splash guard
39 Gravity disc
40 Spring-loaded buffer
41 Spring bearing and casing
42 Oil discharge sight glass
43 Pump pinion shear pin
44 Pump shaft ball race
45 Height adjustment ring
46 Wormwheel shaft ball bearings

E8/9 LP rotary blower

'A' class units were fitted with a single Reavell low pressure rotary blower, designed to discharge 1100cu ft of free air per minute at 11–15lb sq in. This was used to bring the boat to full buoyancy after surfacing, to reduce the expenditure of HP

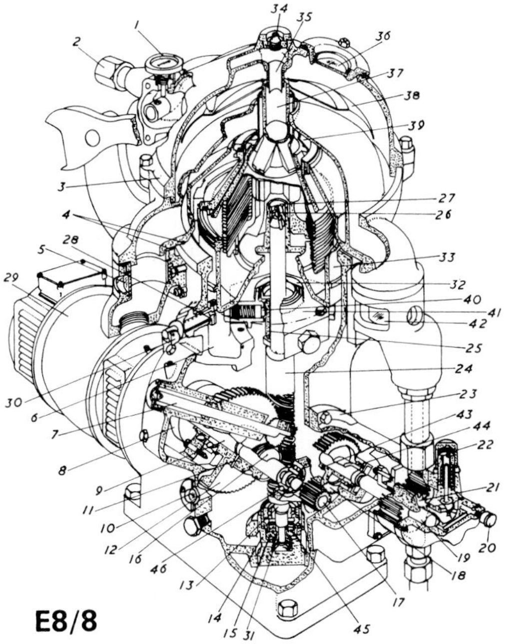

E8/8

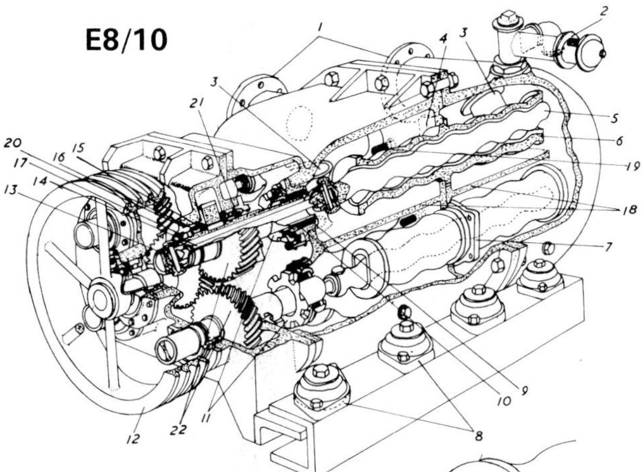

E8/10

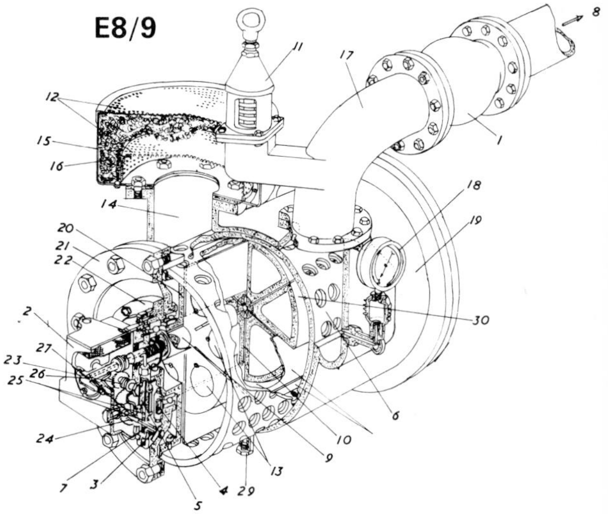

E8/9

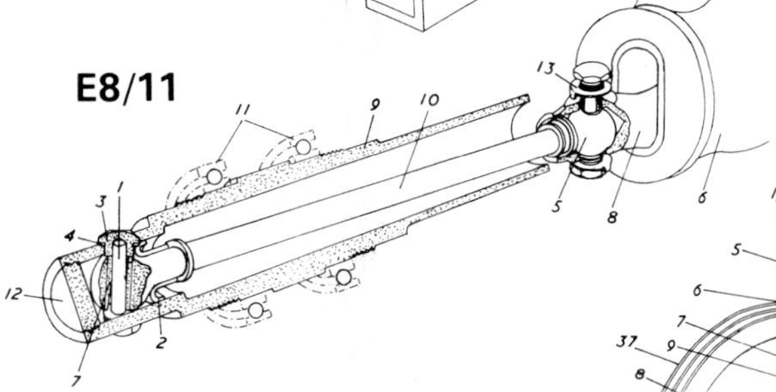

E8/11

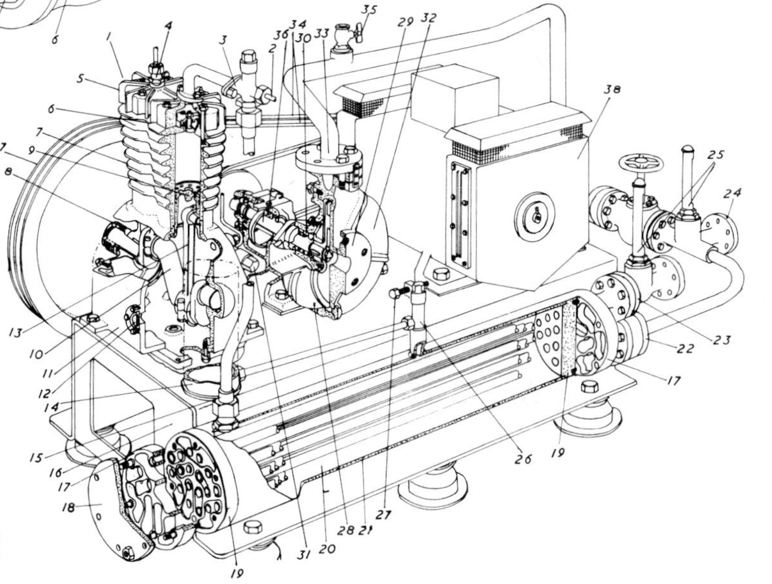

E8/12

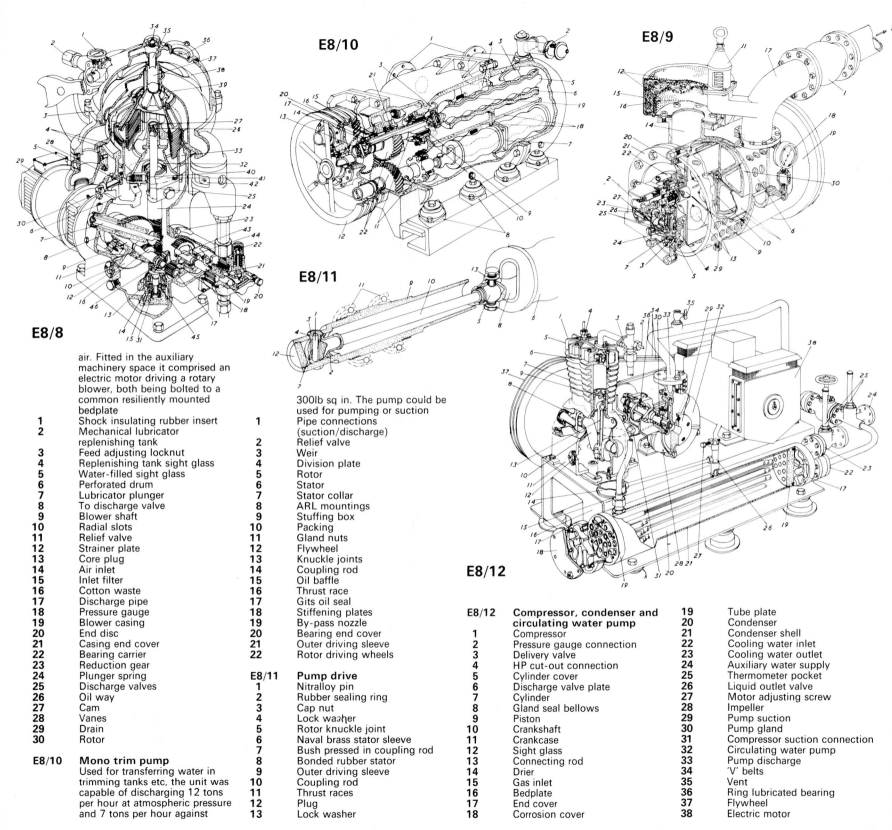

air. Fitted in the auxiliary machinery space it comprised an electric motor driving a rotary blower, both being bolted to a common resiliently mounted bedplate

1 Shock insulating rubber insert
2 Mechanical lubricator replenishing tank
3 Feed adjusting locknut
4 Replenishing tank sight glass
5 Water-filled sight glass
6 Perforated drum
7 Lubricator plunger
8 To discharge valve
9 Blower shaft
10 Radial slots
11 Relief valve
12 Strainer plate
13 Core plug
14 Air inlet
15 Inlet filter
16 Cotton waste
17 Discharge pipe
18 Pressure gauge
19 Blower casing
20 End disc
21 Casing end cover
22 Bearing carrier
23 Reduction gear
24 Plunger spring
25 Discharge valves
26 Oil way
27 Cam
28 Vanes
29 Drain
30 Rotor

E8/10 Mono trim pump

Used for transferring water in trimming tanks etc, the unit was capable of discharging 12 tons per hour at atmospheric pressure and 7 tons per hour against 300lb sq in. The pump could be used for pumping or suction

1 Pipe connections (suction/discharge)
2 Relief valve
3 Weir
4 Division plate
5 Rotor
6 Stator
7 Stator collar
8 ARL mountings
9 Stuffing box
10 Packing
11 Gland nuts
12 Flywheel
13 Knuckle joints
14 Coupling rod
15 Oil baffle
16 Thrust race
17 Gits oil seal
18 Stiffening plates
19 By-pass nozzle
20 Bearing end cover
21 Outer driving sleeve
22 Rotor driving wheels

E8/11 Pump drive

1 Nitralloy pin
2 Rubber sealing ring
3 Cap nut
4 Lock washer
5 Rotor knuckle joint
6 Naval brass stator sleeve
7 Bush pressed in coupling rod
8 Bonded rubber stator
9 Outer driving sleeve
10 Coupling rod
11 Thrust races
12 Plug
13 Lock washer

E8/12 Compressor, condenser and circulating water pump

1 Compressor
2 Pressure gauge connection
3 Delivery valve
4 HP cut-out connection
5 Cylinder cover
6 Discharge valve plate
7 Cylinder
8 Gland seal bellows
9 Piston
10 Crankshaft
11 Crankcase
12 Sight glass
13 Connecting rod
14 Drier
15 Gas inlet
16 Bedplate
17 End cover
18 Corrosion cover
19 Tube plate
20 Condenser
21 Condenser shell
22 Cooling water inlet
23 Cooling water outlet
24 Auxiliary water supply
25 Thermometer pocket
26 Liquid outlet valve
27 Motor adjusting screw
28 Impeller
29 Pump suction
30 Pump gland
31 Compressor suction connection
32 Circulating water pump
33 Pump discharge
34 'V' belts
35 Vent
36 Ring lubricated bearing
37 Flywheel
38 Electric motor

E Machinery

E8/13

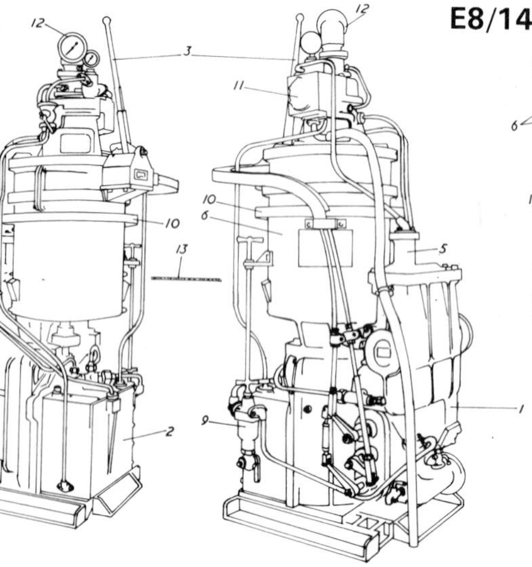

E8/14

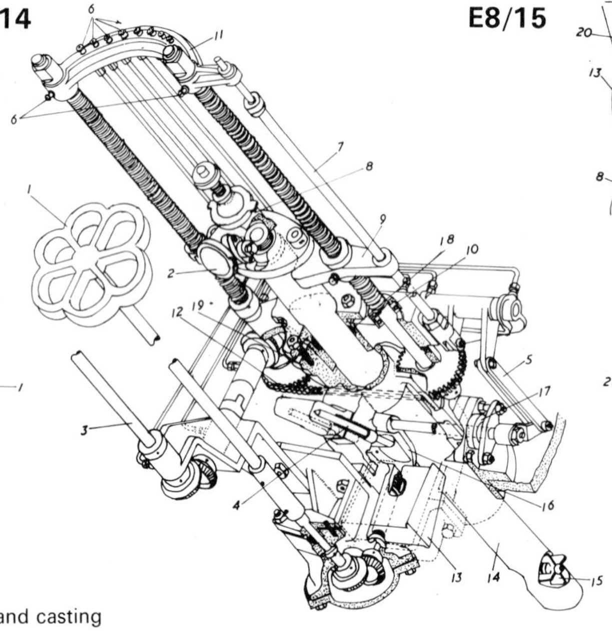

E8/15

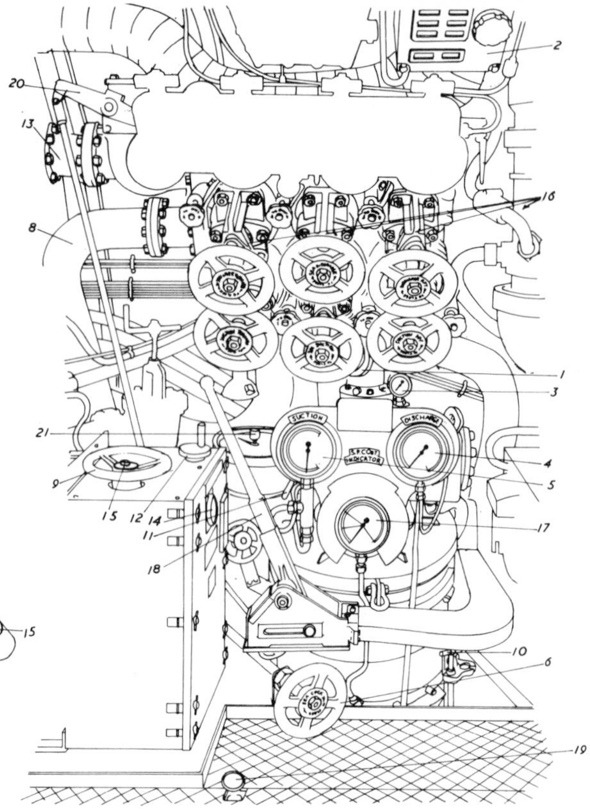

E8/16

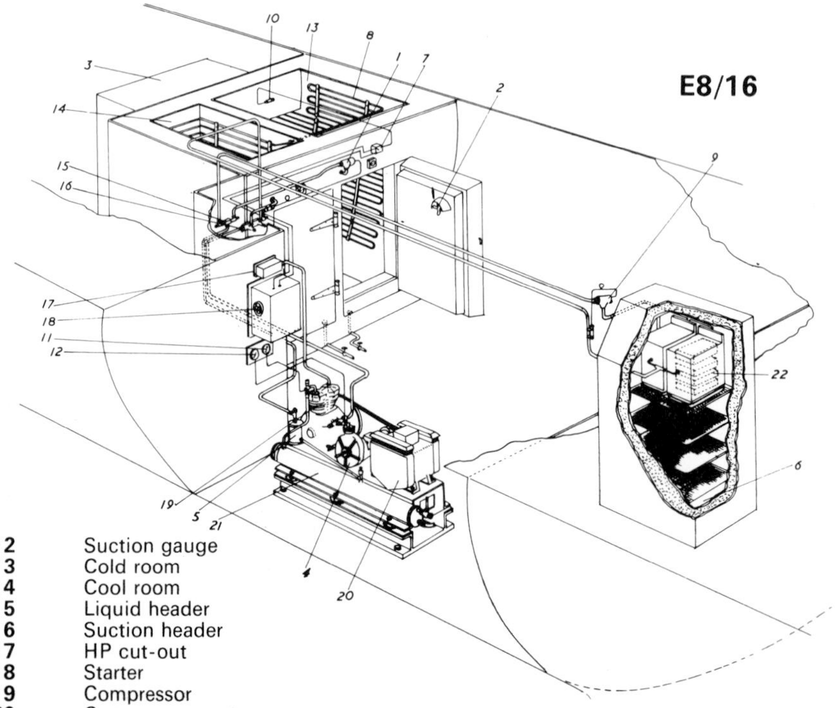

E8/13 Drysdale four-stage series/parallel ballast pump

1 Water pump
2 Cooling chamber for air pump
3 Lever for main control cocks
4 Common suction chamber
5 Needle valve chest
6 Electric motor casing
7 Main discharge
8 Main suction
9 Auto klean strainer
10 Buffer ring
11 Air pump
12 Tacometer
13 Deck level

E8/14 Submarine log Mk 4

The speed and distance recorders were operated by a Chernikeef type water-driven impeller working a simple electrical make and break fitted on the starboard side of the auxiliary machinery space. The log being lowered through a gland under the hull, could be used at any depth but it was difficult to lower below 400ft

1 Sluice valve handwheel
2 Terminal box
3 Raising and lowering shaft
4 Spring-loaded plunger
5 Link mechanism
6 Grease nipples
7 Interlock shaft
8 Oil injector
9 Log carrier
10 Thrust bearing
11 Yoke
12 Driving chain
13 Sluice valve
14 Log tube
15 Impeller
16 Flap valve
17 Dog clutch
18 Tube gland
19 Gland casting

E8/15 Detail view of pump with controls and associated equipment (as seen from the operator's position at deck level; the main body of the pump is below the grating)

1 Tachometer
2 Pump order instrument
3 Air pump vacuum gauge
4 Compound discharge
5 Compound suction
6 Sea cock
7 Starter box
8 Suction pipe to pump
9 Starter handwheel
10 Auto klean strainer handle
11 Air pump control cock
12 Rheostat for speed control
13 Discharge pipe from water pump
14 Ammeter
15 Plunger
16 Six-way valve chest
17 Series/parallel control indicator
18 Lever for series/parallel control
19 Pedal of discharge non-return flap valve
20 Non-return flap valve on pump discharge
21 Flowmeter

E8/16 Refrigeration plant general arrangement

1 Cold and cool room expansion valve
2 Air circulating fan impeller
3 Extension of cold room
4 Circulating water pump
5 Combined drier and strainer
6 Ready-use cupboard
7 Thermostatic control unit
8 Evaporator coils
9 Expansion valve
10 Thermostat bulb
11 Pressure gauge
12 Suction gauge
13 Cold room
14 Cool room
15 Liquid header
16 Suction header
17 HP cut-out
18 Starter
19 Compressor
20 Compressor motor
21 Condenser
22 Ice trays

F Armament

F1 EXTERNAL TORPEDO TUBES, TYPES SE I* AND SE II (all except F1/1 and F1/2 no scale)
Each tube consisted of three gunmetal sections bolted together with spigot joints. All flanges, pads for external fittings and the combined firing and venting pipe were cast solid with the tube. The tube was bored to 21.1in diam; hence they were termed 'dry close fit' type. The SE II tube has a top groove extending its whole length to take the shallow top lug of the torpedo. Note that mines were not discharged from the external tubes and only M Mk V and S Mk VI were carried in the 'A' class internal tubes, which had to be flooded. All the forward edges of the mine were smoothed down to minimise the possibility of damage to the Dermatine rings

F1/1 Forward torpedo tube arrangements (1/96 scale)

1. Open to sea
2. Air inboard vent (AIV) tank
3. Firing pipe
4. Torpedo hatch
5. External firing unit
6. Overhead loading rail
7. Torpedo operating tank
8. 21in dry close fit type external torpedo tube
9. 21in dry semi-slack fit type internal torpedo tube
10. Internal torpedo guide plate
11. Bow shutter in fire position
12. AIV tank inboard vent
13. Mk V mine
14. Torpedo press
15. Torpedo stowage compartment

F1/2 After torpedo tube arrangements (1/96 scale)

1. Orifice for launching torpedo
2. Stern cap open
3. 21in dry close fit type external torpedo tube
4. 21in dry semi-slack fit type internal torpedo tube
5. Firing pipe
6. Mk V mine
7. AIV tank inboard vent
8. AIV tank
9. Torpedo lifting press
10. Torpedo operating tank
11. Torpedo stowage compartment
12. Torpedo loading hatch

F1/1

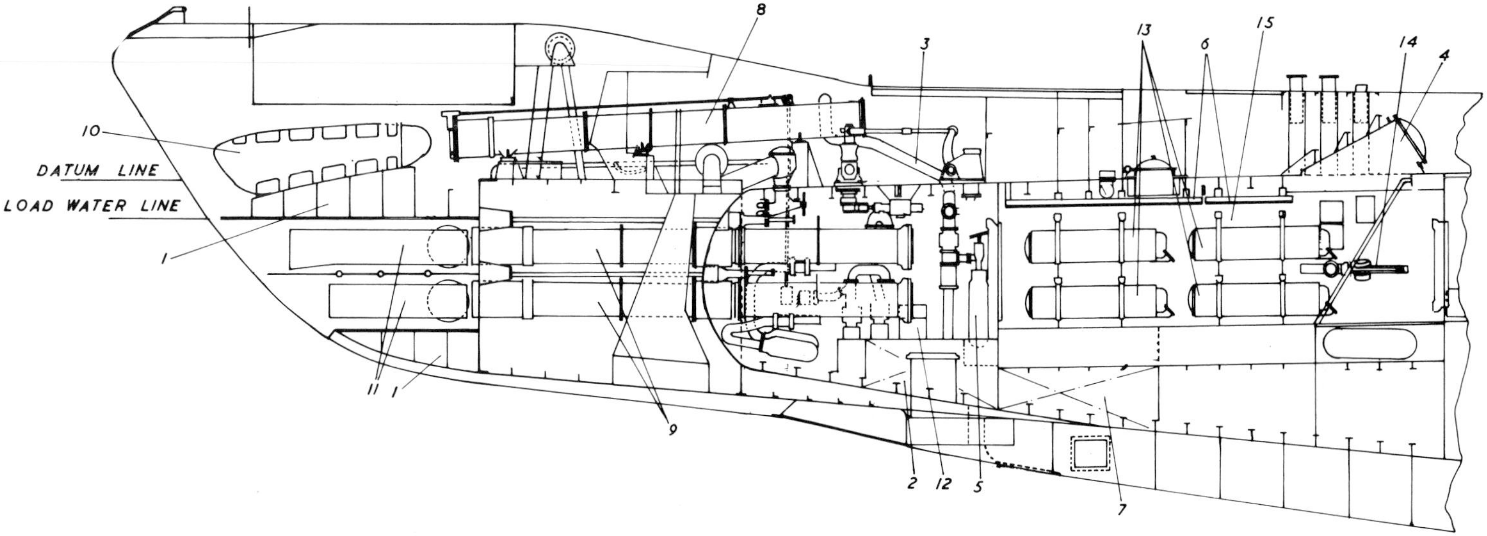

F1/2

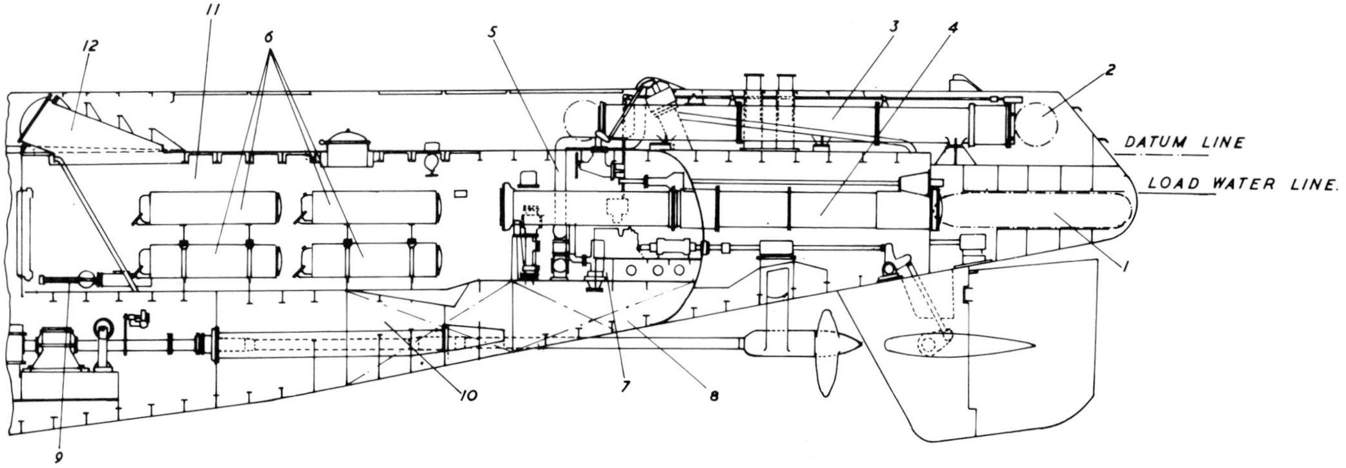

F Armament

F1/3 Diagrammatic arrangement of pipe connections (arrows indicate direction of motion or flow when door is opening)

1 Operating cylinder
2 Ramrod
3 Front door
4 Pressure hull stop valves
5 Pressure gauge
6 Replenishing tank (glycerine and water)
7 Semi-rotary pump
8 Suction valve
9 Relief valve
10 Shut-off cock
11 Open end for tank filling
12 Glycerine by-pass valve
13 Control valves
14 Power cylinder
15 Relief valve
16 Drain to bilge
17 Glycerine and water cylinder
18 Telemotor pressure
19 Telemotor control cock
20 Telemotor return

F1/4 Diagrammatic arrangement of HP firing gear

1 Side stop
2 Tube
3 Pressure gauge
4 Hand firing valve
5 To head space
6 Hull drain valve
7 Front door interlock
8 Interlock
9 Hand emergency cock
10 Two-way test cock
11 Water non-return valve
12 Filter
13 Vent unit
14 Open end pipe
15 Drain
16 AIV cock and motor
17 Tundish
18 60lb relief valve
19 Compensating unit
20 AIV tank
21 Charging valve
22 Relief valve
23 Drain valve
24 To bilge
25 Impulse cut-off vent unit
26 Small firing valve and motor
27 HP firing gear and reservoir
28 Capacity chamber and differential valve

F1/5 Air interlock on hand emergency cock

1 To tube
2 From hand firing valve
3 Cap
4 Air interlock
5 Spring catch
6 To power-operated side stop
7 Piston valve
8 Hand emergency cock operating lever
9 Drain to bilge
10 To air inboard vent tank

F1/3

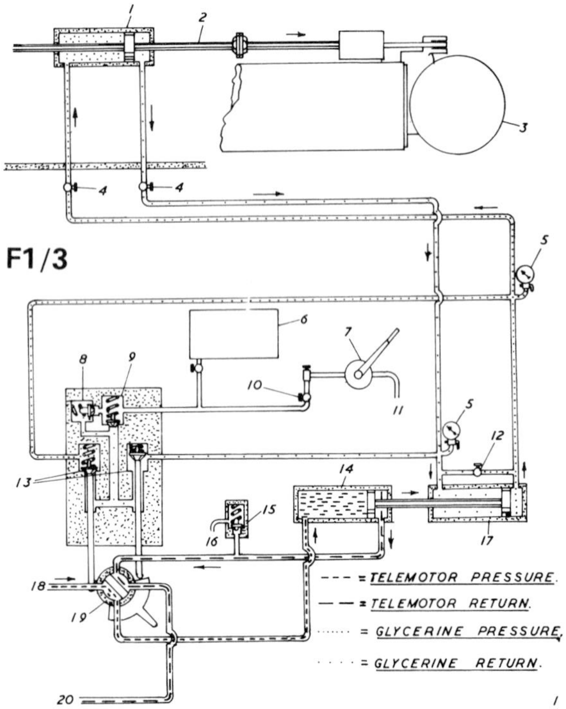

F1/4

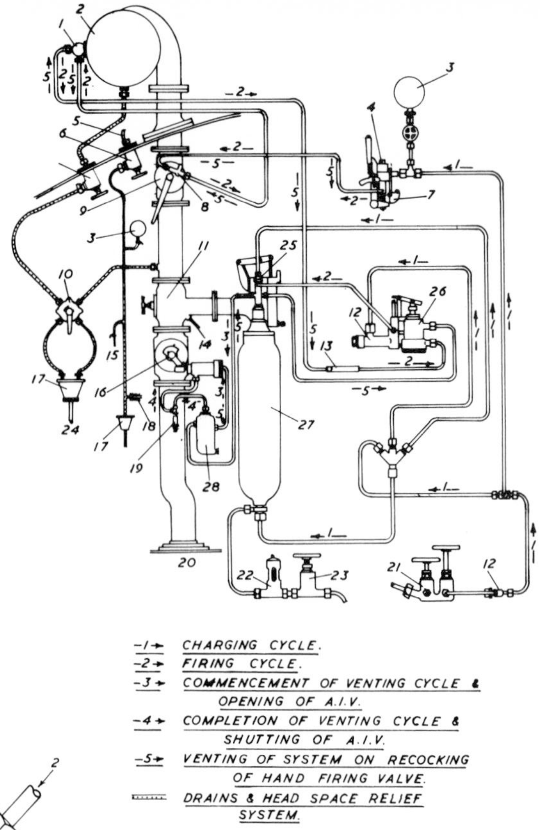

F1/5

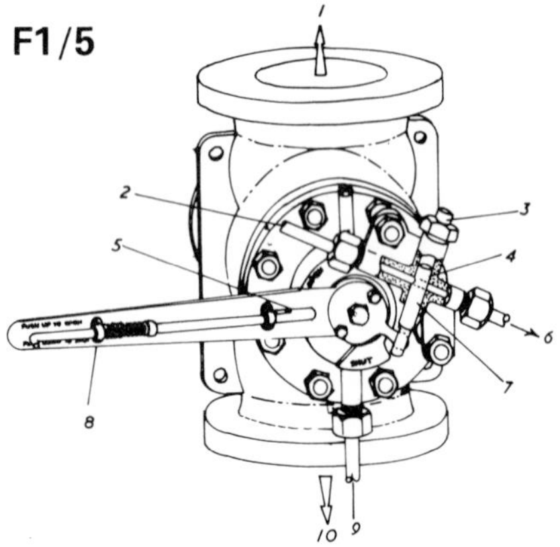

F1/6

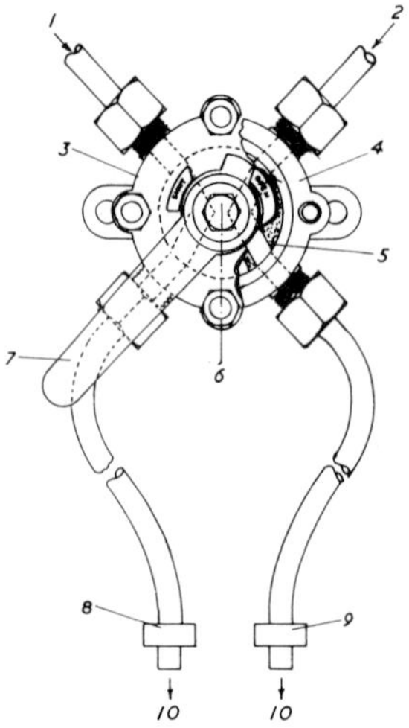

F1/7

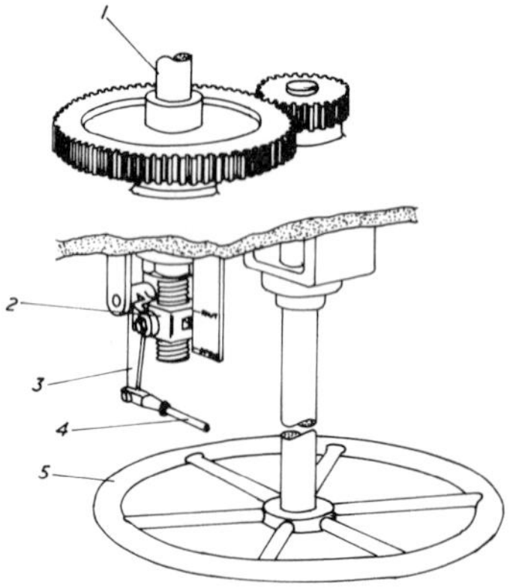

F1/6 Arrangement of two-way test cock

1 From tube drain
2 From combined firing and venting pipe
3 Cover
4 Body cover partly removed
5 Plug sectioned to show port
6 Centreline of handle in shut position
7 Handle
8 Tube drain
9 Firing pipe drain
10 To tundish

F1/7 Screw-operated interlock (hand-operated)

1 Front door operating shaft
2 Screwed block
3 Bell crane lever
4 Arens control cable to hand firing valve
5 Handwheel

F1/8 Screw-operated interlock (power-operated)

1 Front door operating shaft
2 Indicator
3 Arens control cable to hand firing valve
4 Single toothed wheel
5 Single toothed rack
6 Handwheel

F1/8

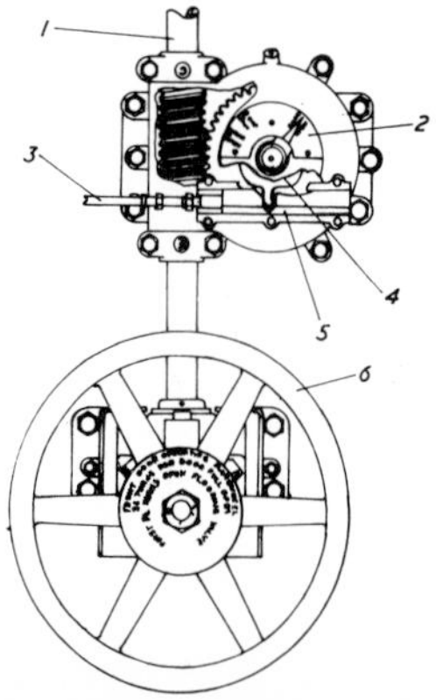

F1/9

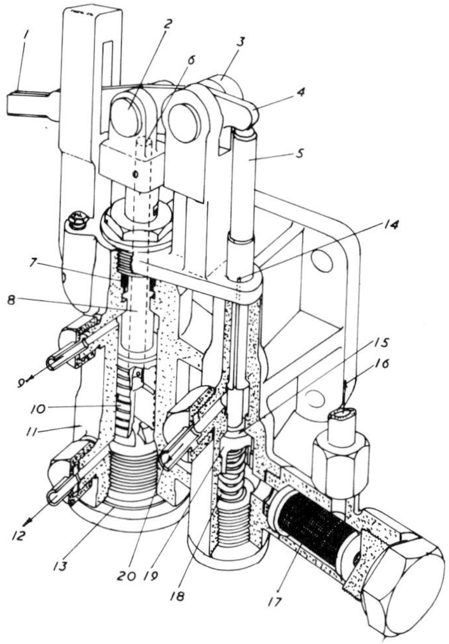

F1/10

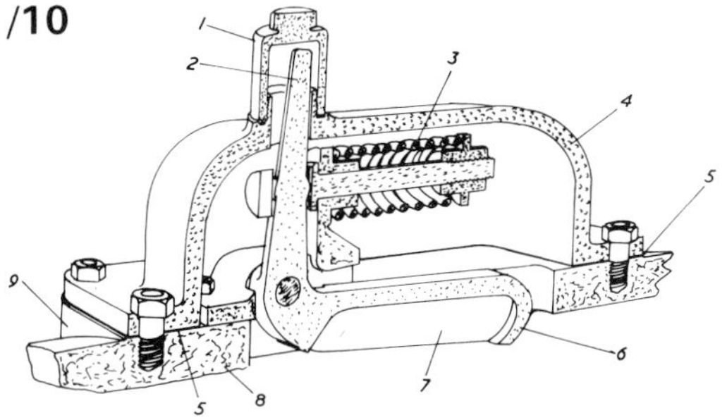

F1/11

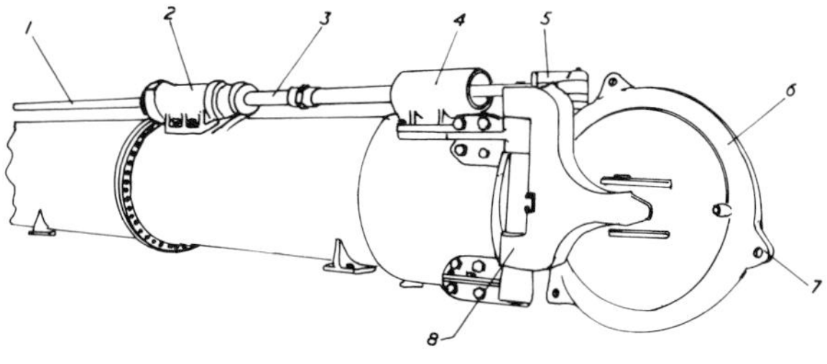

F1/12

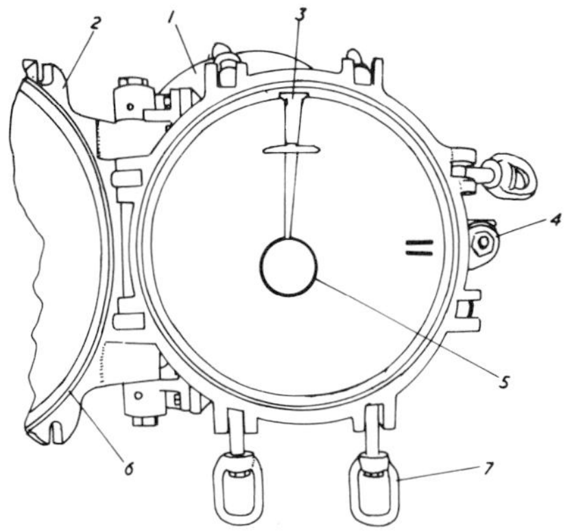

F1/13

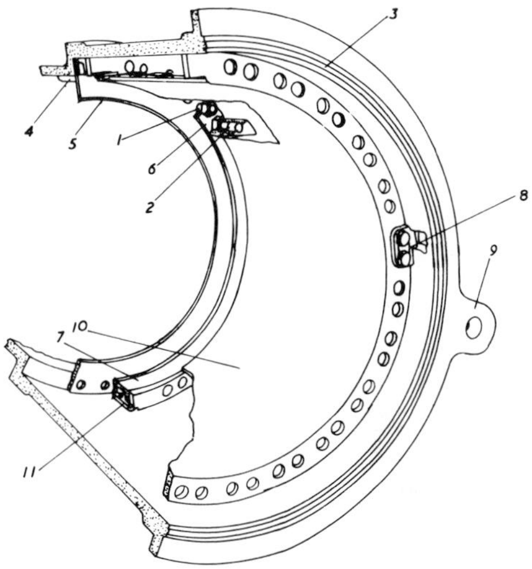

F1/14

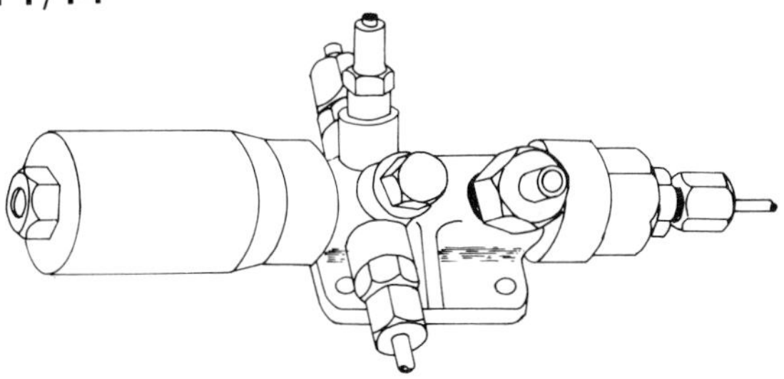

F1/9 Small firing valve and motor
1 Lever extension
2 Crosshead
3 Pivot
4 Lever
5 Valve stem
6 Leak-off to atmosphere
7 Gland
8 Piston rod
9 To valve unit HP firing gear
10 Piston
11 Small firing valve motor
12 To power-operated side stop
13 Joint washer
14 Exhaust groove
15 Valve seating
16 To HP firing reservoir
17 Strainer
18 Spring
19 Small firing valve
20 To HP firing gear

F1/10 Latch-tripper, SE II tube
1 Tripper cap
2 Handle
3 Spring
4 Tripper box
5 Rubber insertion
6 Latch tripper
7 Webb
8 Tube
9 Tube pad

F1/11 Front section, SE II tube
1 Shaft
2 Operating cylinder
3 External ramrod
4 Crosshead and guide
5 Link
6 Front door
7 Door lug
8 Hinge

F1/12 SE II tube (looking inside from rear end)
1 Combined firing and vent pipe
2 Rear door
3 Top groove
4 Power-operated side-stop
5 Dermatine washer
6 Joint washer
7 Ring nut

F1/13 Arrangement of head space, SE II tube
1 Stud
2 Dowel pin
3 Bead
4 Top groove
5 Dermatine ring
6 Retaining ring
7 Floating ring
8 Keep plate
9 Door lug
10 Lantern frame
11 Locating plate

F1/14 Impluse out-off unit

F2 **INTERNAL TORPEDO TUBES (all except F2/1 to F2/5 no scale)**
Each tube was made in two sections called the inboard and outboard lengths. The inboard length was approximately 110in long made of 0.375in steel plate rolled and welded so that the internal diameter was 21.75in. A flange was welded to one end of the inboard length and the rear door flange to the other. The outboard length was in two portions: a long portion of 0.5in steel plate rolled and welded to 21.75in internal diameter. Outboard was a 40in head space of enlarged internal diameter

F2/1–2 **Layout of HP firing gear and AIV pipes (1/48 scale)**

F2/1 **Profile**

F2/2 **Cross-section**

1. Steel pipe
2. Differential valve and capacity chamber
3. Small firing valve
4. Power-operated side stop
5. HP firing unit
6. Water non-return valve
7. Firing motor
8. Air inboard vent sluice valve
9. EIV cock
10. Valve unit

F2/3–5 **Arrangement of bow cap operating gear (1/48 scale)**
The function of the bow cap was to form a water-tight joint at the outboard end of the tube at any depth at which the submarine may operate. A hinged shutter was fitted in conjunction with the bowcap to preserve the streamline of the vessel when the cap was closed. Outside the bow or stern cap the casing was cut away to provide an orifice of suitable shape to ensure that the torpedo was fired clear of the ship without risk of fouling; holes were cut in the plating to allow a free flow of water during the venting cycle obtaining invisible discharge

F2/3 **Profile**

F2/4 **Cross-section**

F2/5 **Plan view**

1. No 1 torpedo tube
2. No 2 torpedo tube
3. No 3 torpedo tube
4. No 4 torpedo tube
5. Bow cap open
6. Outline of emerging torpedo

F2/1

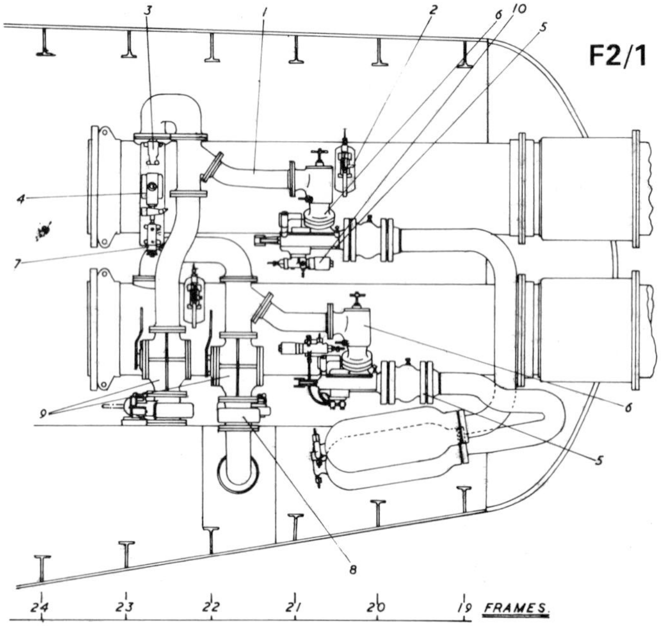

F2/2

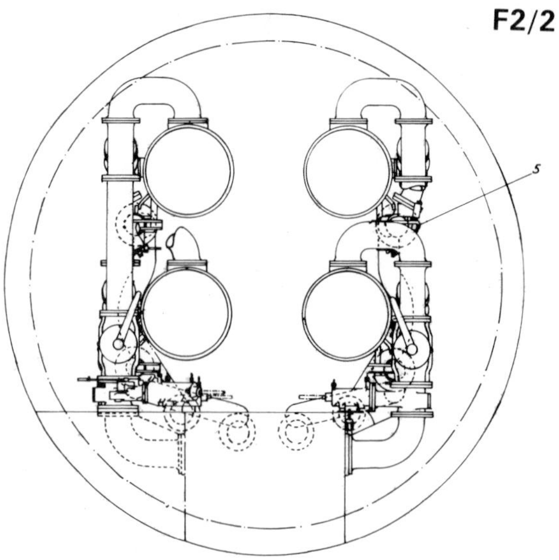

F2/3

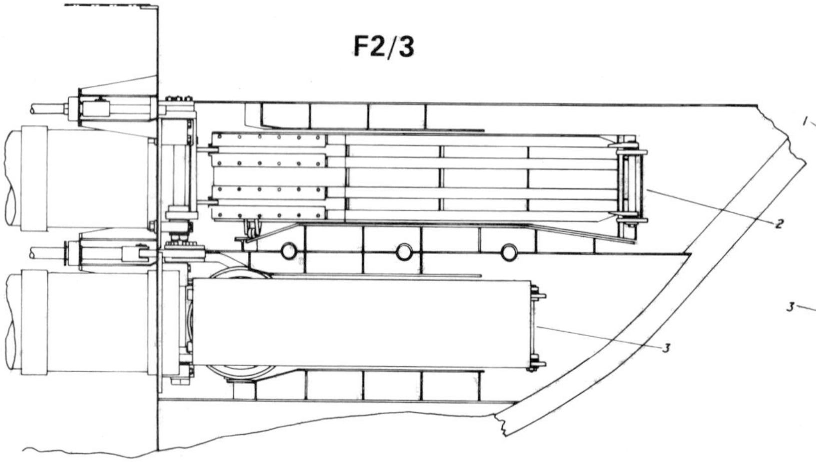

F2/4

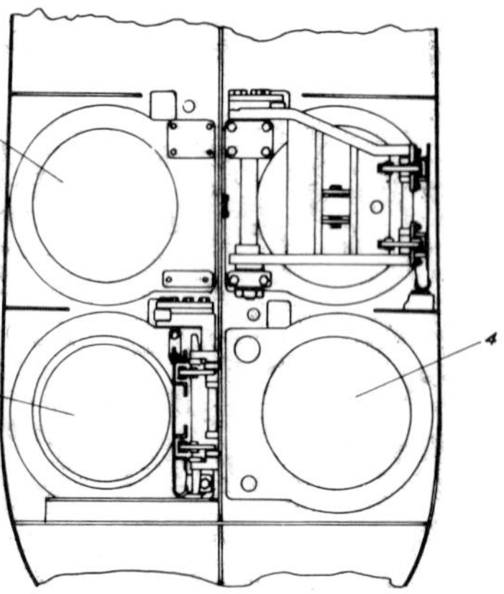

F2/5

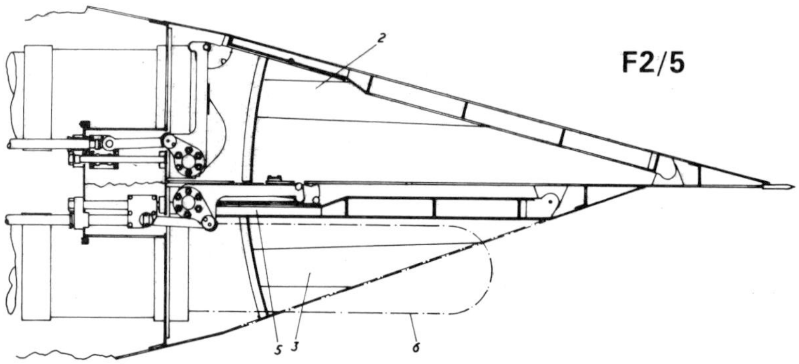

F2/6

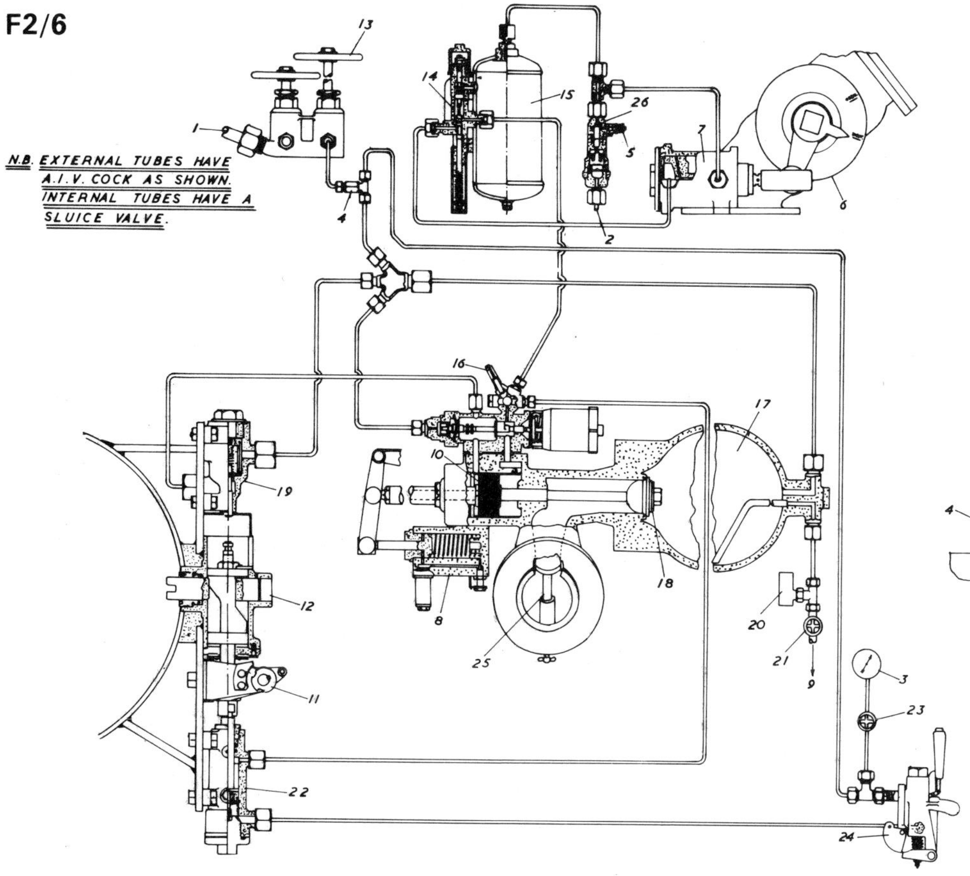

N.B. EXTERNAL TUBES HAVE
A.I.V. COCK AS SHOWN.
INTERNAL TUBES HAVE A
SLUICE VALVE.

F2/9

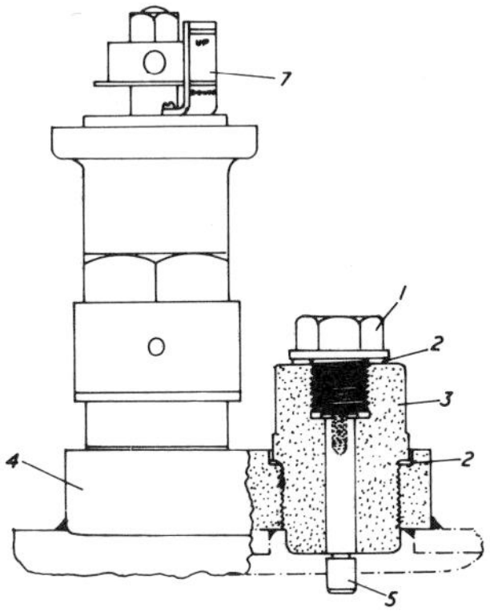

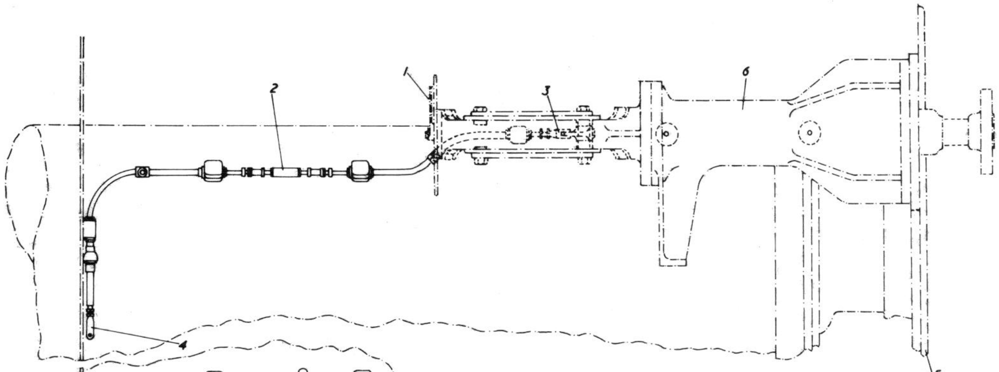

F2/7

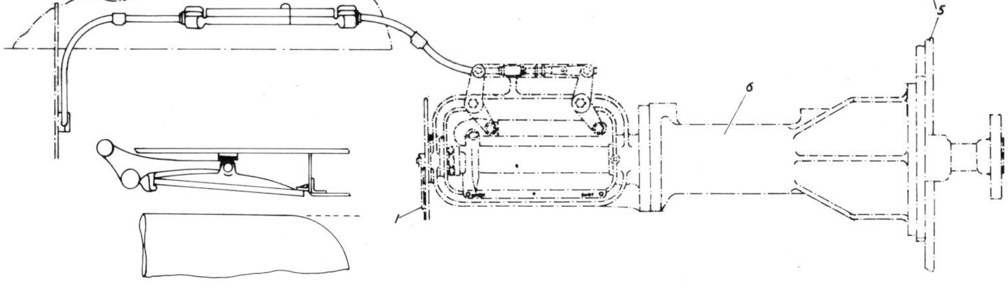

F2/8

F2/6	**Diagrammatic arrangement of HP firing gear**
1	Air from main line through strainer
2	Water at sea pressure
3	Reservoir pressure gauge
4	Strainer
5	Leak off
6	AIV cock
7	AIV motor
8	Dashpot
9	To bilge
10	Piston
11	Limit stop
12	PO side stop
13	Charging valve
14	Differential valve
15	Capacity chamber
16	Release valve
17	Firing reservoir
18	Large firing valve
19	Small firing valve
20	Relief valve
21	Drain valve
22	Firing motor
23	Stop valve
24	Hand firing valve
25	Water non-return valve
26	Compensating unit
F2/7–8	**Bow cap interlock**
F2/7	**Port tube looking outboard**
F2/8	**Plan of port tubes**
1	Bow cap indicator
2	Turnbuckle for adjustment of Arens control
3	Arens control connection to link mechanism
4	Arens control connection to cam positioned under the hand firing valve
5	Torpedo tube compartment bulkhead
6	Bow cap power cylinder
F2/9–10	**Mine-stop**
	For location of 'M' Mk V mine when loaded into the internal tube. The shear pin shears on discharge
F2/9	**Hand mine-stop**

F2/10

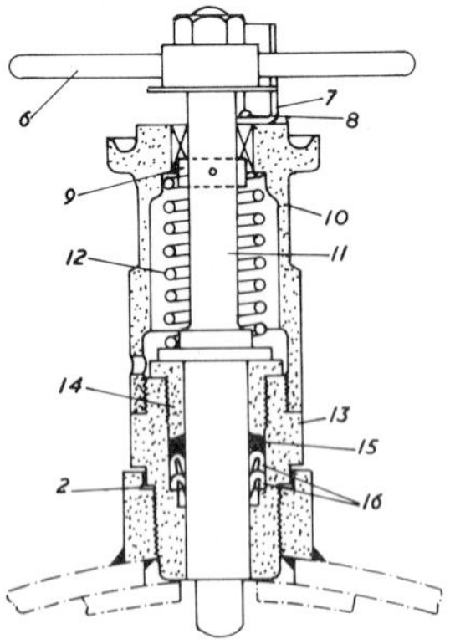

F2/11

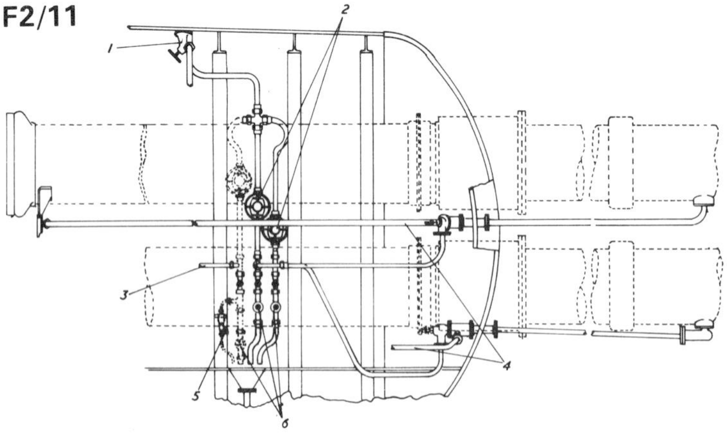

F2/13

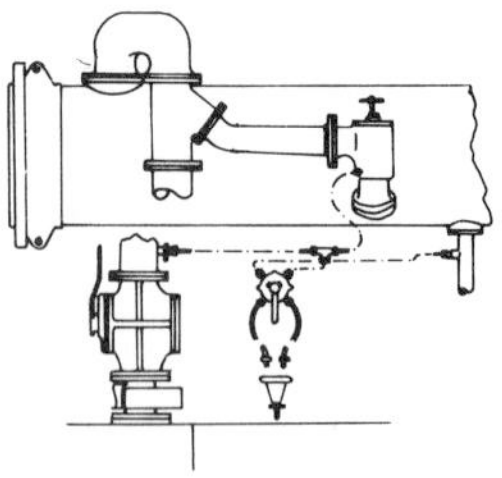

F2/14

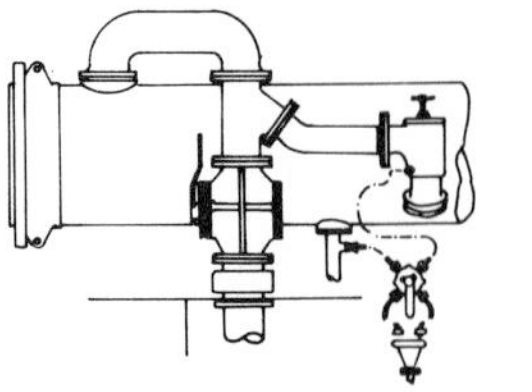

F2/15

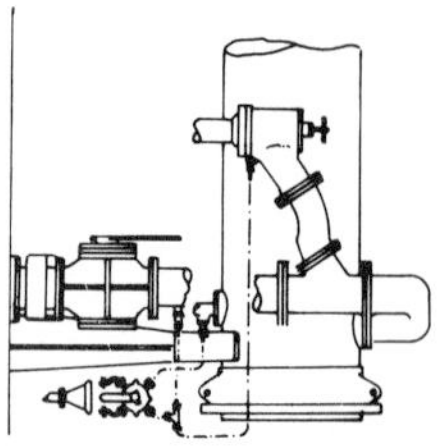

F2/10 Shear pin-stop
1 Plug
2 Washer
3 Adaptor
4 Pad
5 Pin
6 Handwheel
7 Indicator
8 Round head screw
9 Cotter
10 Spring box
11 Spindle
12 Spring
13 Adaptor
14 Gland nut
15 Plastic header
16 SEA ring

F2/11 Arrangement of head space flooding valves
1 1¼in bore hull valve
2 1¼in diameter bore screw-down valves
3 To hull valve for external tube
4 Pipe lead to rear door interlock cock
5 Drain cock
6 Relief valves

F2/12 View looking forward from 26 water-tight bulkhead (Acheron)
1 Recess for external HP air reservoir
2 AIV tank
3 AIV sluice valve and motor
4 Draining and flooding valves
5 Emergency valve
6 Rear door and head space drain interlock
7 HE cock
8 Reservoir drain and relief valves
9 Capacity chamber
10 Depth gear
11 Valve unit
12 Charging valves
13 Hand firing control valves
14 Control panel
15 Head space flooding valves
16 Side stop space flooding valve and firing motor
17 Master valve
18 GA gear Mk XI
19 GA gear Mk VIII

F2/13–15 Arrangement of two-way test cock (diagrammatic view of starboard tubes)

F2/13 No 1 tube

F2/14 No 3 tube

F2/15 No 7 tube

F2/12

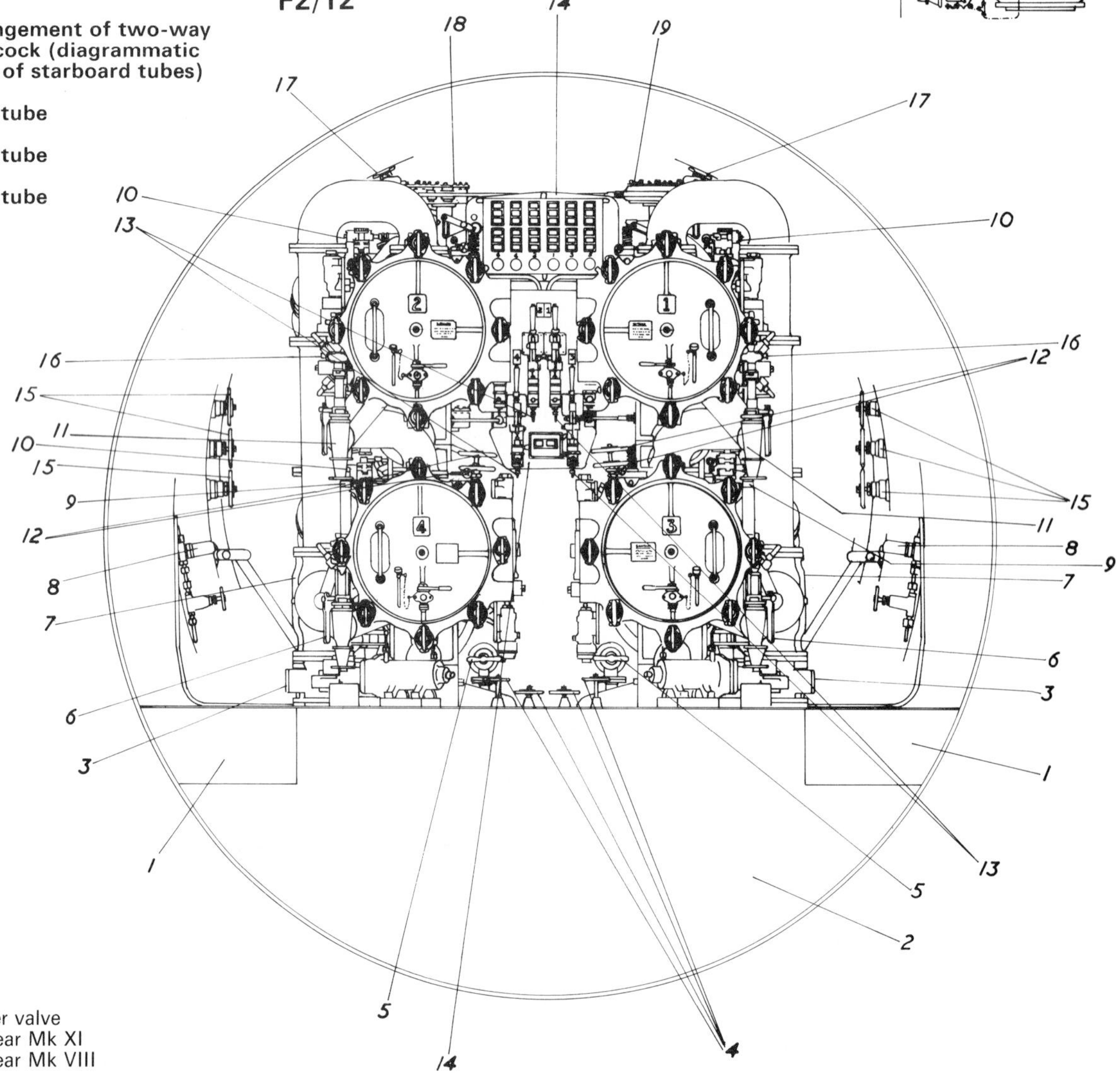

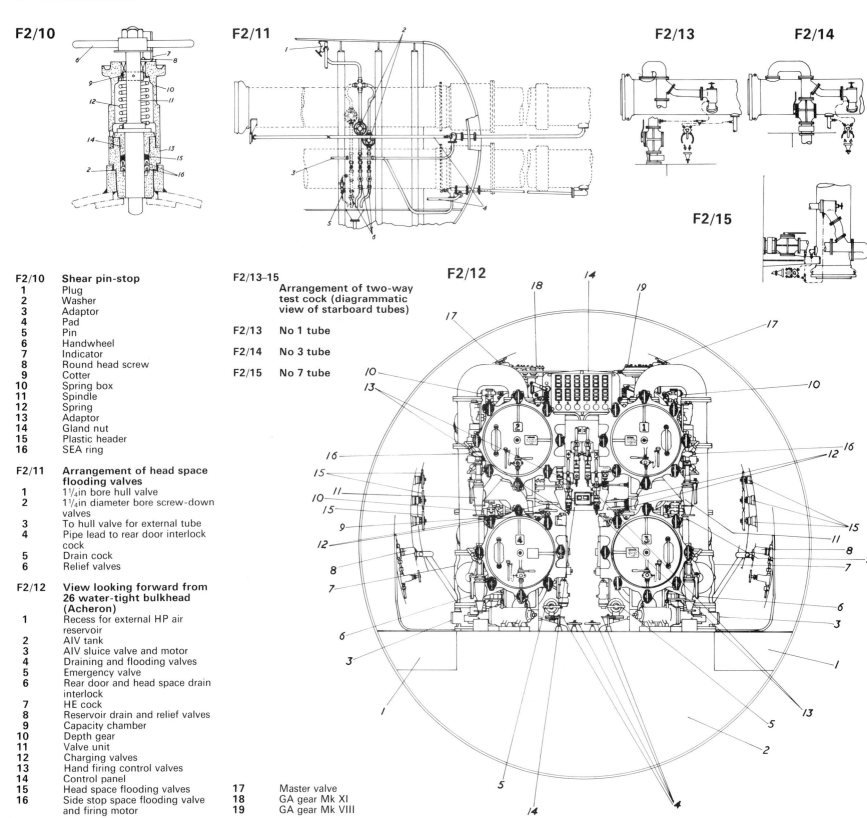

F3/1

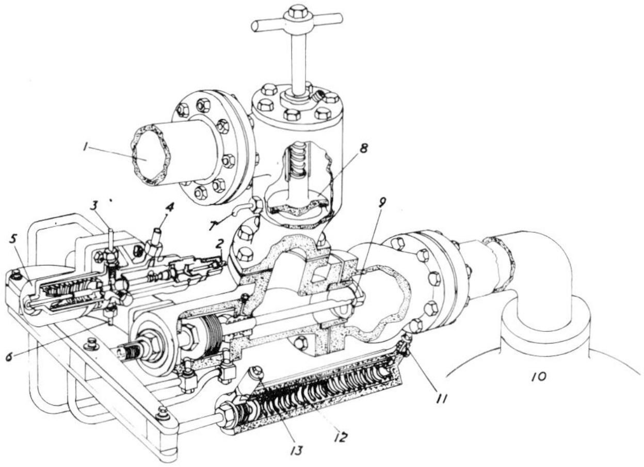

F4/1

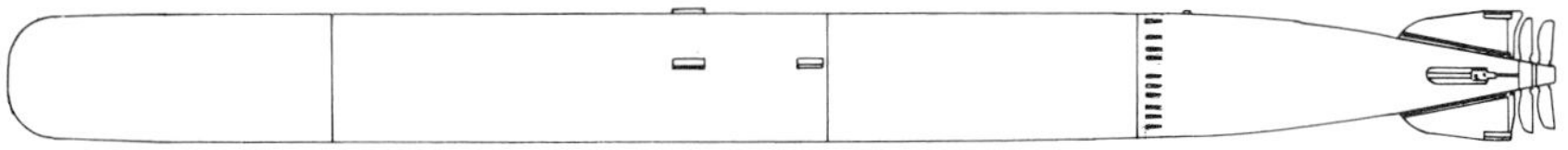

F4/2

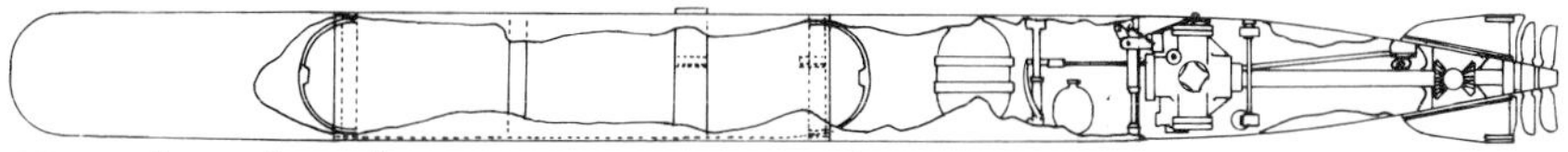

F4/3

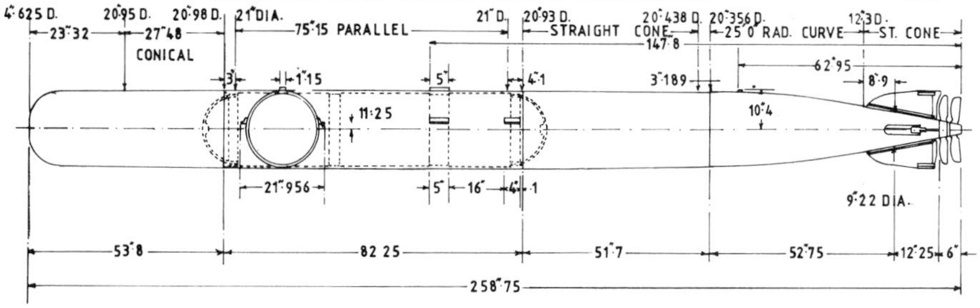

F4/4

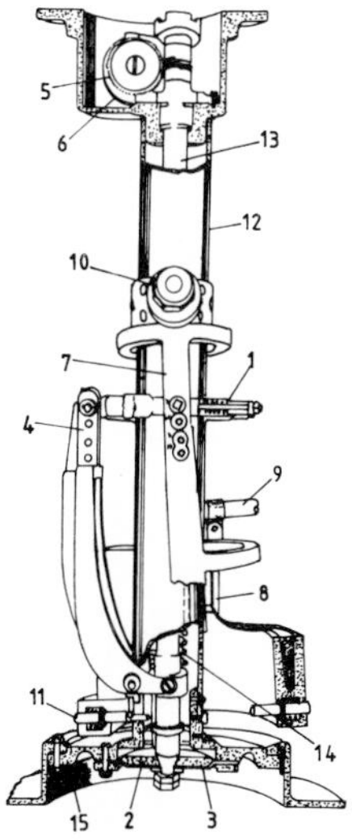

F4/5

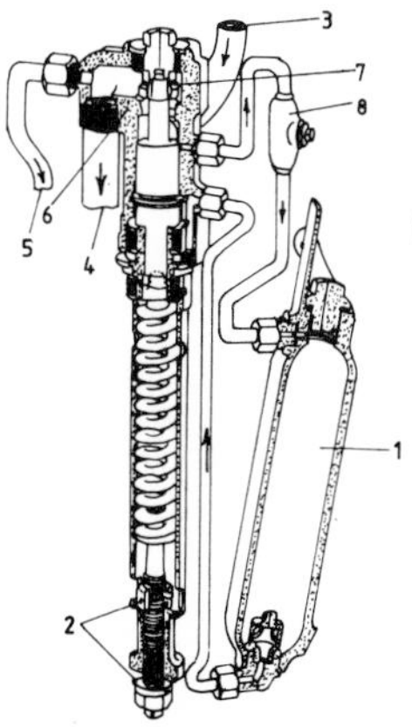

F4/6

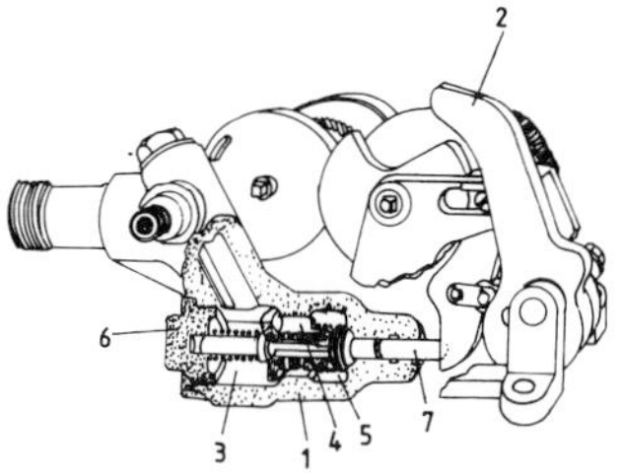

F3 TORPEDO TUBE FITTINGS AND EQUIPMENT (no scale)

F3/1 Components of HP firing gear
1 To torpedo tube
2 From reservoir charging valve
3 To shutting side of small firing valve
4 From small firing valves
5 Adjusting sleeve
6 To differential valve
7 Drain to two-way test cock
8 Water non-return valve
9 Large firing valve
10 Firing reservoir
11 Control valve
12 Dashpot
13 Reservoir

F4 21in Mk VIII TORPEDO

F4/1 External view

F4/2 Sectional elevation

F4/3 Details of dimensions

F4/4 LTA (depth gear)
1 Spring link box
2 Valve plate
3 Neoprene disc
4 Bell crank lever
5 Wormwheel
6 Depth index plate
7 Gallows arm
8 Supporting rod
9 Gab rod
10 Pivot cap
11 Buffer stop
12 Centre tube column
13 Depth adjusting spindle
14 Hydrostatic valve spring
15 Hydrostatic valve casing

F4/5 Main reducing valve and valve lubrication
1 Reducer oil bottle
2 Limit stops
3 Air from group valve
4 Air to generator
5 Air to check valve
6 Plug valve seating
7 Plug valve
8 Non-return oil valve

F4/6 Starting valves
1 Valve casing
2 Air lever
3 Supply chamber
4 Main valve
5 Discharge chamber
6 Cap
7 Starting valve plunger

F4/7 **60lb safety valve buoyancy chamber**
1 Valve
2 Access door
3 Spring
4 Spindle
5 Split pin
6 Washer
7 Disc valve facing

F4/8 **Igniter firing gear**
1 Breech blocks and strikers
2 Igniter pockets
3 Firing spring
4 Igniter hammers
5 Cocking spring
6 Cocking lever
7 Crank lever
8 Firing rod
9 Roller

F4/9 **General arrangement of tail and horizontal rudder connections**
1 Horizontal rudder
2 Vertical rudder
3 Crank
4 Diving rod tube
5 Crosshead pivot
6 Rudder adjustment
7 Rudder crosshead
8 Connecting rod
9 Horizontal slider
10 Diving rod
11 Vertical rudder bearer

F4/10 **Propeller shafts and tail gearing**
1 Baffle plate
2 Main propeller shaft
3 Centre tube
4 Guard ring
5 Forward crown wheel
6 After crown wheel
7 Intermediate wheel
8 Forward propeller
9 After propeller
10 Crosshead
11 Six-spline coupling
12 Vertical stabilising fin
13 Vertical rudder

F4/11 **Steering engine and vertical rudder connections**
1 Air leads from gyro
2 Guard ring
3 Crosshead
4 Vertical rudder
5 Piston
6 Inner pintle
7 Oil bottle
8 Distance rod
9 Securing screw

F4/12 **Engine detail, cooling water system**
Water passes through channels in engine casing and is sprayed on to crank and connecting rod
1 Piston
2 Connecting rod
3 Crank pin and bush

F4/7

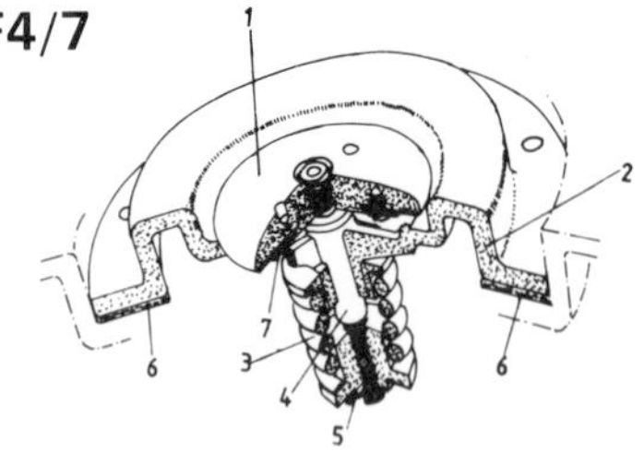

F4/8

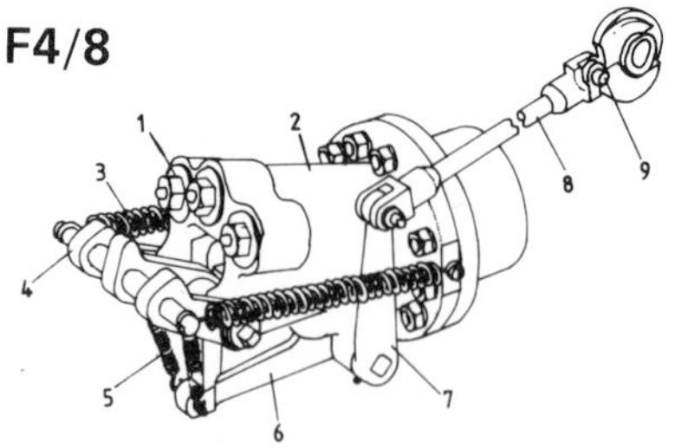

F4/9

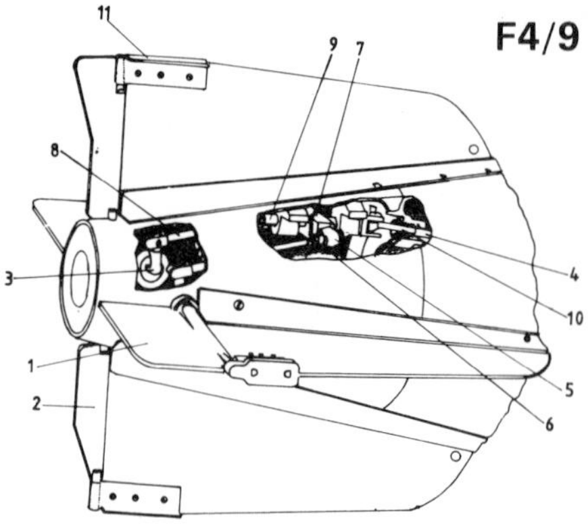

F4/10

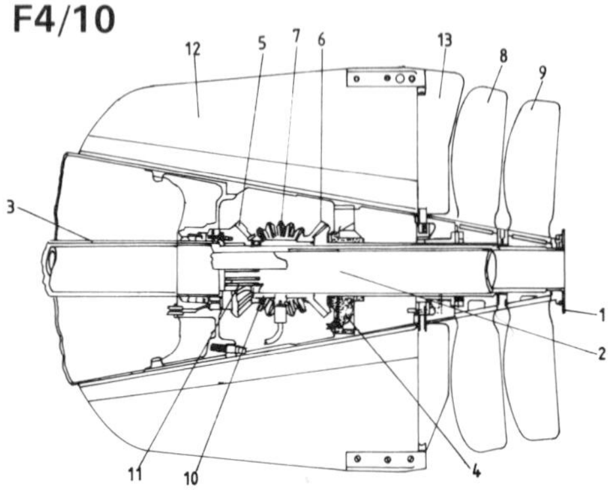

F4/13

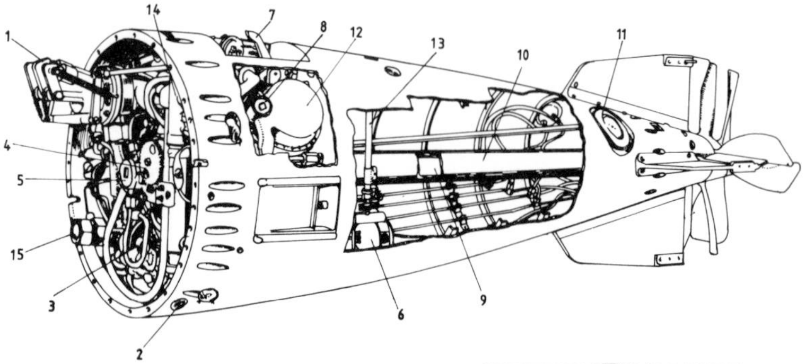

F4/11

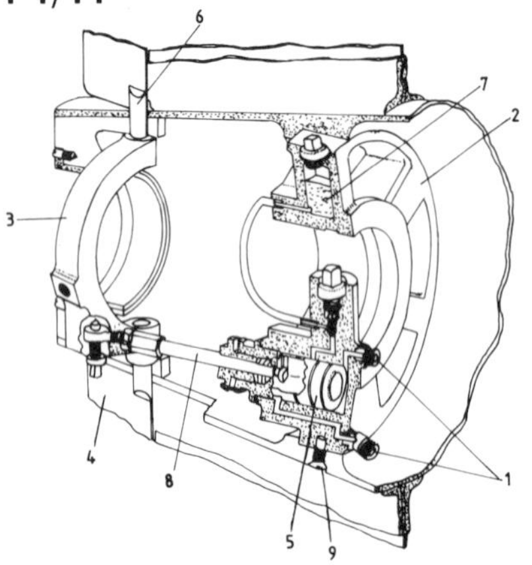

F4/12

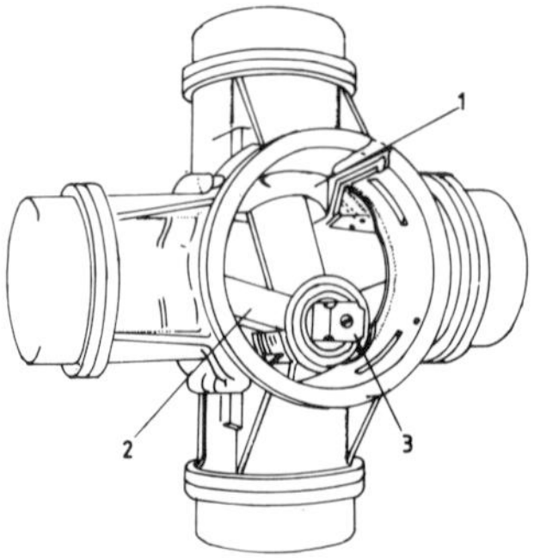

F4/14

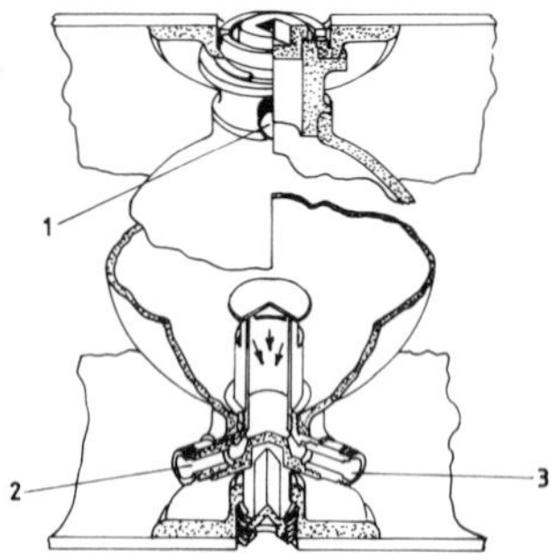

F4/15

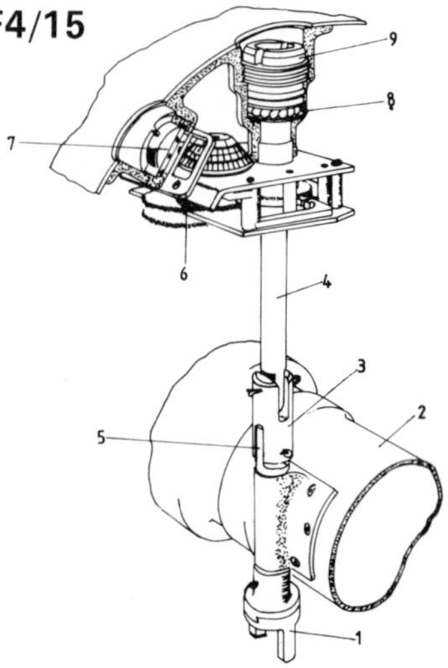

F4/13 **Torpedo afterbody**
1 Hammers
2 Speed setting location
3 Oil distributor
4 Water pump
5 Fuel timing valve
6 Air blast gyro
7 Air lever
8 Valve cap
9 Main propeller shaft
10 Centre tube
11 60lb safety valve
12 Cylinder head
13 Gyro angling spindle
14 Main reducer
15 Multiple pipe coupling

F4/14 **Fuel bottle**
1 Air inlet
2 Injection fuel to strainer in engine room
3 Pilot fuel to strainer in engine room

F4/15 **External gyro angling gear**
1 Forked clutch
2 Centre tube buoyancy chamber
3 Jaw coupling
4 Angling spindle
5 Intermediate spindle
6 Sighting frame
7 Window disc
8 Single thrust bearing
9 Retaining nut

F4/16

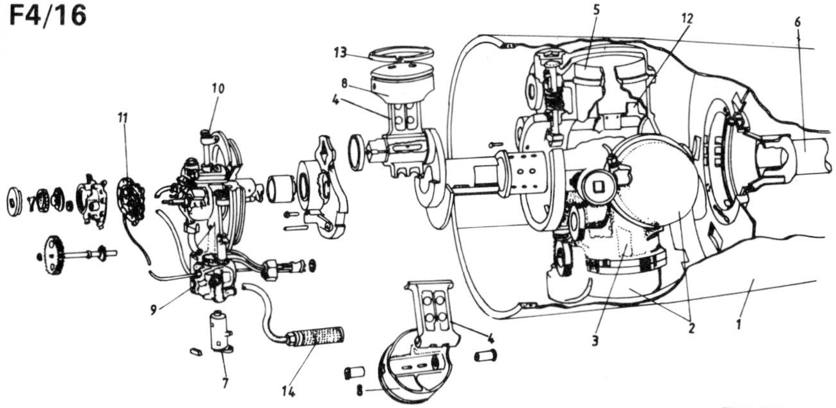

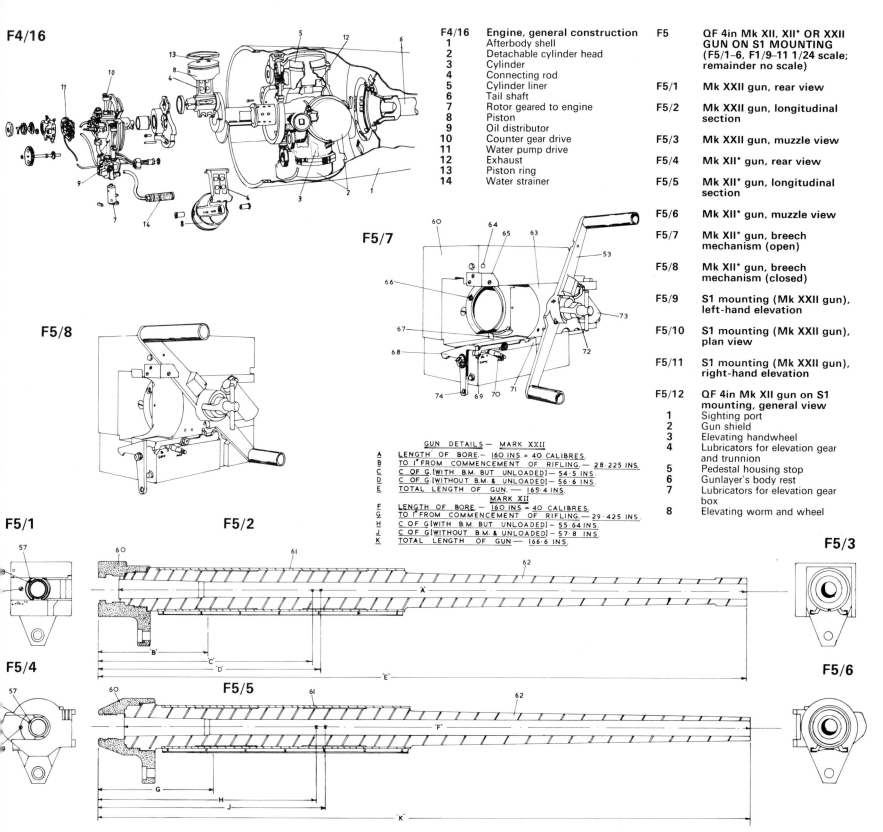

F4/16 **Engine, general construction**
1 Afterbody shell
2 Detachable cylinder head
3 Cylinder
4 Connecting rod
5 Cylinder liner
6 Tail shaft
7 Rotor geared to engine
8 Piston
9 Oil distributor
10 Counter gear drive
11 Water pump drive
12 Exhaust
13 Piston ring
14 Water strainer

F5/7

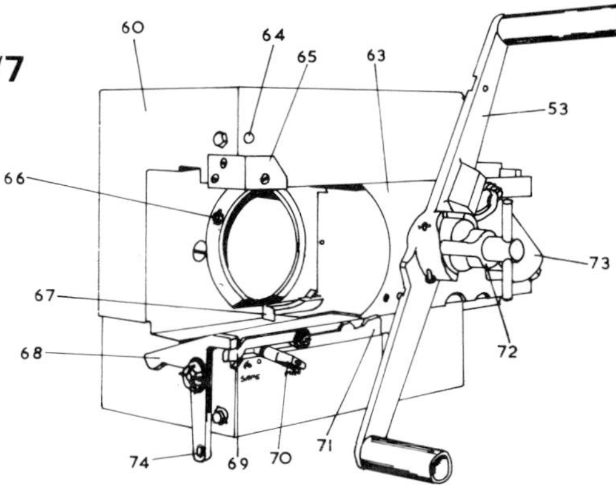

F5/8

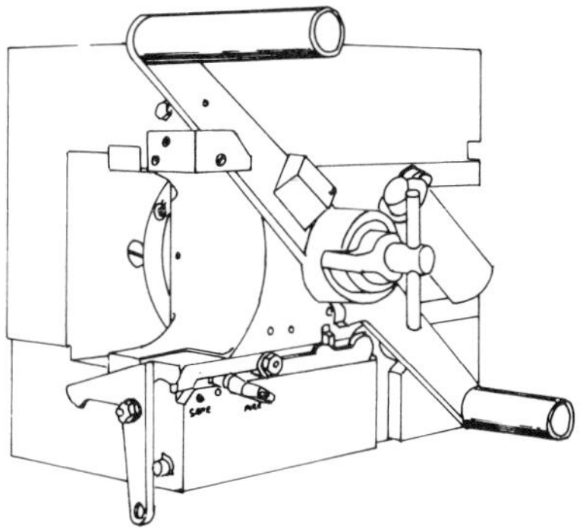

GUN DETAILS — MARK XXII

A LENGTH OF BORE.— 160 INS. = 40 CALIBRES.
B TO 1" FROM COMMENCEMENT OF RIFLING.— 28·225 INS.
C C OF G.[WITH B.M. BUT UNLOADED] — 54·5 INS.
D C OF G.[WITHOUT B.M. & UNLOADED] — 56·6 INS.
E TOTAL LENGTH OF GUN.— 165·4 INS.

MARK XII

F LENGTH OF BORE.— 160 INS. = 40 CALIBRES.
G TO 1" FROM COMMENCEMENT OF RIFLING.— 29·425 INS.
H C OF G[WITH B.M. BUT UNLOADED] — 55·64 INS.
J C OF G[WITHOUT B.M. & UNLOADED] — 57·8 INS.
K TOTAL LENGTH OF GUN — 166·6 INS.

F5 **QF 4in Mk XII, XII* OR XXII GUN ON S1 MOUNTING (F5/1–6, F1/9–11 1/24 scale; remainder no scale)**

F5/1 **Mk XXII gun, rear view**

F5/2 **Mk XXII gun, longitudinal section**

F5/3 **Mk XXII gun, muzzle view**

F5/4 **Mk XII* gun, rear view**

F5/5 **Mk XII* gun, longitudinal section**

F5/6 **Mk XII* gun, muzzle view**

F5/7 **Mk XII* gun, breech mechanism (open)**

F5/8 **Mk XII* gun, breech mechanism (closed)**

F5/9 **S1 mounting (Mk XXII gun), left-hand elevation**

F5/10 **S1 mounting (Mk XXII gun), plan view**

F5/11 **S1 mounting (Mk XXII gun), right-hand elevation**

F5/12 **QF 4in Mk XII gun on S1 mounting, general view**
1 Sighting port
2 Gun shield
3 Elevating handwheel
4 Lubricators for elevation gear and trunnion
5 Pedestal housing stop
6 Gunlayer's body rest
7 Lubricators for elevation gear box
8 Elevating worm and wheel

F5/1

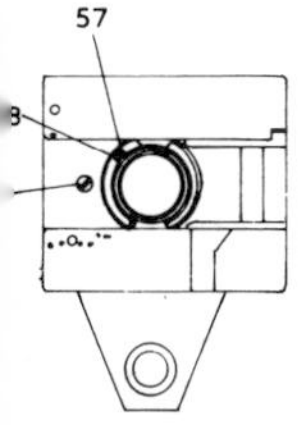

F5/2

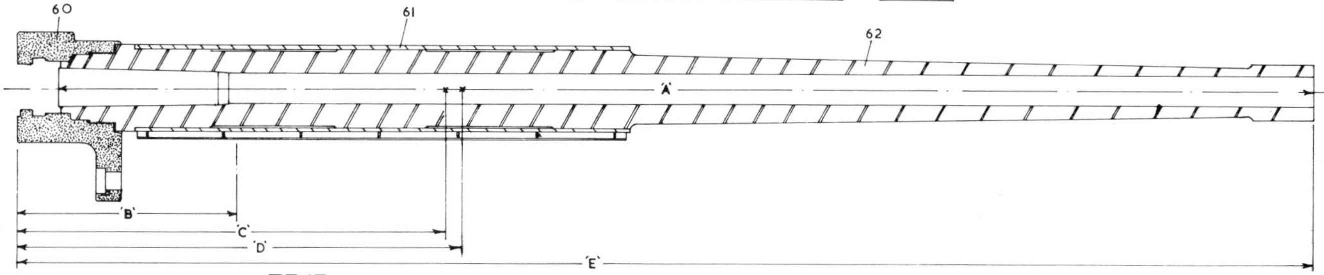

F5/3

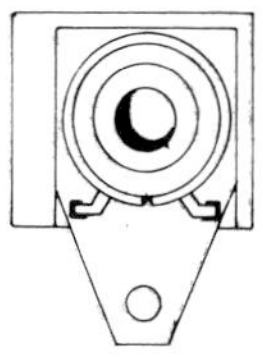

F5/4

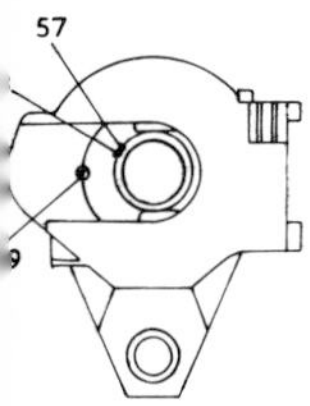

F5/5

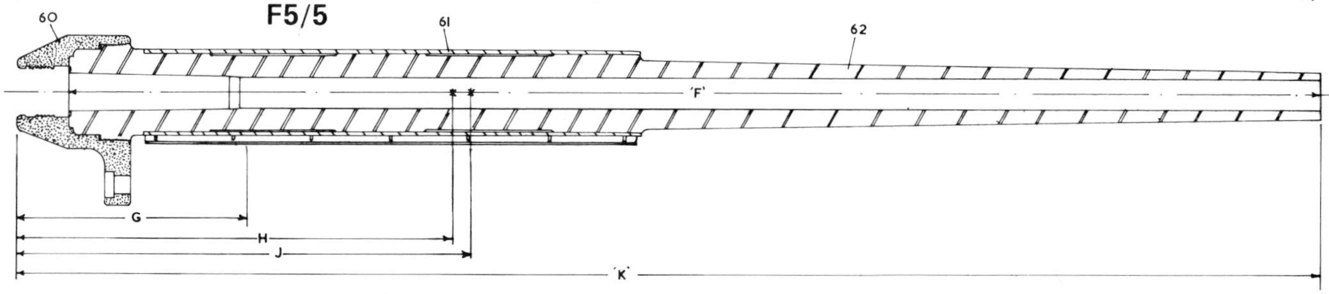

F5/6

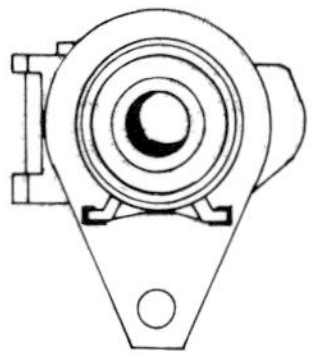

F5/9

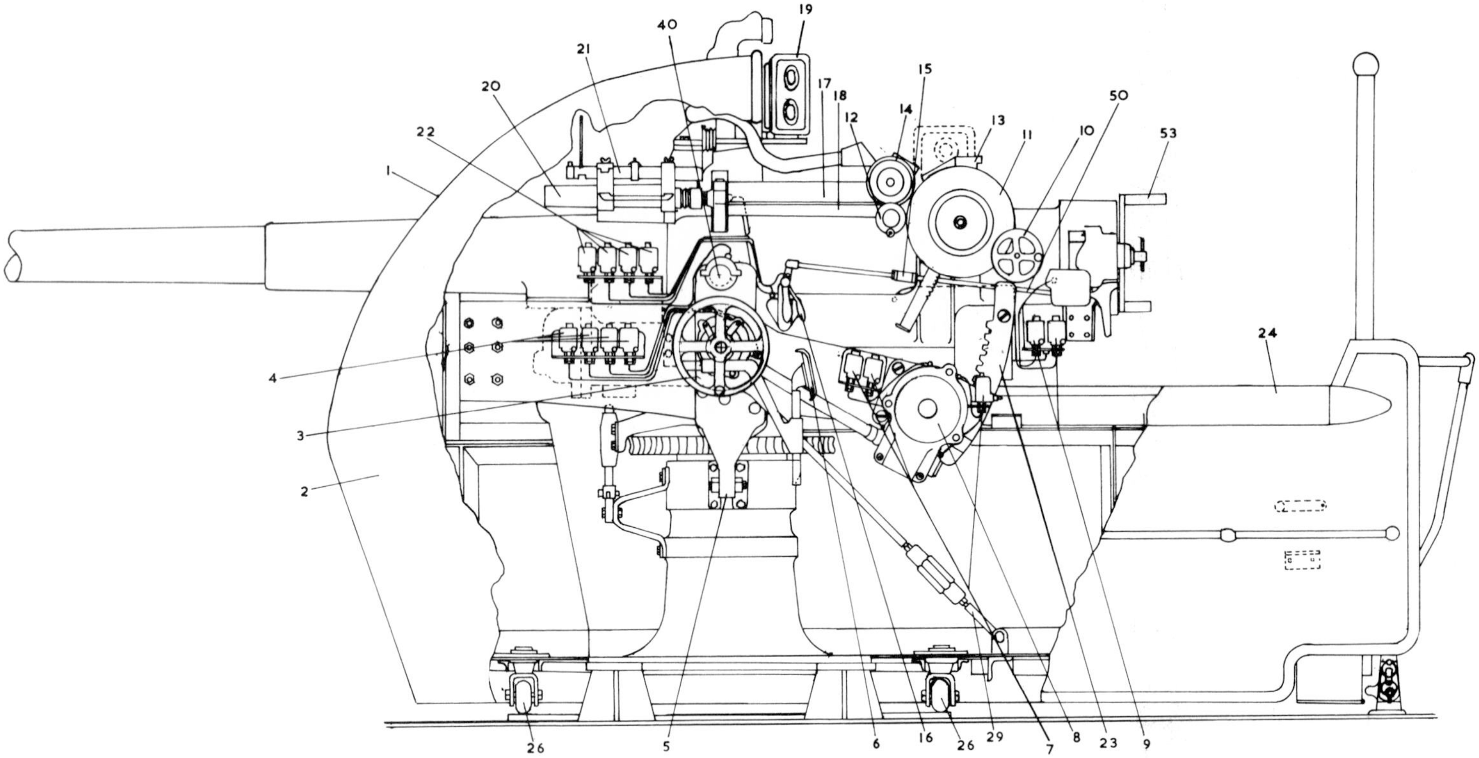
1
2
3
4
5
6
7
8
9
10
11
12
13
14
15
16
17
18
19
20
21
22
23
24
26
26
29
40
50
53

F5/10

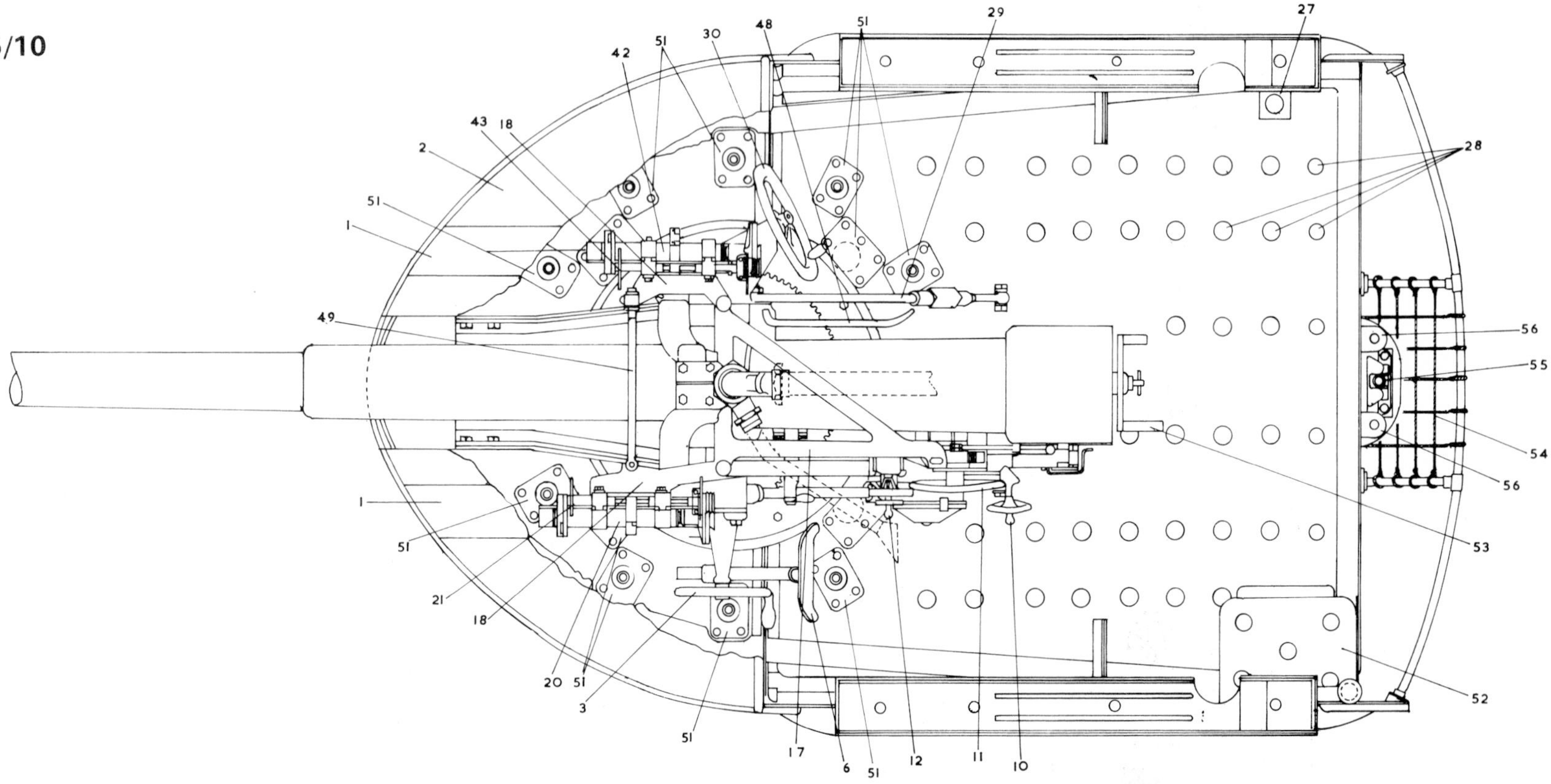
1
1
2
3
6
10
11
12
17
18
18
20
21
27
28
29
30
42
43
48
49
51
52
53
54
55
56
56

9 Lubricators for cradle slide and firing gear
10 Range handwheel
11 Range dial
12 Deflection handwheel
13 Clicker gear
14 Deflection dial
15 Adjustment
16 Firing handle
17 Sight frame
18 Deflection bar
19 Range and deflection receiver
20 Gunlayer's telescope
21 Gunlayer's barrage and open sight
22 Lubricators for cradle slide sight pivot and firing
23 Elevating arc and pinion
24 Stowage for one ready-use round
25 Lubricators for cradle slides
26 Rollers
27 Spare lock stowage
28 Drainage holes
29 Stay
30 Training handwheel
31 Pedestal
32 Training stop
33 Training rack
34 Safety depression cam
35 Lubricators for training gear
36 Safety depression stop
37 Gun carriage
38 Controlling unit
39 Gun cradle
40 Gun trunnion
41 Saddle
42 Trainer's telescope
43 Trainer's barrage and open sight
44 Lubricator for voice pipe pivot
45 Voice pipe connection to bridge
46 Alternative position of range and deflection receiver
47 Lubricator for trunnion
48 Trainer's body rest
49 Convergence bar
50 Firing rod
51 Rollers
52 CO's platform
53 Breech mechanism (BM) lever
54 Rope catch net
55 Cab housing stop
56 Eyes for securing chains
57 Check screw
58 Breech disc stop stud
59 Breech ring securing screw
60 Breech ring
61 Sleeve
62 Barrel
63 Breech block
64 BM lever retaining catch
65 BM lever retaining bracket
66 Breech disc stop stud for aiming rifle
67 Lower extractor
68 Firing lever
69 Intermediate firing lever
70 Safety catch
71 BM lever boss
72 Cocking sleeve
73 Buffer
74 Eye for firing lanyard
75 Firing rod lever
76 Lanyard lever
77 Intermediate rod lever
78 Firing plunger
79 Sear
80 Striker
81 Striker case body
82 Striker case retaining catch
83 Main spring
84 Saddle
85 Recoil cylinder
86 Support for range gear
87 Upper bearing surface
88 Lower bearing surface
89 Locking plate
90 End cap
91 Run-out cylinder
92 Reservoir
93 Grooves
94 Upper extractor
95 Firing pin
96 [not used]
97 Crosspiece
98 Cocking handle
99 Firing hole bush
100 Securing bolt
101 Breech block buffer case

F5/11

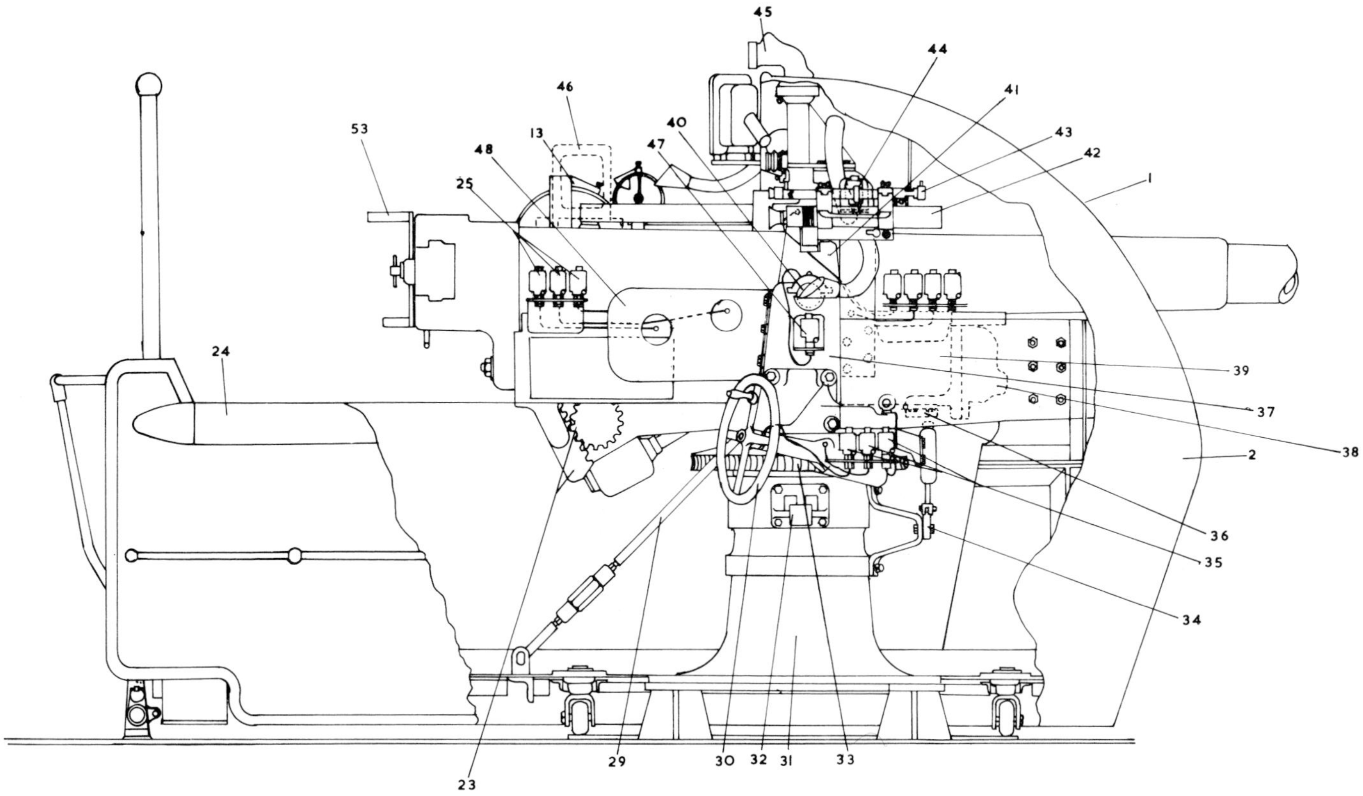

F6 **QF 4in Mk XXIII GUN ON S2 MOUNTING (no scale, except where noted)**

F6/1 **Mk XXIII gun, breech view**

F6/2 **Mk XXIII gun, longitudinal section**
('A' to 1in from commencement of rifling 21.98in; 'B' centre of gravity without BM 44.8in; 'C' total length 137.56in; chamber bore and rifling nickel-plated; external diameter nickel-plated between 'a' and 'b')

F6/3 **Breech open**

F6/4 **Breech closed**

F6/5 **S2 mounting, left-hand elevation (1/24 scale)**

F6/6 **S2 mounting, plan view (1/24 scale)**

F6/7 **S2 mounting, rear view (1/24 scale)**

F6/8 **S2 mounting, right-hand elevation (1/24 scale)**

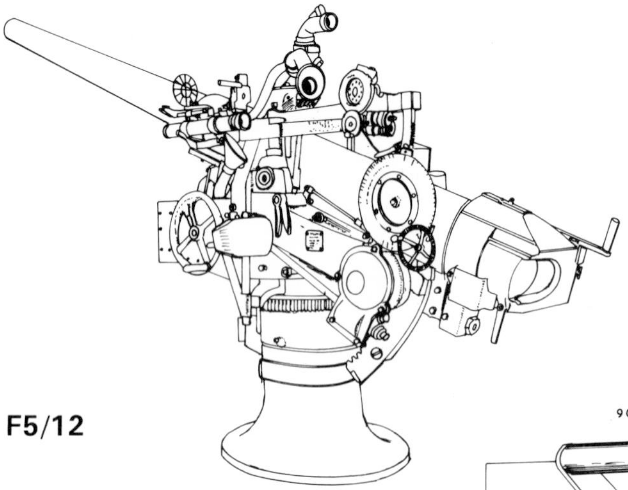

F5/12

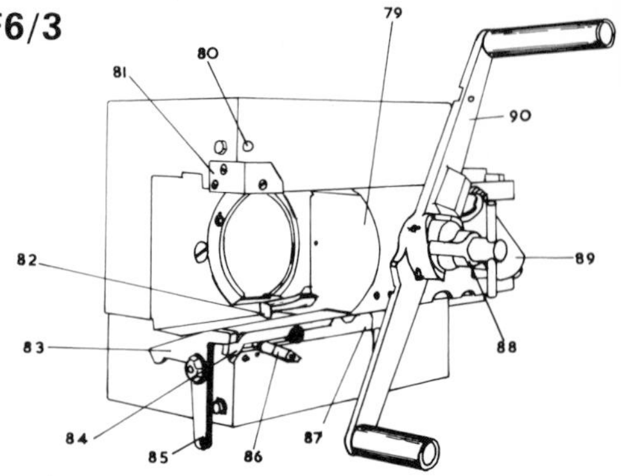

F6/3

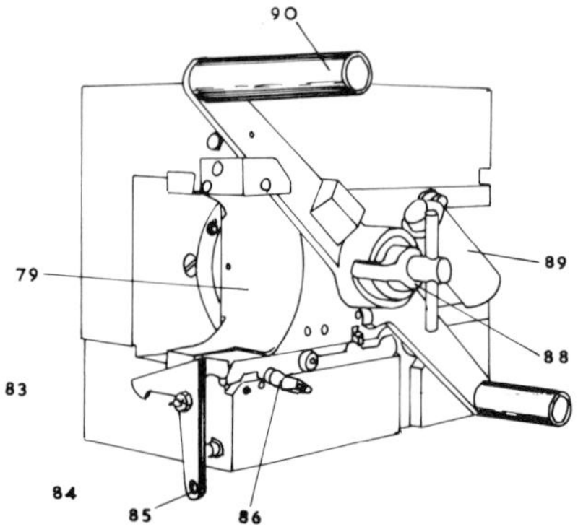

F6/4

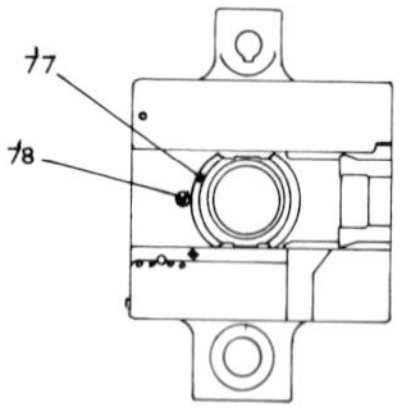

F6/1

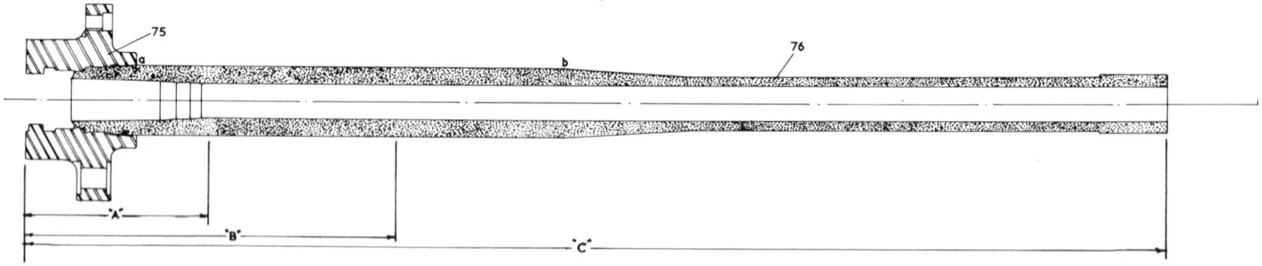

F6/2

F6/9 **Detail view of right side of mounting**

F6/10 **Detail of recoil cylinder, filling adaptor and drain plug**

F6/11 **Section through trunnions**

F6/12 **Cradle, recoil and run-out gear**

F6/13 **QF 4in Mk XXIII gun on S2 mounting, general view**

F6/14 **Firing gear, left-hand elevation**

F6/15 **Firing gear, plan view**

F6/16 **Firing gear, section through cam fulcrum**

F6/17 **Firing pedal**

F6/18 **Section through firing pedal shaft**

F6/19 **Hand firing lever and section through spring box**

F6/20 **Hand firing lever, section through 'Z–Z'**

F6/21 **Firing levers with sections through slave cylinder and return-spring box**

F6/22 **Fulcrum bracket and levers**

1	Open sight for control officer
2	Deflection handwheel
3	Voice pipe
4	Oil supply tank hydraulic firing gear
5	Shield
6	Open sight
7	Gunlayer's seat
8	Layer's telescope
9	Safety depression control gear
10	Firing gear foot pedal
11	Cam rail safety depression control gear
12	Elevating worm gear bracket
13	Training stop
14	Elevating handles
15	Training handles
16	Firing gear handlever
17	Gun guide
18	Elevating arc
19	Firing lever
20	Rear stool for control officer
21	Housing stop
22	Revolving platform
23	Ammunition trough
24	Stanchion
25	Range handwheel
26	Range and deflection receiver
27	Training index
28	Cover plate over access hole for lubrication of rollers
29	Trainer's telescope
30	Open sight
31	Recoil make up tank
32	Portable plate to allow for the removal of rollers
33	Forward stool for control officer
34	Cartridge catch net
35	Range dial
36	Deflection dial
37	Elevating pinion
38	Sight port
39	Detachable plate
40	Drain holes
41	End cover
42	Front compressor plate
43	Right-hand spring
44	Compressor rod
45	Run-out spring case
46	Separating plate
47	Left-hand spring
48	Support bracket
49	Dowel pin
50	Spring case housing
51	Tail piece
52	Upper breech ring lug
53	Nut
54	Beating face
55	Breech ring
56	Piston air release valve
57	Cradle
58	Cam plate (safety depression gear)
59	Recoil piston road
60	Control rod
61	Control valve
62	Recoil cylinder
63	Recoil control ring
64	Cylinder closing plug
65	Inner nut
66	Beech lug
67	Capsquare
68	Oil level

69 Air and filling plugs
70 Screwed plug
71 Cover plate with anti-corrosion plate on inside face
72 Trunnion bracket
73 Cylinder air release valve
74 Trunnion pin
75 Breech ring
76 Barrel
77 Stud stop breech disc
78 Screw securing breech ring
79 Breech block

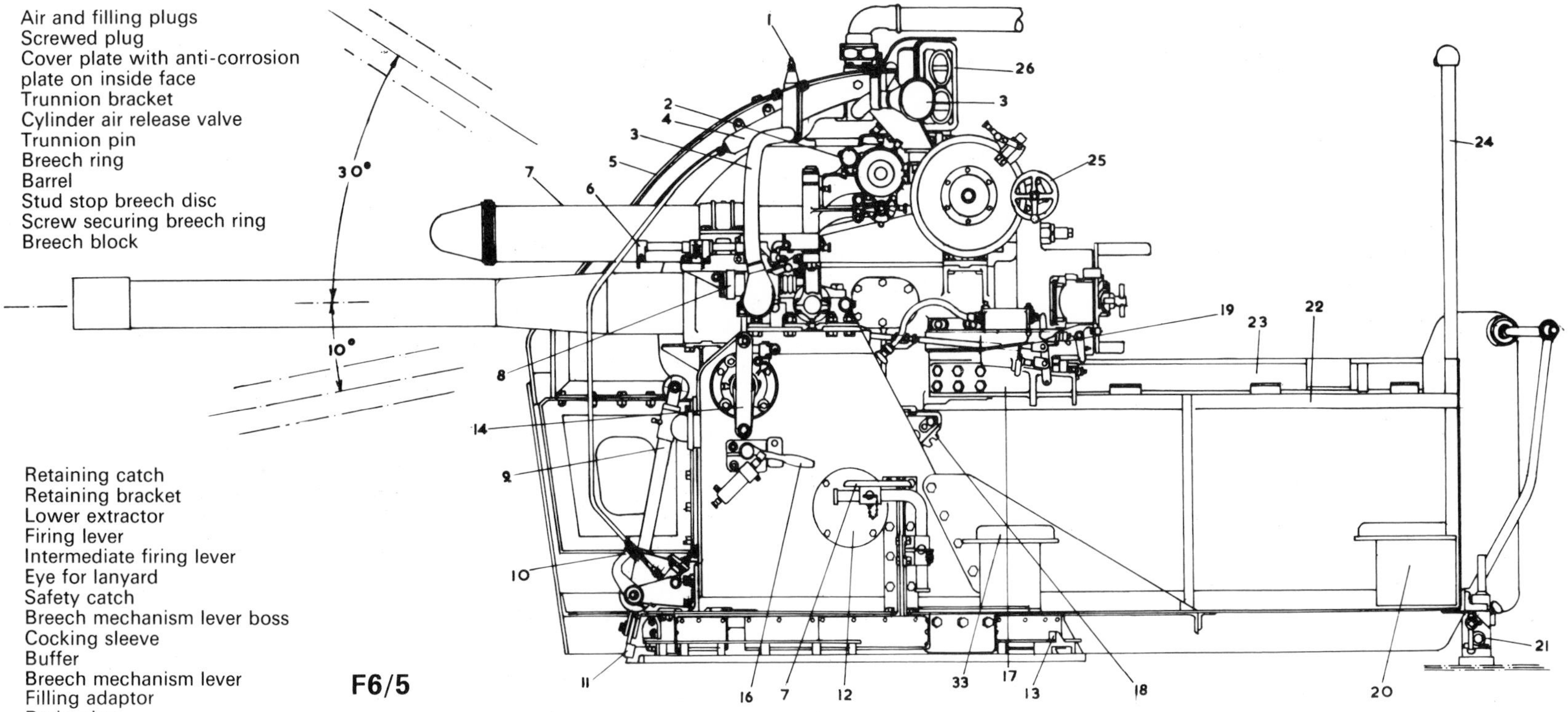

F6/5

80 Retaining catch
81 Retaining bracket
82 Lower extractor
83 Firing lever
84 Intermediate firing lever
85 Eye for lanyard
86 Safety catch
87 Breech mechanism lever boss
88 Cocking sleeve
89 Buffer
90 Breech mechanism lever
91 Filling adaptor
92 Drain plug
93 Operating lever
94 Master cylinder
95 Pipe to slave cylinder
96 Spring box
97 Lever
98 Link
99 Roller
100 Firing cam
101 Firing cam fulcrum
102 Flexible hose connection
103 Lanyard firing
104 End piece
105 Piston rod
106 Piston
107 Master cylinder
108 Spring
109 Drain

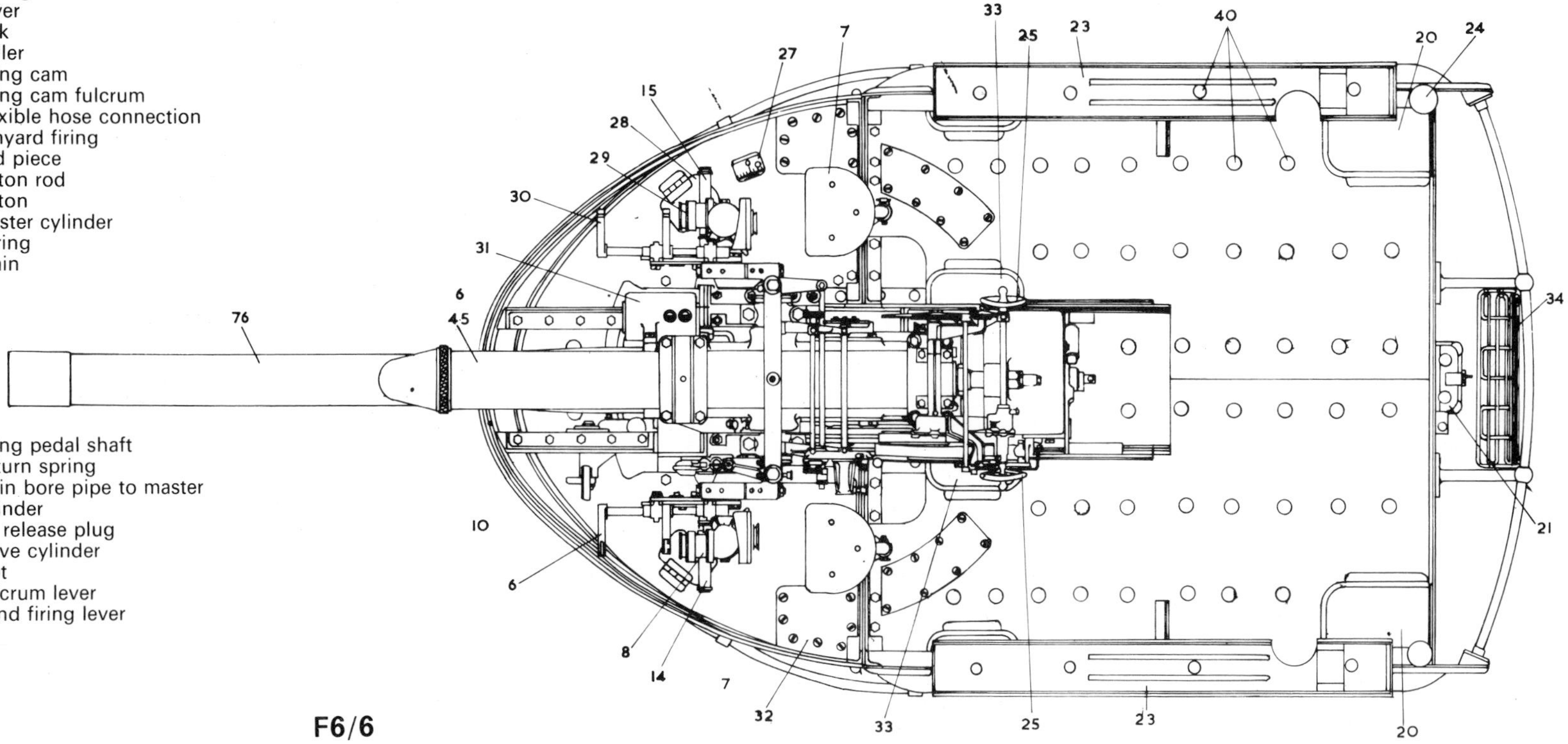

110 Firing pedal shaft
111 Return spring
112 .25in bore pipe to master cylinder
113 Air release plug
114 Slave cylinder
115 Slot
116 Fulcrum lever
117 Hand firing lever

F6/6

F Armament

F6/7

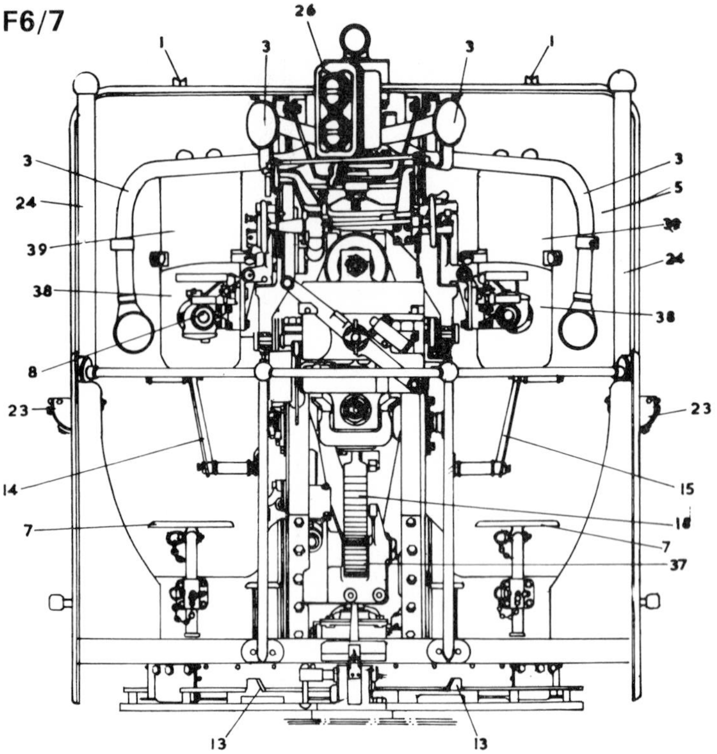

F6/8

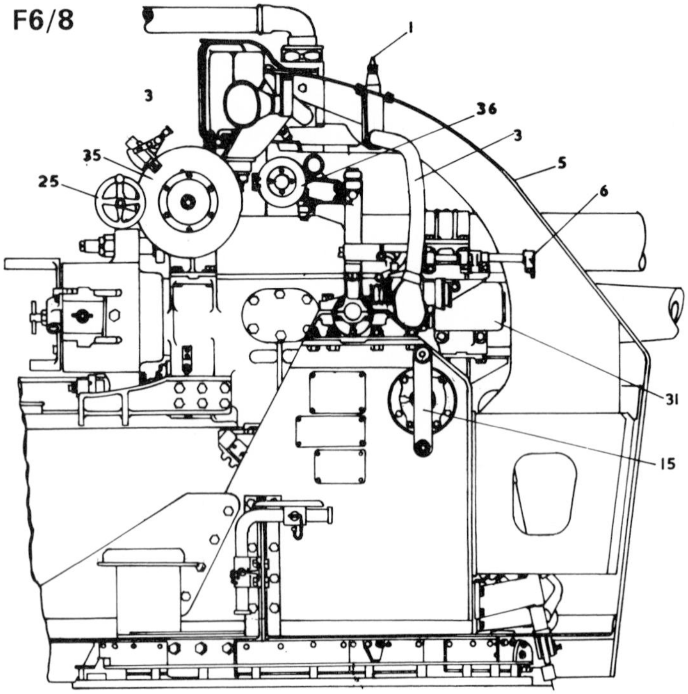

F6/10

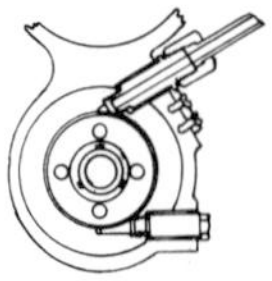

F6/9

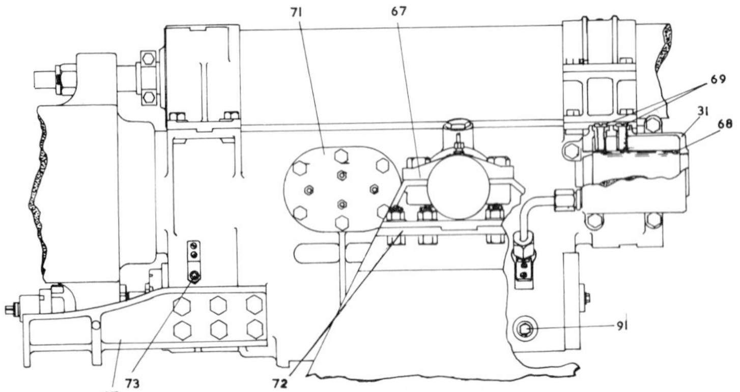

F6/11

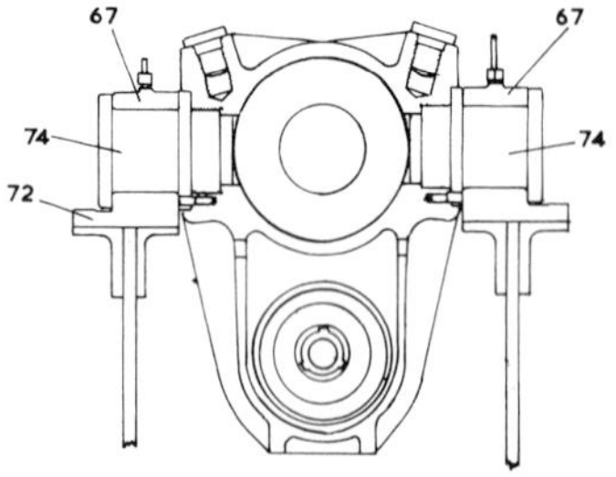

F6/13

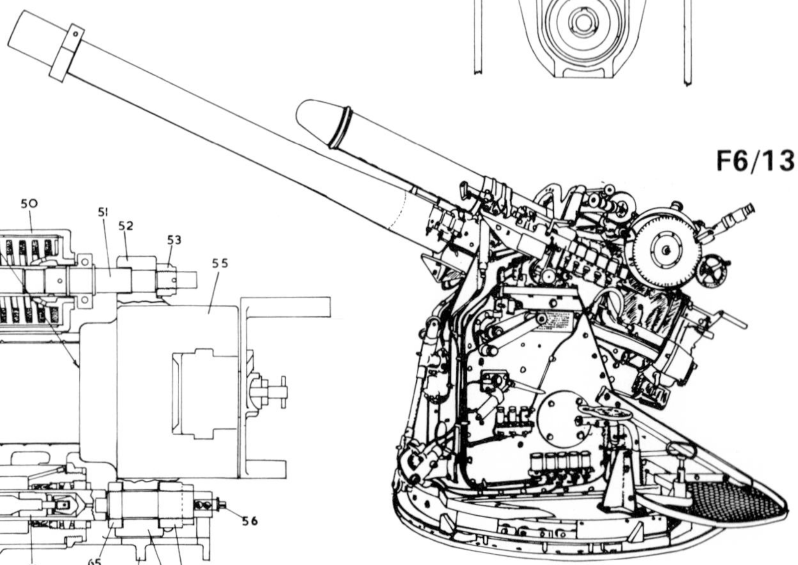

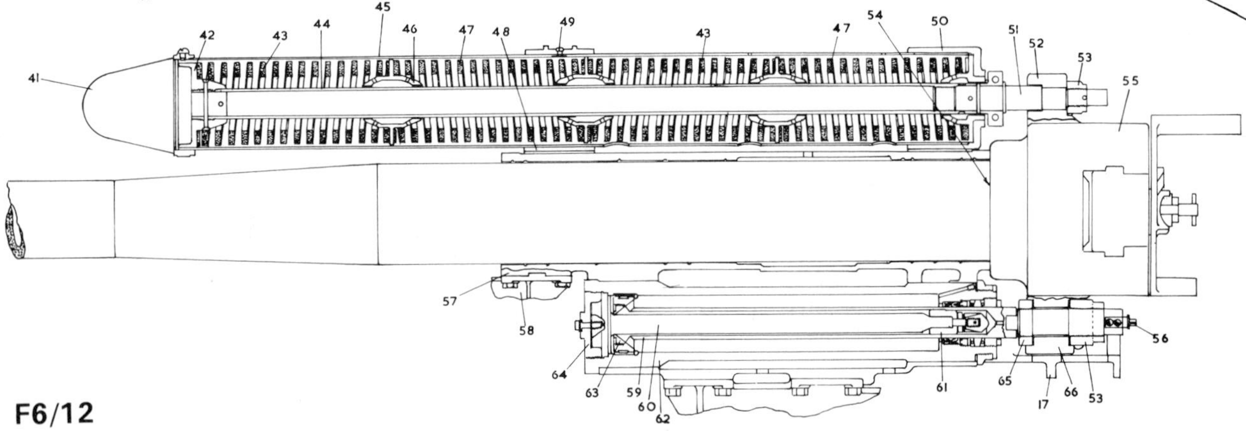

F6/12

F6/14

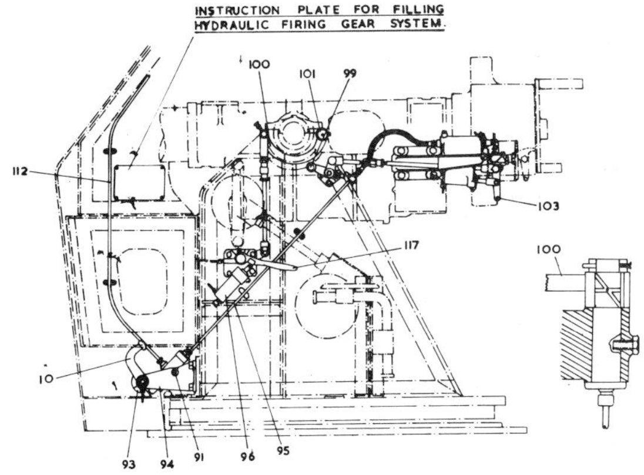

F6/16

F6/22

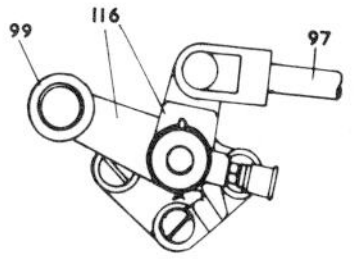

F6/15

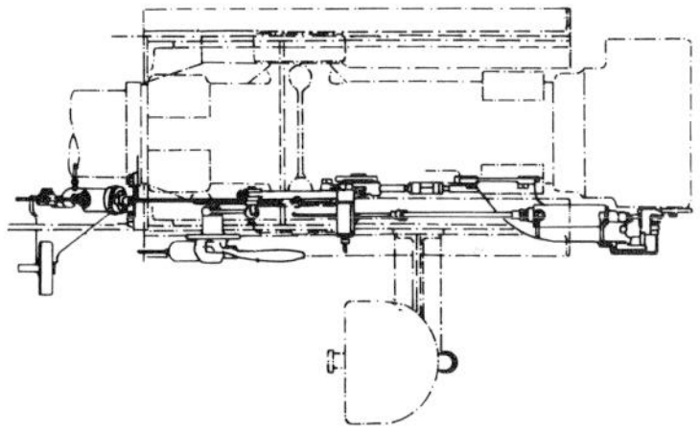

F6/21

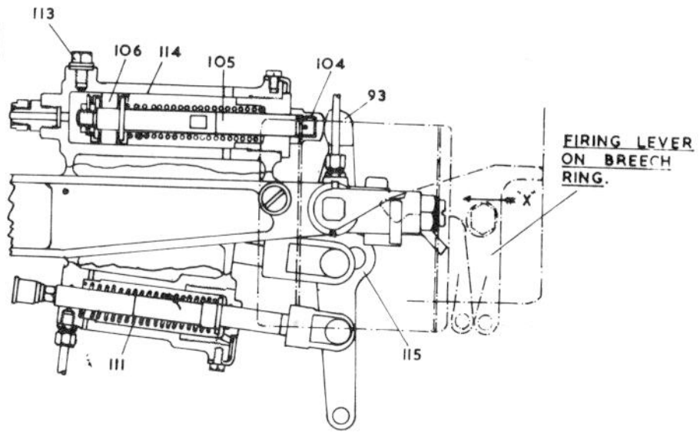

F6/17

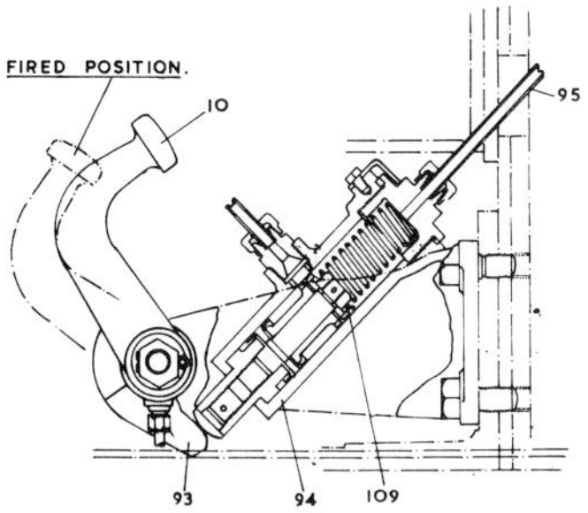

F6/19

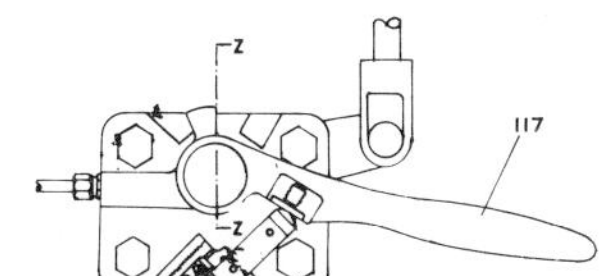

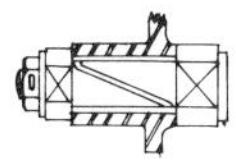

F6/20

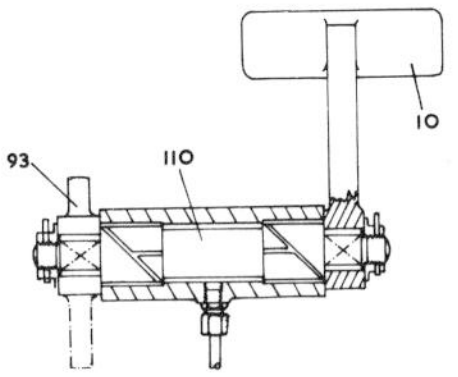

F6/18

F7	**20mm OERLIKON GUN (1/12 scale)**
F7/1	**Sectional plan of gun**
F7/2	**Sectional elevation of gun**
1	Hand grip
2	Trigger
3	Safety catch
4	Cocking stud
5	Breech cotter
6	Bolt
7	Striker
8	Barrel spring casing
9	Buffer
10	Left barrel spring
11	Right barrel spring
12	Breech
13	Barrel
14	Magazine support shoulder
F7/3	**Section 'A–A'**
F7/4	**Section 'B–B'**
F7/5	**Section 'C–C'**
F7/6	**Section 'D–D'**
F7/7	**Section 'E–E'**

F7/1

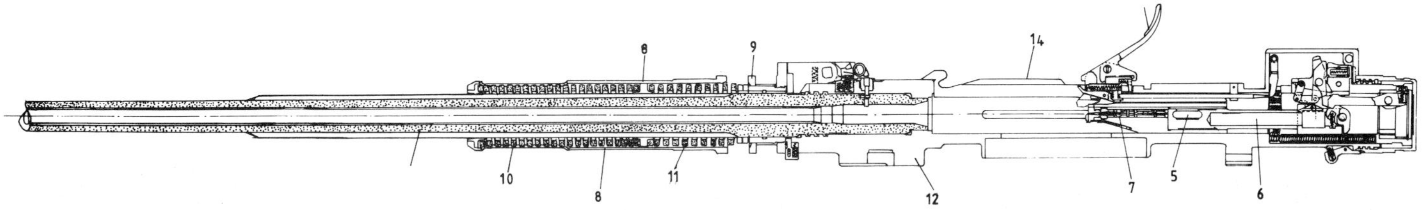

F7/2

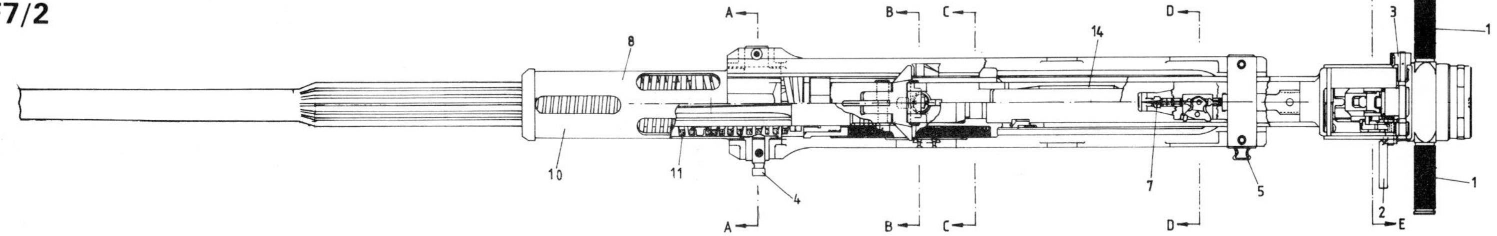

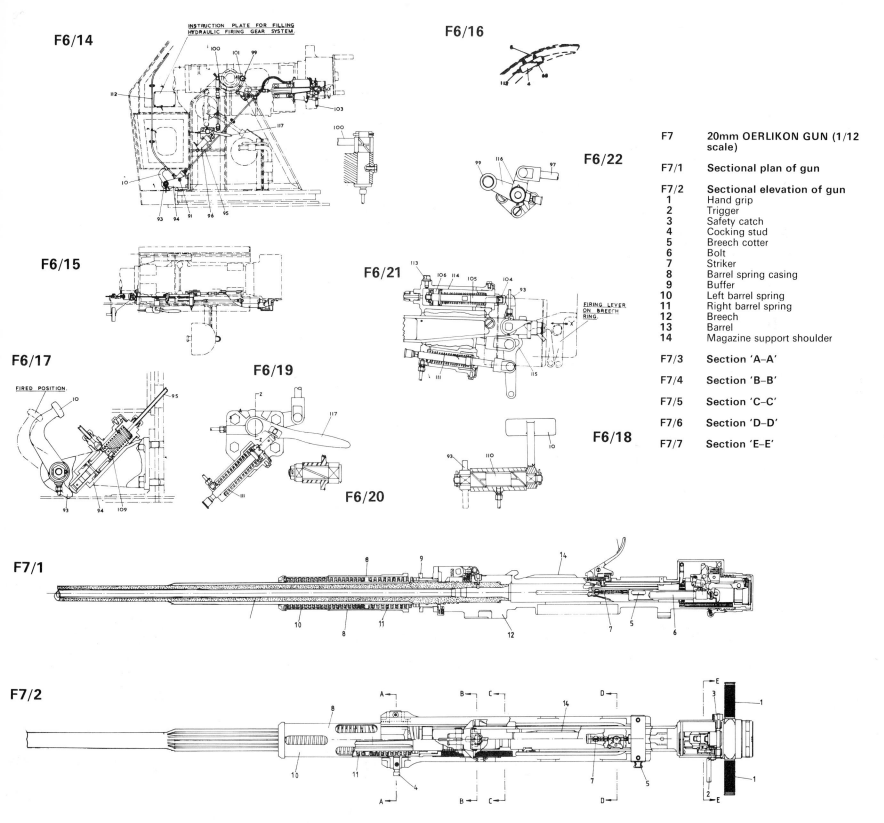

F7/8 Oerlikon magazine detail (no scale)
1 Cover plate
2 Mouth piece
3 Cartridge feeder
4 Rollers
5 Feed block
6 Drum
7 Indicator block
8 Spiral path
9 Clock spring

F7/9 Gun, general view (no scale)
1 Barrel
2 Barrel spring casing
3 Left barrel spring
4 Right barrel spring
5 Buffer
6 Magazine catch lever
7 Left breech bar
8 Trigger box cover
9 Trigger
10 Safety catch
11 Hand grip
12 Cocking stud
13 Breech cotter
14 Magazine support shoulder

F7/10 Mk II striker (no scale)

F7/11 Mk VIIA mounting, left side view (note that the submarine mounting had no splinter shield; 1/36 scale)

F7/12 Mk VIIA mounting, front view (1/36 scale)
1 Cartridge chute
2 Gun carriage
3 Chain for balance weight
4 Cam
5 300-knot foresight
6 Pedestal
7 Shield

Note: Details of the 0.303in Vickers machine gun and the 20mm twin Mk 12A mounting occasionally carried, and the proposed 6pdr Mk IIA can be found in the companion volume in this series on the Fairmile 'D' type MTB.

F7/3

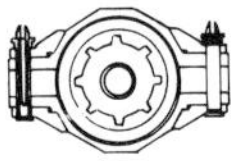

F7/4

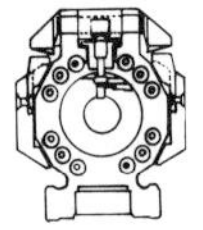

F7/5

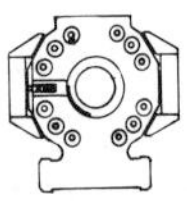

F/76

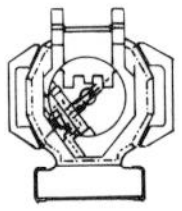

F7/8

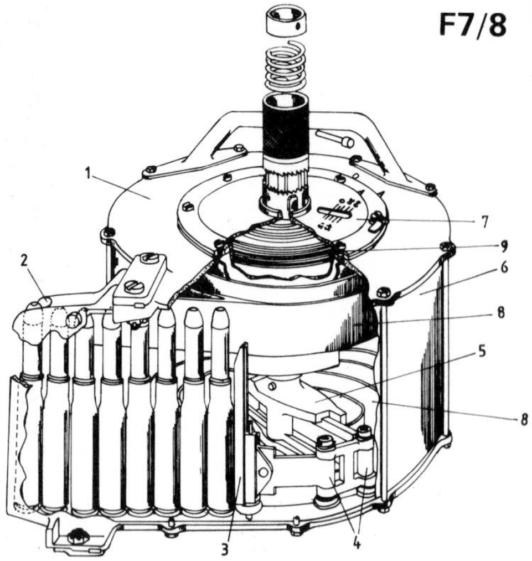

F7/7

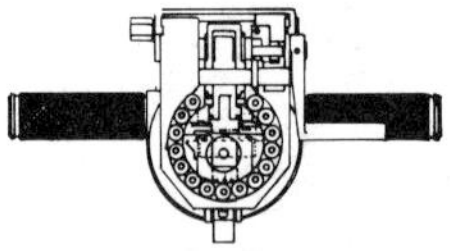

F7/10

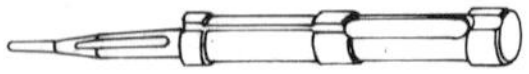

F7/9

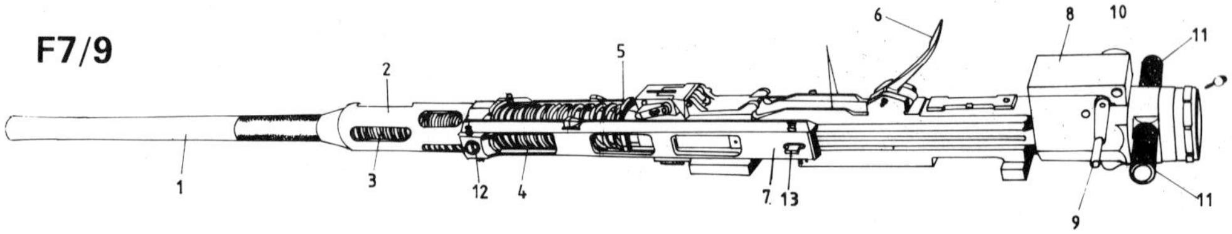

F7/11

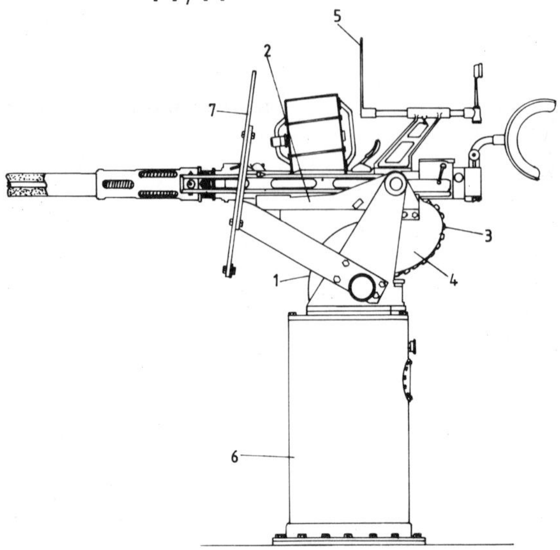

F7/12

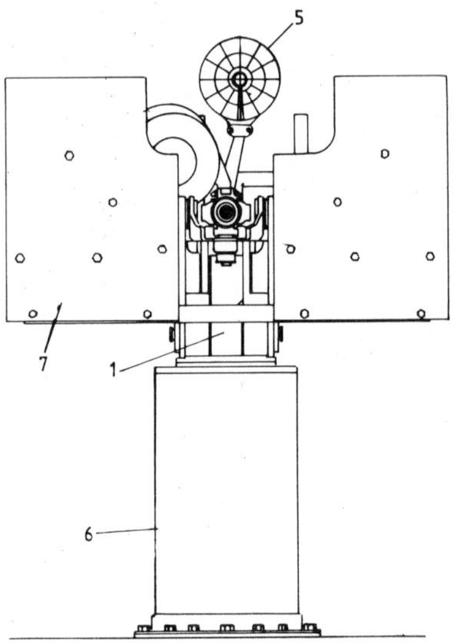